Marion R. Faulds.

November 1968.

BASIC STATISTICAL METHODS

SECOND EDITION

N. M. DOWNIE

PURDUE UNIVERSITY

R. W. HEATH

EDUCATIONAL TESTING SERVICE

A HARPER INTERNATIONAL STUDENT REPRINT

JOINTLY PUBLISHED BY

HARPER & ROW, New York, Evanston & London
AND JOHN WEATHERHILL, INC., Tokyo

CONTENTS

TABLES

APPENDIX

INTRODUCTION
TO THE SECOND EDITION

*" He who knows not mathematics cannot
know any other science, and he cannot,
moreover, become aware of the extent of
his own ignorance."*
UNKNOWN RENAISSANCE SCHOLAR

In my introduction to the first edition of this book I pointed to the mathematical deficit under which the present and prospective users of statistics
labor—students and workers in education, psychology, and sociology.
That deficit is still only slightly if at all reduced. The notion that the
answer to a mathematical problem is absolutely either correct or wrong is
deeply imbedded in our culture. Probabilistic thinking is largely a product
of the twentieth century and the exactitudes of the arithmetic learned in
elementary and secondary education transfer somewhat negatively to the
concept of estimates inherent in statistics.

The success of the first edition of this book, measured by its many adop-
tions, attests to its usefulness to those for whom it was written. This
revision, I am confident, will prove even more useful than the first edition.
Experience with teaching with the first edition has led the authors to some
reorganization, increased emphasis on some concepts, and the addition of
some other concepts—for example in Chapter 15, the concept of covariance.
The addition of a table of random numbers to the Appendix and the prepa-
ration of a student workbook to accompany the textbook (with step-wise,
detailed solution of illustrative problems) will enhance the book's use as a
teaching tool.

The computer science that only recently grew up between the interstices
of mathematics and electronics is by way of quantifying data beyond the
hopes of less than two or three decades ago—and is revolutionizing our
ways of life and work. To be able to read the professional journals in the
social sciences requires more than ever an understanding in the ways of
thinking to which this book is a notably clear and straightforward
introduction.

H. H. REMMERS

INTRODUCTION
TO THE FIRST EDITION

Until you have measured it,
you don't know what you are talking about.
LORD KELVIN

The clock, the calendar, high hopes, and deep convictions have for long been, and still are to too great an extent, the major criteria of educational achievement. Until J. McKeen Cattell in the late nineteenth century convinced Wilhelm Wundt that individual differences were worth systematic study in their own right, psychological study was aimed at establishing general laws of the "mind," and individual differences tended to be regarded as annoying anomalies, somewhat analogous to early disciples of Linnaeus ascribing species of living organisms that did not fit his binomial nomenclature to the work of the devil.

Mathematical invention and discovery in statistics applied to the biological and social sciences has seen phenomenal development, particularly in the last four decades. Statistics thus applied, however, is still largely not a part of the intellectual furniture of those charged with responsibility for educating the young—teachers and administrators—who, for varying reasons, tend to shy away from courses that would provide them with a functional modicum of this powerful tool for analysis and synthesis of data.

One of the reasons for this deficiency is doubtless a lack of mathematical knowledge and skills and hence a fear of the unknown in the form of difficult subject matter. Therefore, a book that takes into account this lack of training and that approaches prospective teachers and administrators as they are is a most desirable addition to the literature of education. Without making unwarranted assumptions concerning the mathematical sophistication of the student, this textbook is in my judgment notably successful in presenting in simple, clear language the logic and content of statistics as needed by the beginning student of education and psychology. The introduction to distribution-free or nonparametric statistics—in my view destined to be much more used than heretofore—is particularly salutary, since the assumptions underlying parametric statistics are often dubious in the social sciences.

The introductory discussion of analysis of variance will lead the student to realize that, for drawing inferences from data, other powerful aids are available to those who wish to go on to more complete mastery of the tools requisite to more effective and valid control of the educational process.

Not the least valuable aspect of this book is its thorough consideration of the technology of tests and measurements, an area with which all students of education and psychology need to be concerned.

This book by my colleagues Professors Downie and Heath is a highly successful attempt to provide an effective learning aid. It affords me pride and pleasure to see it included in the series for which I have editorial responsibility.

H. H. R.

PREFACE

This elementary statistics book, like its predecessor, is written to meet the need for a short, clear book for the beginning student of the social sciences. We believe that such a book should treat the computation, interpretation, and application of commonly used statistics. No extensive attempt has been made to derive formulas or to involve statistical theory, since the mathematical training of the typical student using this book probably precludes effective presentation of such topics.

Like the earlier edition, this book comprises three parts. The first eight chapters present descriptive statistics, the next seven introduce inferential statistics, and the last three treat materials usually not included in a first course in statistics. These are (1) a survey of various correlational techniques, (2) test theory and test construction, and (3) the more frequently encountered nonparametric statistical tests.

Many parts of the original text have been rewritten and new material has been added. In a rapidly developing field such as this, new techniques and new methodologies are appearing at a rapid pace, while some older methods become less widely used. We have attempted to present an up-to-date elementary statistical textbook.

Problems designed to offer practice in the techniques discussed in each chapter appear throughout the book. The answers to these problems are presented in the back of the book. At the request of many users of this textbook, a new, separate workbook has also been written by the senior author.

Many sincere thanks are due to various authors and publishers who gave us permission to use the materials which appear in the tables in the Appendix. Special acknowledgment of this is given in footnotes appearing at the bottom of each table.

We are especially indebted to the late Sir Ronald A. Fisher of Cambridge, to Dr. Frank Yates of Rothamsted, and to Messrs. Oliver and Boyd, Ltd., of Edinburgh, for permission to reprint Tables III, IV, and VI from their book *Statistical Tables for Biological, Agricultural, and Medical Research.*

N. M. DOWNIE
R. W. HEATH

April, 1965

BASIC
STATISTICAL
METHODS

1

INTRODUCTION

This book is an introduction to statistics, written primarily for students of education, psychology, and sociology. The student may ask why he should take time to study this subject. We believe that in addition to the value of statistics in a general education there are at least five specific reasons why students would want to study this subject.

1. *Daily Use.* Statistics are of immediate and practical utility. They help us get our work done more quickly and efficiently. They aid teachers in the assignment of grades and in the construction of tests. They help psychologists interpret the measurements and observations they make. The sociologist finds them of similar use in evaluating the data with which he must work. In all the behavioral sciences, statistics have become a familiar part of the working day. In these fields effectiveness and ease of operation require a knowledge of the basic statistical methods.

2. *Problem Solving.* Often, research is conducted on a limited scale, not to test a theory, but to uncover information vital to the solution of a practical problem. We may be asked such questions as: "How can this test be improved?" "Which members of the group have the lowest morale?" "Does this method do a better job than that one?" "Is this variable related to another?" Such questions call for the application of statistical methods to the available data.

3. *Theoretical Research.* As the behavioral sciences have grown in sophistication, they have become more quantitative. The development of theories serves to organize our information. Theories predict what we expect to observe in specified circumstances. Theories of physical science which did not lend themselves to operational testing have long since been abandoned. The means by which we test the theories of education, psychology, sociology, and economics are largely statistical.

4. *Comprehension and Use of Research.* The competent practitioner, regardless of his field, must keep abreast of technical advancements. He must be able to read with understanding reports of applied and theoretical

research. In the behavioral sciences, this requires that he must know the meaning of certain statistical terms and when particular methods should be used. Unfortunately, not all research is good research, and the burden of evaluation ultimately falls upon the reader. Statistics can be misused and misinterpreted, but to those who understand them, they tell the truth or they say nothing.

5. *Enjoyment.* To many students, it may seem that collecting and analyzing data would be anything but fun. Perhaps this is because such activities are frequently approached with an overwhelming pomposity and a deadly serious intent.

However, it does seem to be in the nature of men to enjoy such activities if they are left to their own devices. A real thrill can result when one finds that, in an apparently chaotic and jumbled reality, he can see orderly and lawful relationships. When one successfully completes a puzzle or a game of solitaire, he probably experiences a dilute form of such an experience. When the pieces of the puzzle have social significance, and when the solution brings an understandable order to the behavior of people, the thrill is magnified many times. If puzzles were too easy, they would be no fun. It would be a tragedy if we let their often exaggerated difficulties frighten us away.

BRIEF HISTORY OF STATISTICS

Statistics has a long and venerable history. Perhaps the earliest use of statistics was when an ancient chief counted the number of effective warriors that he had or the number he would need to defeat his enemy, or when he figured how much might judiciously be collected in taxes. In later times, statistics were used to report death rates in the great London plague and in the study of natural resources. These uses of statistics, which encompass a broad field of activity referred to as "state arithmetic," are purely descriptive in nature.

In the seventeenth and eighteenth centuries, mathematicians were asked by gamblers to develop principles that would improve the chances of winning at cards and dice. The two most noted mathematicians who became involved in this, the first major study of probability, were Bernoulli and DeMoivre. In the 1730s DeMoivre developed the equation for the normal curve. Important work on probability was conducted in the first two decades of the nineteenth century by two other mathematicians, LaPlace and Gauss. Their work was an application of probability principles to astronomy.

Into the nineteenth century statistics had been mathematical, political, and governmental. A famous Belgian statistician, Quetelet, applied these new research tools to investigations of social and educational problems. Walker (1929)[1] credits Quetelet with developing statistical theory as a

---

[1] Complete references are given at back of book.

general method of research applicable to any observational science. Beyond any doubt, the individual who had the greatest effect upon the introduction and use of statistics in the social sciences was Francis Galton. In the course of his long life he made notable contributions in the fields of heredity and eugenics, psychology, anthropometry, and statistics. Our present understanding of correlation, the measure of agreement between two variables, is credited to him. The mathematician, Pearson, collaborated with Galton in later years and was instrumental in developing many of the correlation and regression formulas that are in use today. Among Galton's contributions was the development of centiles or percentiles.

The famous American psychologist James McKeen Cattell studied in Europe in the 1880s and contacted Galton and other European statisticians. On his return to the United States he and his students, including E. L. Thorndike, began to apply statistical methods to psychological and educational problems. The influence of these men was great; in a few years, theoretical and applied statistics courses were commonly taught in American universities.

In the twentieth century, new techniques and methods were applied to the study of small samples. The major contributions in small-sample theory were made by the late R. A. Fisher, an English statistician. While most of his methods were developed in an agricultural or biological setting, it was not long before social scientists recognized the utility of Fisher's methods and made use of his ideas. Today, statistics is the major tool of the research worker in the social sciences.

WHAT CAN BE DONE WITH STATISTICS

Educators and social scientists are collectors of many different types of data. Much of these data come from educational and psychological measuring instruments. A knowledge of statistics aids in the correct interpretation and analysis of these data.

Consider some of the information that can be obtained from such data. Suppose that a teacher, a psychologist, or a sociologist has just made some measurements. What are some of the things that can be done to get the maximum information from the results? Here is a list of possibilities:

1. Averages can be calculated. These averages give a picture of the typical performance of the groups.

2. The variability of the measurements can be determined. By using the average as a point of reference, one can determine how scores or observations spread about this central point.

3. Graphs, tables, and figures can be prepared to portray clearly the nature of the group or groups.

4. The "raw" scores can be transformed into a more meaningful form. The most common of these forms are centiles (or percentiles) and standard scores. When dealing with classroom performance, raw scores can be

changed into letter grades. When dealing with vocational tests, scores can be converted to job classifications. In sociological studies, scores might indicate group membership.

5. The relationship of one variable to another can be determined. These statistics are called correlation coefficients and are among the most useful. For example, it might be of interest to find the relationships between an intelligence test and classroom tests; between abilities and interests; or among various measures of physical development. Variables such as age may be related with measures of achievement and with psychological and sociological characteristics.

6. The *reliability* of the measurement instruments can be determined. This is done by making two measurements of the same individuals with the same or "parallel" devices and finding the correlation between the two sets of data. As will be seen, there are also other ways of computing reliability coefficients.

7. The *validity* of the measurements can be determined. With regard to statistical validity, the correlation between scores made on one test and performance on another measurement, called a criterion, is an index of validity. For example, intelligence tests are often validated by correlating scores on these tests with grade point averages. If the intelligence tests are valid, those who obtained the highest scores will also receive the highest academic grades.

8. One set of measurements, or a combination of variables, can be used to predict future status or behavior. This is probably the major end of all correlational work; in themselves correlation coefficients are of little value.

9. From the measurement of a sample of individuals, inferences can be made about the larger population from which the sample was drawn. The drawing of statistical inferences is one of the chief activities of modern research. Information about a small sample is usually of limited use. The research worker hopes to generalize and draw conclusions about a larger group.

10. The performance of one group can be compared with that made by another, and the significance of any difference can be tested. Suppose that a school is trying out a new reading curriculum. We have two groups; one is handled in the usual way in the course of a semester or a year and the other, an experimental group, is treated in a new fashion. That is, the experimental group is exposed to the new reading curriculum. At the end of the school year, the same reading test is administered to both groups. The scores made by each group on this test can be averaged. By inspection we cannot tell whether or not the averages are significantly different. At this point a test of significance can be made to see whether or not the difference is attributable to chance variation. The processes of drawing inferences, making predictions, and testing significance are examples of *sampling* or *inferential* statistics. The other methods mentioned are included in what is called *descriptive* statistics. Modern experimental research in fields of knowledge from anthropology to zoology uses sampling statistics.

It is hoped that the student will become more judicious in the use of statistics as a result of studying this book. In some circles statistics and statisticians have a bad name; it has been said that a person can use statistics to prove anything, so statisticians and liars have been lumped together in one breath. A book by Huff (1954) contains a good summary of the ways in which statistics are misused by individuals who wish to prove a point or misrepresent facts. As will be shown throughout this book, there is a time and place for every statistical method. Certain techniques are to be used when particular conditions prevail. We hope that the student will become aware of the conditions which justify the use of each statistic. In summary, statistical methods are powerful tools that aid the social scientist in his efforts to extend the limits of knowledge.

It is probable that many students using this text may have found mathematics unpleasant or difficult in the past. Since this book is concerned with numbers and formulas, they may fear that the subject is complicated and obscure. These students should set their minds at ease. One does not have to be a genius, or fond of mathematics, to learn the methods presented here. We believe that a grasp of the elements of seventh- and eighth-grade arithmetic will suffice. About the only further prerequisites are the ability to take square roots and to subtract negative numbers. A few will need to brush up a bit on these with a couple of hours' practice.

A more important problem for most students is that of precision or accuracy. It has been our experience that most errors come not from using the wrong principle but merely from carelessness in the simple operations of addition and subtraction.

Statistics, it will be found, is one of those subjects that cumulates. One topic leads to another, and the second is built upon the first. The work has to be kept up to date. If knowledge of statistics is built on an incomplete foundation, the whole structure will surely topple. The problems found at the end of each chapter will help to test the stability of the student's progress.

2
A REVIEW OF
FUNDAMENTALS

In this chapter we shall be concerned with two topics: a review of simple arithmetic and elementary algebra and a discussion of the fundamental nature of measurement. Many of the errors which occur in statistical computations are not caused by a lack of knowledge of statistics but by mistakes in very simple arithmetic. Hence we shall start with a rapid review of the rules that must be followed if computations are to be correct.

REVIEW OF ARITHMETIC

Decimals

Addition and Subtraction. When adding or subtracting decimals, align the numbers with the decimal point of one number directly below that of the one above.

To add 3.094, 235.67, and 45.7, we align the numbers like this:

$$
\begin{array}{r}
3.094 \\
235.67 \\
45.7 \\
\hline
284.464
\end{array}
$$

Multiplication. In multiplying decimals, the product has as many decimal places as there are in both the multiplicand and the multiplier taken together, as shown below:

$$
\begin{array}{r}
1.072 \\
\times\ .02 \\
\hline
.02144
\end{array}
\qquad
\begin{array}{r}
.00007 \\
\times\ .2 \\
\hline
.000014
\end{array}
\qquad
\begin{array}{r}
1.2 \\
\times\ 1.2 \\
\hline
1.44
\end{array}
$$

Division. When two decimals are divided, the number of decimal places in the quotient is equal to the number of decimal places in the dividend minus the number of places in the divisor when there is no remainder.

$$\frac{.012}{.3} = .04 \qquad \frac{2.0648}{.2} = 10.324 \qquad \frac{.008}{8} = .001$$

Fractions

Addition and Subtraction. When two or more fractions are to be added or subtracted, they must first be reduced to fractions having the same or a common denominator, as below:

$$\frac{1}{2} + \frac{1}{3} - \frac{3}{6} + \frac{2}{6} = \frac{5}{6} \qquad 2\frac{3}{4} + \frac{1}{2} = \frac{11}{4} + \frac{2}{4} = \frac{13}{4} = 3\frac{1}{4}$$

$$\frac{3}{8} - \frac{3}{16} = \frac{6}{16} - \frac{3}{16} = \frac{3}{16} \qquad \frac{x}{y} + \frac{a}{b} = \frac{xb}{yb} + \frac{ya}{yb} = \frac{xb + ya}{yb}$$

Multiplication. To multiply fractions, multiply all the numerators and place this quantity over the product of all of the denominators, as shown:

$$\frac{1}{2} \times \frac{2}{3} = \frac{2}{6} = \frac{1}{3} \qquad \left(\frac{3}{4}\right)\left(\frac{2}{3}\right)\left(\frac{4}{6}\right)\left(\frac{4}{5}\right) = \frac{96}{360} = \frac{4}{15}$$

When multiplying fractions, considerable time is saved if terms common to both the numerator and denominator are canceled. This is equivalent to dividing the numerator and denominator of a fraction by the same number. The size of the product is not changed. Let us rework the last example:

$$\frac{\overset{1}{\cancel{3}}}{\underset{1}{\cancel{4}}} \times \frac{\overset{1}{\cancel{2}}}{\underset{1}{\cancel{3}}} \times \frac{\overset{1}{\cancel{4}}}{\underset{3}{\cancel{6}}} \times \frac{4}{5} = \frac{4}{15}$$

First we cancel the first 3 in the numerator with the 3 in the denominator. Next the first 4 in the numerator is canceled by the 4 in the denominator. The 2 in the numerator is divided into the 6 in the denominator, leaving a 3 in that position. Then we have $1 \times 1 \times 1 \times 4$ in the numerator and $1 \times 1 \times 3 \times 5$ in the denominator. The product of all terms in the numerator is equal to 4; the product of those in the denominator is 15. Four-fifteenths is again our answer.

Division. To divide one fraction by another, invert the fraction which is the divisor and proceed as in multiplication.

$$\frac{3}{4} \div \frac{2}{3} = \frac{3}{4} \times \frac{3}{2} = \frac{9}{8} = 1\frac{1}{8}$$

$$2\frac{3}{4} \div \frac{11}{7} = \frac{11}{4} \times \frac{7}{11} = \frac{7}{4} = 1\frac{3}{4}$$

$$\frac{x}{y} \div \frac{a}{b} = \frac{x}{y} \times \frac{b}{a} = \frac{xb}{ya}$$

Negative Numbers

Addition.   To add numbers, each of which is negative, add the numbers in the usual fashion and place a minus sign in front of the sum.

$$(-6) + (-8) + (-12) = -26$$

When the signs are mixed and there are only two, that is, one negative and the other positive, subtract the smaller from the larger and give the remainder the sign of the larger

-6	-22	56	19
8	28	-72	-30
2	6	-16	-11

When adding more than two numbers of different signs, add all the positive numbers and then the negative ones and combine the results as above.

$$(-4) + (-7) + (8) + (13) + (-12) + (-5) = 21 + (-28) = -7$$

Subtraction.   To subtract a negative number, change its sign and proceed as in addition.

12	-22	-4.48
$-(-8)$	$-(-8)$	$-(-8.24)$
20	-14	3.76

Multiplication.   When two numbers have the same sign, either positive or negative, the product of the two numbers is positive.   When the sign of one number is positive and that of the other number is negative, the product of the two numbers is negative.

6	-6	6	-6
$\times\ 2$	$\times\ (-2)$	$\times\ (-2)$	$\times\ (2)$
12	12	-12	-12

Division.   As in multiplication, when a positive or negative number is divided by a number of the same sign, the quotient is always positive. When the dividend and divisor are of unlike signs, the quotient is always negative.

$$\frac{6}{2} = 3 \qquad \frac{-6}{-2} = 3 \qquad \frac{6}{-2} = -3 \qquad \frac{-6}{2} = -3$$

Use of Zero

The chief rule to remember when using zero is: when any number is multiplied by zero, the product is 0.

$$2 \times 0 = 0$$
$$(.5)(3.55)(0)(4976) = 0$$

Square Root

In statistical operations, the student will find that there are many occasions on which it is necessary to extract a square root. Table I in the Appendix contains the square root of the whole numbers from 1 to 1000. Unfortunately, many of the numbers which we use are not whole and hence cannot be read directly from the tables.

Suppose that we want to take the square root of a simple number like 144. Table I in the Appendix shows that the square root of this number is 12. Suppose that we did not have a table. This is what we would do:

$$
\begin{array}{r}
1 \quad 2. \\
\sqrt{1 \quad 44.} \\
\underline{1} \\
\end{array}
$$

$$
\begin{array}{r}
2\,(?) \\
\times\,(?)
\end{array}
\left|
\begin{array}{l}
44 \\
44
\end{array}
\right.
$$

Starting at the decimal point, we move to the left, making pairs. The last pair consists of only one digit, 1. We take the first pair and find the largest square contained in it. In this case, the largest square in 1 is 1. We write this under the 1 and subtract. Then we place the square root of this square, 1, above the square root sign. We bring down the next pair of numbers. Then we bring the first number above the radical sign down and multiply it by 2. We write this 2 at the left of 44. Then we find a digit that can be placed where the (?) is, such that, when multiplied by the entire number, the product will be as close to 44 as possible, but will not exceed 44. This digit is 2. A 2 is then placed where the question marks are, the multiplication is made, and the answer comes to 44. Hence 2 becomes the second digit in the answer and is written above the second pair of digits, 44. This time we have no remainder and the operation is complete.

Let us extract the square root of 876.457.

$$
\begin{array}{r}
2\;9.\;6\;0\;5 \\
\sqrt{876.457000} \\
\underline{4} \\
\end{array}
$$

$$
\begin{array}{rr}
49 & \left| \begin{array}{l} 476 \\ \underline{441} \end{array} \right. \\
\times\,9 & \\
586 & \left| \begin{array}{l} 3545 \\ \underline{3516} \end{array} \right. \\
\times\,6 & \\
59205 & \left| \begin{array}{l} 297000 \\ \underline{296025} \end{array} \right. \\
\times\,5 & \\
& 975
\end{array}
$$

Again, starting at the decimal point we make pairs. To the left of the decimal point, our first pair is 76 and the next is 8. To the right, the first pair is 45 and the next one is 70. Note that a zero was added here to make a pair. If we begin as before, the largest square contained in 8 is 4. A 4 is written below the 8, subtracted from 8, and the next pair, 76, is brought down.   The square root of 4 is placed above the 8 and becomes the first digit in the answer.   Next, this 2 in the answer is brought down and, as it is, it is multiplied by 2 and a 4 is placed to the left of 476.   Then we look for the digit which, when placed to the right of this 4 and the whole number multiplied by this digit, will come as close to 476 as possible but remain less than 476.   The digit is 9.   So a 9 is placed as the second digit of the answer. Then 441 is placed below 476 and subtracted, and the next pair, 45, is brought down.

Now we bring down the two digits which appear in our answer and multiply them by 2 which gives us 58.   Again by trial and error, we see that a 6 will serve as our multiplier in the space to the left of 3545, and 6 becomes the third digit in the answer.   Note that the decimal point in the answer appears directly above the decimal point in the original number. We bring down the next pair, 70, and place it to the right of the remainder. This gives us 2970.

This time we take the three digits in our answer, 296, multiply them by two, and have 592.   An inspection of the values shows that there is no number that can be used this time, since no matter how we multiply 592(?) the product will be larger than 2970.   So we place a 0 in the answer and bring down the next pair.   This next pair consists of a pair of zeros which we have added at the end.   It might be noted that we can add as many pairs of zeros as we wish and continue the extraction of the square root to many decimal places or until it happens to come out even.   Again we repeat the process, multiplying the four digits in our numerator by 2 and continuing as above.   This time a 5 appears in our answer and we stop the operation at this point.

It must be emphasized that it is most important when extracting a square root to point off into pairs and to start at the decimal point.   Here are some illustrations of pairing off.

45678.9	04 56 78 . 90
4567.89	45 67 . 89
4.56789	04 . 56 78 90
45.6789	45 . 67 89
.04567	. 04 56 70

We can get very close approximations of square roots by using Table I in the Appendix.   Suppose that we extract the square root of 45360.9 using this table.   We look in the column labeled n^2 until we come as close to 45360 as possible.   The closest number in the table is 45369.   Reading in the column to the left of 45369 we find the square root to be 213.   Next, let us look up the square root of 453609.   This time we go down the n^2 column until we come to 452929.   Our value is about half-way between this number and the next one, and the square root is read as 673.5.   It should be noted that when we take the square root of 4536.09 we proceed in the same way, going down the table until we come to 452929.   The only difference is that we point off differently.   In this case our answer is 67.35.

In a similar fashion, the square root of 4.53609 would be approximately 2.13.

Exponents

We shall have limited use of exponents in elementary statistics, but the student should know what an exponent is and what it means. For example, in 2^3, the 3 is the exponent, and it means to multiply $2 \times 2 \times 2$ or to raise 2 to the third power.

$$3^2 = 3 \times 3 = 9$$
$$4^3 = 4 \times 4 \times 4 = 64$$
$$x^4 = (x)(x)(x)(x)$$

Removing Parentheses and Simplifying

Sometimes it is necessary to simplify a rather complex term. The general rule is to start by performing operations so that the parentheses located on the inside can be removed.

$$[(12 + 4)4] - [(3 + 10) + (6 \times -12)]$$
$$= [(16)4] - [(13) + (-72)]$$
$$= 64 - (-59)$$
$$= 64 + 59$$
$$= 123$$

Proportions and Percentages

A proportion, the symbol for which is p, is defined as a part of a whole. If a pie is cut into six equal parts, each slice is a proportion and we can write that $p = \frac{1}{6}$ or .167.

To use another example, suppose that in a given class of 400 students, 40 receive A's as their final grade; 100, B's; 150, C's; 70, D's; and 40, F's. What proportion received each letter grade?

	N	p	P
A	40	$\frac{40}{400} = .10$	10
B	100	$\frac{100}{400} = .25$	25
C	150	$\frac{150}{400} = .375$	37.5
D	70	$\frac{70}{400} = .175$	17.5
F	40	$\frac{40}{400} = .10$	10
	$N = 400$	1.000	100.0

It should be noted that the sum of the proportions for a given example is always 1 and the maximum value of any single proportion is 1.

A percentage is obtained by multiplying a proportion by 100. The symbol for a percentage is P. For our example, the corresponding percentages are shown in the column at the right. It will be noted that the percentages for our data add up to 100.

A word of warning should be given about percentages and proportions. When the number of cases is small, percentages are unstable. That is, a change in one case can cause a relatively large change in the percentage. For example when there are ten cases, a change in one case causes a change of 10 in terms of percent. It might be desirable to follow a rule that, when the number of cases is less than 100, the use of percentages should be avoided. In fairness to the reader of the results of a study, the number of cases on which a percentage is computed should always be reported with the percentage.

A recent article stated that there was an increase of 132 percent in the number of new teachers of Russian between one year and the next, whereas there was only a 16.5 percent increase in the number of new high school teachers of English. It should have been noted in the article that there were 11,966 new teachers of English, but only 65 new teachers of Russian.

Rounding Numbers

In rounding numbers to the nearest whole number or to the nearest decimal place, we proceed as follows:

To the nearest whole number   7.2 = 7

7.8 = 8

To the nearest tenth   7.17 = 7.2

7.11 = 7.1

.09 = .1

To the nearest hundredth   7.177 = 7.18

.674 = .67

1.098 = 1.10

The general rule is that if the last digit is less than 5, it is dropped; if the last digit is more than 5, the preceding digit is raised to the next higher digit. The only complication arises when numbers end in 5. There is a general rule for this case. When the digit preceding the 5 is an odd number, this digit is raised to the next higher one; when it is an even number, the 5 is dropped. The following examples illustrate this rule:

8.875 = 8.88   5.25 = 5.2

8.05 = 8.0   66.975 = 66.98

Significant Digits. The question frequently arises in recording numbers as to how many digits we should have in our answers. As a general rule the answer should have only one or two digits more than exist in the raw data.   For example, if we have a series of test scores, each of which contain two digits, then ordinarily we would have no more than three digits in the average or mean which we compute from these data.   There is nothing to be gained in computing these averages to five or six decimal places.   No meaningful accuracy is obtained from these large decimals.   As a matter of fact, such large decimals mean nothing when computed on the basis of two-place numbers.   A good rule is to have one more significant digit in the answer than was present in the original numbers.   Here are some examples of the number of significant digits in a series of numbers.

78	two	1008	four
786	three	1976.09	six
78.2	three	.0025	two (the two zeros merely point off the number in this case)

Sometimes students get into trouble as a result of rounding numbers in their problems too freely.   Suppose that we have an operation which consists of six distinct steps.   At the conclusion of the computations for each step, the student rounds his results.   A series of a half dozen such roundings in the course of the solution of a problem causes inaccuracies to enter the work.   If we are going to express our answer to the nearest tenth, a good rule is to carry all operations through in terms of hundredths and round to the nearest tenth in the last step.

HOW VARIABLES ARE CONSIDERED IN STATISTICS

Types of Measurements

We can classify data into two types: continuous and discontinuous, or discrete.   Feet, pounds, minutes, and meters are examples of continuous data.   With these we can make measurements of varying degrees of precision.   For example, we can break meters into centimeters, centimeters into millimeters, and with intricate devices we can make measurements which are more and more precise.   Such data can be considered as points on a line.   The size and accuracy of the measurements that we can make along this line depend on the way that the measurements are made.

To illustrate, suppose that we measure a boy and we say that he is 57 inches tall.   Does this mean that he is exactly 57 inches tall?   Probably not.   In reading our scale, we merely read that number of inches to which the boy's height was closest.   This 57 inches includes then a segment of our line; that is, the segment extends from 56.5 to 57.4999 inches.   We can round the latter and then say that 57 includes everything from 56.5 to 57.5 inches.   Similarly a reading of 58 extends from 57.5 to 58.5.   Each reading which represents continuous data has a lower limit and an upper limit, as shown in Fig. 2.1.

Discontinuous or discrete data, on the other hand, are based upon measurements which can only be expressed in whole units.   The counting of people, for example, can only occur in whole units in contrast to measurements of length which can be divided into smaller and smaller units.   Other examples of discrete units are the number of words spelled correctly, the number of objects assembled, and the number of cars passing a point during

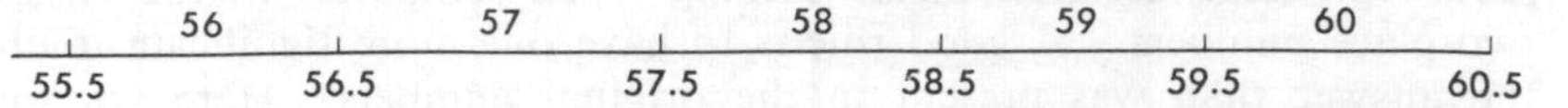

	56		57		58		59		60	
55.5		56.5		57.5		58.5		59.5		60.5

FIGURE 2.1   The upper and lower limits of continuous data.

a certain period of time.   The student will note, however, that in statistical work most data tend to be treated as continuous, so we make such statements as: the typical graduate of college A has 2.8 children.   The student should become accustomed to thinking of every number as having an upper and a lower limit.

In statistics and measurement it is customary to describe four types of measures: *nominal, ordinal, interval,* and *ratio.*   As these are listed, the lowest type occurs first.   When a *nominal* scale is used, a number or name is used to designate a class or a category.   For example, a sample of voters may be classified into three categories: Democrat, Republican, and Independent.   Another example of such a scale is two groups designated on the basis of sex.   After the groups are designated, the numbers in each group can be determined and the simplest types of statistics used.   Nominal scales indicate that individuals belong in different categories.

When measurements are arranged on an *ordinal* scale, they are placed in rank order, starting with either the largest or the smallest.   When data are on this scale, simple statistics such as the median, centiles, and the Spearman rank-order correlation coefficient may be used.   Ordinal scales indicate which objects are larger or smaller than another.

The next highest type of scale is the *interval* scale.   Scales of this type must have equal units of measurement.   The commonly used Fahrenheit or centigrade thermometers represent scales of this type.   Interval scales show that an object is so many units larger or smaller than another.

The final type of scale, the *ratio* scale, has an absolute zero in addition to equal units.   Such a scale is the Kelvin scale.   Its absolute zero is the point at which there is the absence of heat, or $-273°C$.   Measurements made in feet, pounds, gallons, and the like are also ratio scales.

When data are in terms of feet, we can say that one length is twice or half that of another.   When our measurements are on an interval scale, we cannot do this and make sense.   For example, suppose that the maximum temperature today is 60°; the same day last year it was 30°.   In this case we cannot state that it is twice as warm today as it was on the same date last year.   What is the difference between these two conditions?   When we were dealing with feet, we were using a measuring scale that was based upon an absolute zero; in the second case we are using a scale which started 32 degrees below the freezing point of water.   When measurements are on a ratio scale, meaningful comparisons can be made. As a matter of fact, when data are of this type, all of the usual mathematical and statistical manipulations may be made. However, in actual practice, many of our measurements are based upon interval scales and we apply practically all of our statistical techniques to these measurements.

What can we say about the measurements that we make in education, sociology, and psychology? First of all, we frequently assume that they have equal units of measurement. An inspection of certain of these, such as intelligence quotients, reveals that this assumption is not likely to be true. Furthermore, our scales do not possess an absolute zero. The physicist can describe absolute zero on his heat scale. It is not difficult to visualize zero inches, pounds, or meters. But what does zero IQ mean? Or what does it mean when a boy gets a score of zero on a geography test? Actually we do not know what these scores of zero mean. Then it follows that we have no basis for stating that a child with an IQ twice the size of the IQ of another child is twice as bright. Neither can we say that the child whose score on an arithmetic test is double that of another child knows twice as much arithmetic as the first child.

SAMPLES AND POPULATIONS

It is important to distinguish between these two terms, and to do this let us use an illustration. Suppose that we are interested in the mental ability of children in the second grade. One way to investigate this is to give intelligence tests to second graders. We begin by obtaining permission to administer the test to one group of second graders. We compute the average or mean score for the group; this mean score is a statistic and gives us the average test score of our sample. Since there are so many second-grade pupils, we could continue this process for a long time by drawing sample after sample. If each of these samples is a *random sample* (random sampling procedures will be discussed in Chapter 10), we can combine all the sample averages or means to obtain a grand mean. This grand mean will be our best estimate of the average intelligence of all the second graders. That is, the average of all of the means of our samples is used to tell us something about the population value. All second graders in the United States make up the population or universe from which the various samples are drawn. Values which refer to populations are referred to as *parameters*; in contrast, *statistics* are reserved to describe samples. Populations, as the term is used in statistics, are arbitrarily defined groups. They need not be as large as the one used here as an illustration. We could define the 552 seniors in a certain school system as our population, and from this we could draw samples. One of the major aspects of statistical research is making inferences about population characteristics on the basis of one or more samples that have been studied.

Statistical Symbols

The student will soon find that there are a number of symbols used in statistics. However, there is no absolute conformity in the use of these symbols, and notational usage will vary somewhat from author to author. A common and simple statistical equation is

$$\Sigma f = N$$

This equation is read, capital sigma (Σ), *summation of*, or *the sum of*, the frequencies (f) is equal to N, the number of cases. Σ is one of the most widely used statistical symbols.

If we are dealing with one variable (a variable being a characteristic that manifests differences in magnitude or quantity), it is customary to designate it as "x." One measurement or observation of a variable is usually symbolized by the corresponding capital letter; hence X is one measure for variable x and Y is one measure for variable "y." Different individual measures on the same variable are denoted by numeric subscripts; $X_1, X_2, X_3, \ldots, X_N$.

The student will find it useful to be familiar with the following expressions:

$$X = Y \qquad X \text{ equals } Y$$
$$X \neq Y \qquad X \text{ does not equal } Y$$
$$X > Y \qquad X \text{ is greater than } Y$$
$$X < Y \qquad X \text{ is less than } Y$$
$$X \geq Y \qquad X \text{ is equal to or greater than } Y$$
$$X \leq Y \qquad X \text{ is equal to or less than } Y$$

As mentioned earlier in this chapter, the characteristics of a population are called *parameters* while the characteristics of a sample are called *statistics*. In this book, as in most statistical writing, different symbols are used for *parameters* and *statistics*.

Characteristic	Parameter	Statistic
Mean	m	$\overline{X}$
Standard Deviation	σ	s
Variance	σ^2	s^2
Proportion	p	p
Pearson correlation coefficient	R	r
Number of cases	n	N

In many instances lowercase Latin letters are used to represent statistics and lowercase Greek letters for parameters.

Exercises

1. Subtract the following:
    (a) 26.09   (b)   87.54   (c)   .0987   (d) 14.67
          7.76   − 22.13   − .9987   32.53

    (e) − .0987   (f) − 54.89   (g)   1.0987   (h) 67.87
          .9872   − 6.76   11.6009   − 7.13

2. Multiply the following:
    (a) 45.67   (b) 12.345   (c) .0008   (d) − 11.098
          8   .006   .07   .06

    (e) 456.89   (f) − .0768   (g) − .777   (h) − 6.578
          − 2   − .4   1.000   − .9

3. Divide the following:
    (a) 16/.4   (b) 81/.009   (c) .125/5   (d) − 2.525/.05
    (e) 144/ − .4   (f) − .49/ − .007 (g) 100.58/ − 10 (h) − 16.16/ − 4

4. Complete the following operations with fractions in the manner indicated:
    (a) $\frac{1}{2} + \frac{3}{4} + \frac{5}{3} + \frac{5}{6} =$ (l) $442\frac{2}{11} - (-.426) =$
    (b) $2\frac{2}{3} + \frac{5}{8} + \frac{7}{12} =$ (m) $(\frac{1}{2})(\frac{2}{3})(0) =$
    (c) $\frac{7}{3} + 2\frac{3}{4} - \frac{2}{3} =$ (n) $4^3 =$
    (d) $\frac{5}{3} + \frac{6}{15} - (-\frac{9}{15}) =$ (o) $(3)^4 - (5)^3 =$
    (e) $\frac{5}{6} - (-2\frac{1}{6}) - \frac{7}{6} =$ (p) $a(ab) =$
    (f) $(\frac{9}{7})(\frac{4}{6}) =$ (q) $(\frac{2}{3})^2 =$
    (g) $(\frac{3}{4})(\frac{5}{2})(-\frac{2}{3}) =$ (r) $(x + y)^2 =$
    (h) $(\frac{3}{4}) \div (\frac{4}{5}) =$ (s) $12 - (-3)^2 =$
    (i) $(\frac{7}{8})(\frac{4}{5}) \div \frac{3}{7} =$ (t) $(fx)x =$
    (j) $6(-8 + 4) - \frac{1}{2}(-3 \div -6) =$ (u) $(x)(xy)(x^2y^2)(z) =$
    (k) $12[286 - (16)^2][198 - (14)^2] =$

5. Find the square root of each of the following:
    (a) 3249   (g) .00025
    (b) 30625   (h) 9.0009
    (c) 306916   (i) $1/9$
    (d) 777.89   (j) − .49
    (e) 8876.9   (k) 76453.678
    (f) .00009

6. Round each of the following to the nearest tenth:
    (a) 14.36   (f) 90.25
    (b) 24.32   (g) 87.95
    (c) 17.798   (h) 56.35
    (d) .098   (i) 48.575
    (e) 1.011   (j) .125

7. How many significant digits are there in each of the following?
    (a) 234.67   (e) 5004.009
    (b) 10.67   (f) .009
    (c) .67   (g) 7.2
    (d) .067   (h) 0.01

3

FREQUENCY DISTRIBUTIONS, GRAPHS, AND CENTILES

Often to make our data more meaningful and convenient, we set up a frequency distribution and draw graphs of various kinds to represent the data.

THE FREQUENCY DISTRIBUTION

Suppose that we have given a geography test yielding the scores shown in Table 3.1. The first step is to determine the range. This is defined as the

TABLE 3.1. Scores on a Geography Test

56	78	62	37	54	39	62	60
28	82	38	72	62	44	54	42
42	55	57	65	68	47	42	56
56	56	55	66	42	52	48	48
47	41	50	52	47	48	53	68

highest score minus the lowest score plus one. In Table 3.1 the highest score is 82 and the lowest is 28. In statistics we let a capital X stand for any raw score or any measurement. If we were working with two sets of data at the same time, we could use a capital Y for any measurement in the other set. The range then is

$$(X_H - X_L) + 1 \quad \text{or} \quad (82 - 28) + 1 = 55$$

The second step is to decide how large each of the intervals in the frequency distribution is going to be. A widely accepted practice is to have between 10 and 20 intervals in the frequency table. When there are less than 10 intervals, the coarseness of the grouping may cause inaccuracies;

18

when there are more than 20, the work becomes laborious.   The size of the intervals can be determined in a trial and error fashion.

If we let each interval cover 10 units, then the range will be included by 6 of these intervals, $55 \div 10 = 5.5$ or 6.   Ten then is too large, as this results in only 6 intervals.   Suppose that this time we try 5.   Five goes into 55 exactly 11 times; hence 5 would be acceptable as the size of our interval. If we try 3, we find that 3 goes into 55 about 18 times; so 3 could be used for the size of the interval.   Let us consider one more, 2.   Two is contained in 55 about 28 times.   We would reject this as the size of the interval, because it results in too many intervals.   Since we need between 10 and 20 intervals in our frequency distribution, we can take the average of 10 and 20, which is 15, and divide this into the range.   In this case the range 55 divided by 15 results in a value between 3 and 4, and either of these could accordingly be used as the interval size (i).

If you observe frequency distributions made by others, you will note that odd numbers are frequently used for the size of the intervals.   The advantage of this is that the midpoints of each of the intervals will be whole numbers.   Such numbers as 3 and 5 are commonly used for interval size (i). An exception to this practice is the use of multiples of 10 which often make convenient intervals.

TABLE 3.2.   Setting Up a
Frequency Distribution

		f
81–83	/	1
78–80	/	1
75–77		0
72–74	/	1
69–71		0
66–68	/ / /	3
63–65	/	1
60–62	/ / / /	4
57–59	/	1
54–56	̷H̷L̷ / / /	8
51–53	/ / /	3
48–50	/ / / /	4
45–47	/ / /	3
42–44	̷H̷L̷	5
39–41	/ /	2
36–38	/ /	2
33–35		0
30–32		0
27–29	/	1
		$N = 40$

Suppose for the data in Table 3.1 we decide to use an interval with a size of 3.   We would note this by writing that $i = 3$.   We start building the frequency distribution that is shown in Table 3.2.   The next problem is to decide where to start.   A common practice is to let the bottom interval begin with a number which is a multiple of the interval size.   In this case our lowest score is 28, the size of our interval is to be 3, so the bottom interval would begin at 27 and end at 29.   These are the *integral limits*.   Remember from the last chapter that in statistics we are going to deal with upper and lower limits (or exact limits), and so this bottom interval actually begins at 26.5 and ends at 29.5.   If we subtract the first of these from the latter, we obtain a value of 3 which is the size of the interval.   This interval size is not apparent unless we are aware of the exact limits of the interval.   This bottom interval also has a midpoint that is one-half of the distance between the lower and the upper limits.   The midpoint for this interval then is 26.5 + 1.5 which equals 28.   As noted above, when the size of an interval is an odd number, the midpoint will be a whole number.

After deciding upon the limits of the bottom interval, we determine the rest of the intervals by increasing each integral limit by 3.   We stop when we reach the interval 81–83 which contains the highest score in the distribution. The usual practice is to set up frequency distributions with the lowest scores at the bottom.

The next task is to tally the scores.   We take the scores one at a time and record each to the right of its appropriate interval by making a tally mark. When this is finished, we combine the tallies in the column to the right. This column is headed with f which stands for frequencies.   This column is summed, and we write the total at the bottom.   We can write a capital N in front of this sum to denote that the number of cases is 40, or we can write $\Sigma f = 40$.   This last symbol which is the Greek capital sigma is, as noted, read as "summation of" or "sum of."   Note that for intervals where there were no tallies, we entered a zero in the f column.   Data in such a frequency distribution are said to be *grouped*, and formulas used with grouped data are applicable to this type of data only.   In contrast, we also have ungrouped data; the formulas applied to them are often referred to as raw score formulas.

Suppose that we organize the same geography test scores in a different frequency table.   This time the size of the interval will be 5.   Since our lowest score is 28, the lowest interval will be 25–29.   This interval has exact limits of 24.5 and 29.5 and a midpoint of 27.   This second table appears as Table 3.3.   This time we have only 12 intervals instead of 19 which resulted when we used an interval size of 3.   In the actual analysis of these data, the interval of 5 would be preferred.

At this point we summarize the steps in organizing a frequency distribution or frequency table.

1. Determine the range.
2. Divide this by 15 to estimate the approximate size of the interval.
3. List the intervals, beginning at the bottom.   Let the lowest interval begin with a number which is a multiple of the interval size.
4. Tally the frequencies.
5. Summarize these under a column labeled f.
6. Total this column and record the number of cases at the bottom.   It might be mentioned here that if this number, obtained by adding the

frequencies, is the same as the known number of cases, it does not follow that no mistake has been made. To check the work, the scores should be retallied.

TABLE 3.3. Setting Up a
Frequency Distribution

		f
80–84	/	1
75–79	/	1
70–74	/	1
65–69	/ / / /	4
60–64	/ / / /	4
55–59	⊬⊬ /·/	7
50–54	⊬⊬ /	6
45–49	⊬⊬ /	6
40–44	⊬⊬ /	6
35–39	/ / /	3
30–34		0
25–29	/	1
		$\Sigma f = 40$

GRAPHS

The Frequency Polygon

Of all the graphic devices used to illustrate statistical distributions, probably the most frequently encountered is the frequency polygon. This is because the frequency polygon is very easy to construct, and it is basically very simple to interpret. Several distributions, using a different type of line for each, may be portrayed on the same axes.

Construction of the Frequency Polygon. In all work with graphs, two axes are used. The vertical axis is always labeled the *Y* axis and values taken along this axis are called *ordinate* values. The other axis, the *X* axis, is called the *abscissa*. It is horizontal and meets the *Y* axis at right angles at a point called the origin (0). In constructing graphs of the frequency polygon type, the *X* axis is longer than the *Y* axis. Usually a ratio of 3 to 2 or 4 to 3 will result in a good graph. For example, if the *X* axis is 6 inches in length, the *Y* axis should be about 4 inches. Or if another graph had an *X* axis of 8 inches, then the *Y* axis should be about 6 inches.

To make graphs that can be easily and accurately read, a good quality graph paper should be used. The type that has ten squares to the inch is very good for statistical work. It is easier to build graphs of the desirable proportions if the *X* axis is placed on the wider side of the graph paper. In building a frequency polygon, the frequency values are always placed on the *Y* axis. A small *f* is placed along the *Y* axis. The scores are placed on the *X* axis. To illustrate this, suppose that we construct a frequency polygon for the data in Table 3.3.   The highest frequency is 7, so we need no more than 7 units on the *Y* axis of Fig. 3.1.   On the *X* axis we have placed score values.

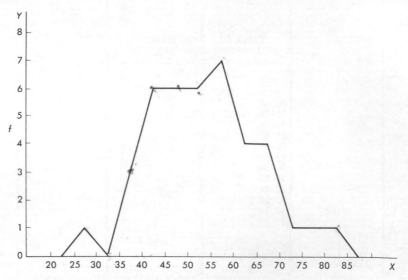

FIGURE 3.1   Frequency polygon for the geography scores in Table 3.1.

The next step is to plot the frequencies.   For any one of the intervals in Table 3.3 we can make an assumption that if all the scores in that interval were averaged, this average would be equal to the midpoint of the interval. Then it follows that the midpoint is the value which best represents any given interval.   Frequency values are plotted above the corresponding midpoints of each of the class intervals.   Let us take the first or bottom interval of our table, 25–29.   This interval has a midpoint of 27 and a frequency of 1. We go along the *X* axis until we come to 27, and then we go up one unit above this point and place a point.   The midpoint of the next interval is 32, and this interval has a frequency of 0.   So a mark is placed at 32 on the *X* axis.   Next, the midpoint of the third interval is 37 with a frequency of 3. So at a point 3 units above 37 on the *X* axis we place our next point.   We proceed like this until all the frequencies have been plotted.   Then with a ruler we connect these points with straight lines.

Rather than leave our graph suspended in space, we assume that there is another interval above and below those shown in our table, and that each of these intervals has a frequency of 0.   So at 22, the midpoint of the lower of these terminal intervals, we place a mark on the *X* axis.   A similar mark is placed at 87 to provide our top.   The graph is now anchored at both ends. Some find it much more convenient to construct frequency polygons with the numerical values of the midpoints of the intervals on the *X* axis rather than the score values shown in Fig. 3.1.   The resulting picture is the same, no matter which method is used in the construction.

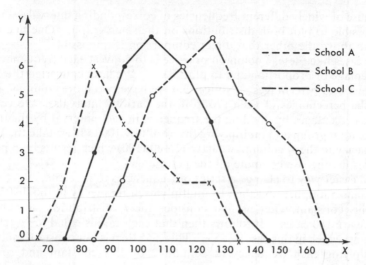

FIGURE 3.2 Distribution of Stanford-Binet IQ's for groups of kindergarten children in three schools of a city.

As mentioned earlier, the frequency polygon is very useful in portraying two or more distributions at once. Figure 3.2 shows the distributions of the intelligence quotients of three groups of kindergarten children in three different schools of a city. In such a graph, similarities and differences are very apparent.

Constructing Frequency Polygons When Frequencies Differ. In many cases, as in Table 3.4, we find that the numbers in the different groups we

TABLE 3.4. Intelligence Test Scores of Children in Two Schools

(1) Scores	(2) School A f_1	(3) School B f_2	(4) P_1	(5) P_2
150–159	1	10	.6	2
140–149	4	20	2.2	4
130–139	8	40	4.4	8
120–129	12	170	6.7	34
110–119	31	180	17.2	36
100–109	69	50	38.3	10
90–99	32	10	17.8	2
80–89	18	10	10.0	2
70–79	4	5	2.2	1
60–69	1	5	.6	1
	$\Sigma f_1 = 180$	$\Sigma f_2 = 500$	100.0%	100%

wish to plot differ considerably. In this table we have the distribution of intelligence test scores for 180 children in one school (f_1) and for 500 children in another school (f_2). If we attempt to plot both these distributions on the same axes as they are now organized, we shall have difficulty.

Because of widely different frequencies in corresponding intervals, it may be impossible to plot both distributions on the same graph.   One line will be so far above the other that direct comparison is impossible.

In cases like these, a common practice is to convert each frequency into a percentage or proportion and to plot these.   We have converted the data in Table 3.4 to percentages.   Notice that we have two more columns, P_1 and P_2, the percentages of each group in the various intervals.   We compute these percentages by dividing the frequency in each interval by the number in the total group and multiplying this result by 100.   If we take the bottom frequency in the f_1 column, we have (1/180)(100) which results in .6 percent. In this manner we compute all the percentages.

An easier way to change a series of frequencies to percentages is to find a constant multiplier and then to multiply each frequency in the distribution by this constant.   Let us first consider the f_1 distribution in Table 3.4. There are 180 cases.   It follows then that each case is equal to (1/180)(100) percent, which in this case is .555.   This .555 then is our constant multiplier; multiplying each frequency in column 2 by this constant and rounding results in the values shown in column 4.   A check on the work is that the sum of column 4 is 100 percent.   Sometimes there are minor variations in this sum caused by rounding.   The f_2 data in column 3 are taken next.

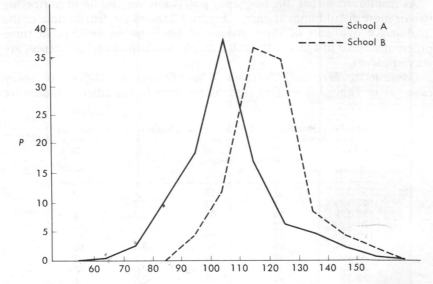

FIGURE 3.3   Distribution of scores on an intelligence test in two schools with the frequencies converted to percentages.

This time the constant multiplier is (1/500)(100) which equals .2.   So we multiply each of the f_2 frequencies by .2 and find the results shown in column 5.

The next step is to construct the frequency polygon as described earlier. This time, though, we place our percentages, instead of the frequencies, on the Y axis.   The largest percentage in columns 4 and 5 is smaller than 40 (38.3); hence the largest value needed on our Y axis is 40.   Along the X axis we have the test scores plotted in the usual manner (see Fig. 3.3). We plot our percentages above the midpoints of the appropriate intervals on the X axis and connect these points with straight lines.   These lines should be constructed using different types of lines or different colors. Since we have two graphs on the same axis, we include a legend showing which polygon represents which set of data.

Types of Curves

After making a few frequency polygons, we soon notice that the curves tend to have shapes that can be classified into types.   Sometimes the frequencies tend to pile up on the left-hand side of the graph with a tail extending to the right, as shown in curve A of Fig. 3.4.   Such a curve is

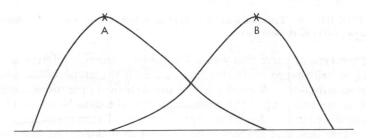

FIGURE 3.4   Types of skewness: curve A is positively skewed; curve B is negatively skewed.

said to be *skewed*.   If the tail goes to the right, we label this type of skew as being *positive*.   (This conforms with the mathematicians' practice of calling the right end of a line positive and the left end negative.)   Curve B shows the tail extending to the left.   This condition is called *negative skewness*. The student should remember that it is the tail of the distribution which determines the sign of the skewness and not the location of the pile-up of scores.

Curves can also be classified on the basis of their peakedness or *kurtosis*. Figure 3.5 shows the three types of kurtosis.   Curve A is peaked and the tails are more elevated above the base line.   Such a curve is said to be leptokurtic.   Curve B is described as being mesokurtic and curve C, decidedly flattened, is said to be platykurtic.   Measures of skewness and kurtosis will be presented in a later chapter.

Another type of curve that is by no means rare is the bimodal curve shown in Fig. 3.6.   This curve has two peaks or modes.   It is also possible for a curve to have more than two modes.

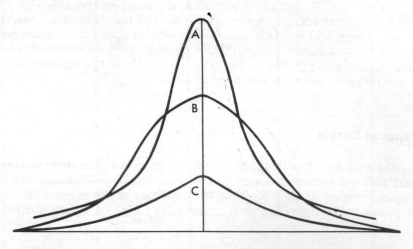

FIGURE 3.5   Types of kurtosis: curve A is leptokurtic; curve B is meso-kurtic; curve C is platykurtic.

The last type of curve that we shall consider is the one referred to as the normal or bell-shaped curve (Fig. 3.7).   This is the graph of the so-called normal distribution.   A good share of the statistical operations covered in this book are based upon the assumption that the data being handled are normally distributed.   Since this type of curve is of such major importance, considerable time and space will be devoted to it later.   At that time we shall discuss its properties and uses.

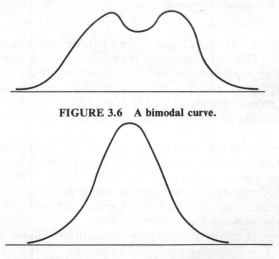

FIGURE 3.6   A bimodal curve.

FIGURE 3.7   The normal or bell-shaped curve.

Other Types of Graphs

The Histogram.   The histogram (Fig. 3.8) is very similar in construction to the frequency polygon.   Everything is the same up to the point of plotting the frequencies.   The histogram in Fig. 3.8 is also based upon the data in

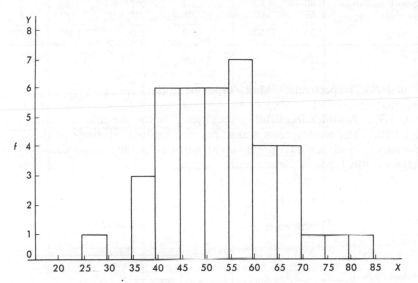

FIGURE 3.8   Histogram for the geography scores in Table 3.3.

Table 3.3.   Here is how this graph is made.   The bottom interval 25–29 has a frequency of 1.   Starting at the lower limit of this interval, 24.5, the interval is marked off, and since the interval has a frequency of 1, this interval has a height of 1 on the Y axis.   The next interval has a frequency of 0; hence there is a gap in our histogram at this point.   At the interval beginning with 34.5, we mark off a bar with a height of 3, since there are three scores in this interval.   We continue this process until we have entered all the frequencies into the graph.   If the midpoints of the top line of each of the columns comprising the histogram were connected, we would have the same frequency polygon previously constructed.

The histogram is more time consuming to construct than the frequency polygon.   Also, only one histogram can be placed clearly on one set of axes unless a second is reversed and plotted below the X axis.   We saw how several frequency polygons were placed on the same axes to make comparisons and illustrate differences.   This cannot be done as easily and clearly with histograms.   Their use is thus more limited than that of some other types of graphs.

Graphs for Frequencies, Proportions, and Percentages.   In Table 3.5 are figures showing the number of seniors in five colleges of two universities. The frequencies have been converted into both proportions and percentages,

TABLE 3.5.   Seniors in the Five Colleges of Two Universities, A and B

College	f A	B	p A	B	P A	B
Engineering	440	640	.48	.58	48%	58%
Liberal Arts	220	220	.24	.20	24	20
Agriculture	120	120	.13	.11	13	11
Home Economics	80	80	.09	.07	9	7
Fine Arts	60	40	.06	.04	6	4
	920	1100	1.00	1.00	100%	100%

p's and P's, respectively.   Many types of graphs can be used to display these data pictorially.   One of the commonest of these is the bar graph (Fig. 3.9).   Another frequently encountered is the pie diagram shown in Fig. 3.10.   The weekly news magazines, the business sections of the daily newspapers, and our own professional journals include many illustrations of the various types of these graphs.

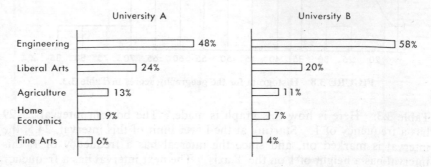

FIGURE 3.9   Bar graphs for the data in Table 3.5.

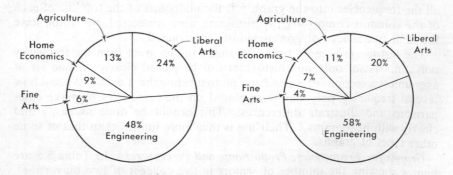

FIGURE 3.10   Pie diagrams for the data in Table 3.5.

CUMULATIVE FREQUENCY DISTRIBUTIONS

In Table 3.6 a frequency distribution of the scores of 376 boys on a test of mechanical ability is presented.   Column 2 contains the frequencies.   In column 3 we have the cumulative frequencies, *cf*.   These are obtained as follows.   We start at the bottom and note how many scores are below the

TABLE 3.6.   Obtaining Cumulative Frequencies,
Proportions, and Percentages

(1)	(2) f	(3) cf	(4) cp	(5) cP
60–64	2	376	1.000	100
55–59	12	374	.995	99.5
50–54	20	362	.963	96.3
45–49	32	342	.907	90.7
40–44	46	310	.824	82.4
35–39	58	264	.702	70.2
30–34	64	206	.548	54.8
25–29	58	142	.377	37.7
20–24	42	84	.223	22.3
15–19	23	42	.112	11.2
10–14	15	19	.050	5.0
5–9	4	4	.011	1.1

$$N = 376$$

upper limit of the bottom interval.   The number is 4.   So a 4 appears as the bottom entry in column 3.   Next we ask how many scores fall below the upper limit of the next interval, that is, how many scores are below 14.5. The answer is 19, the frequency of all scores below this point.   The cumulative frequency for the next interval is $23 + 19 = 42$.   The process is continued by adding the frequency of each interval to the cumulative frequency of all the intervals below the given interval.   If the work is correct, the *cf* of the top interval will equal the number of cases.

Obtaining the Cumulative Proportions and Percentages

As pointed out previously, the easiest way to convert a set of frequencies to proportions is to obtain a constant multiplier by dividing 1 by the number of cases and then multiplying each frequency by this constant to obtain the proportion.   *The dividend that results from dividing 1 by any number is called the reciprocal of that number.*   The reciprocals of the numbers from 1 to 1000 are presented in the fourth column of Table I in the Appendix. For these data, we want to multiply each *cf* by the reciprocal of 376.   In Table I, we find that $1/376 = .00266$.   The products of .00266 and each *cf* are recorded in column 4.   This column is headed *cp*, cumulative proportions. To change these cumulative proportions to cumulative percentages, *cP*, each *cp* is multiplied by 100.   These values appear in column 5.

Constructing the Cumulative Percentage or Ogive Curve

In setting up the cumulative proportion, cumulative percentage, or ogive curve as it may be called, we follow the general rules of building graphs which we discussed earlier.   We attempt to have the ratio of the Y axis to the X axis as 2 is to 3.   The cumulative proportions or cumulative percentages are always placed along the vertical or Y axis.   As in the frequency polygon, the scores are entered on the horizontal or X axis.   The values on the Y axis will range between 0 and 1, or 0 and 100, depending on whether we are using proportions or percentages.   In this case we are going to plot the cumulative percentages.   It may be recalled that when we were plotting a frequency polygon we placed the plotting points above the midpoint of

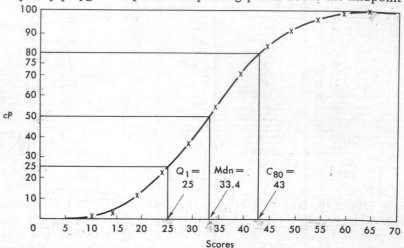

FIGURE 3.11   Cumulative percentage or ogive curve for the ability test scores in Table 3.6.

each interval.   *In plotting the cumulative percentage graph, we use the upper limits of each of the intervals and place our points above these.*   This is consistent with the concept of cumulative frequencies or cumulative percentages.   In finding these from our frequency table, we asked ourselves how many or what percent of the cases fell below the upper limit of each interval.   The construction of one of these curves is shown in Fig. 3.11.

The upper limit of the bottom interval is 9.5.   Hence above 9.5 on the X axis we go up 1.1 points and place our point.   Above 14.5, the upper limit of the next interval, we count off 5 units on the Y axis and again place a mark.   This process is continued until all cP values are plotted.   Then a smoothed curve is drawn.   Some of the plotted points will not be on the curve, some appearing on one side and some on the other.   Smoothed curves of cumulative distributions take the shape shown in Fig. 3.11 and are frequently referred to as S-shaped curves.   The curve is brought to the base line by extending it to the next lower interval and giving that interval a cP of 0.

CENTILES

Reading the Centile Points from the Ogive Curve

If the cumulative percentage curve has been accurately constructed on a large piece of graph paper, centile points may be read from it with a high degree of accuracy. To read the points a ruler is placed on the cP column at the centile point desired and a straight line is drawn over to the curve. From this point on the curve another line is drawn down to make a right angle with the X axis. The point on the X axis where this vertical line meets the X axis indicates the desired centile point. In Fig. 3.11 lines are drawn showing the values for C_{80}, the median C_{50} and C_{25}. These values are approximately 43, 33, and 25, respectively. These values are very close to the computed values for the same statistics which are 43.5, 33.1, and 25.4.

Computation of Centiles

A centile or centile point is defined as a specific point in a distribution which has a given percent of the cases below it. For example, the 88th centile (C_{88}) is that point in a distribution which has 88 percent of the cases below it.

To illustrate the computation of centiles the data in Table 3.6 will be used. First we shall compute C_{50}. By definition, this centile point will have 50 percent of the cases above and below it. That is, it is the midpoint of the distribution and is known as the *median*. Dividing the N of 376 by 2 or taking 50 percent of it gives 188 cases. Hence we are interested in finding that point in the distribution with 188 cases above and below it.

We start by counting up from the bottom until we come as close to 188 cases as possible, but not exceeding it. This brings us to the point at the top of the interval 25–29 or at the bottom of the interval 30–34, this point being 29.5. There are 142 cases below this point. We need 46 more cases, the difference between 188 and 142. We must interpolate, for we need 46 of the 64 cases in the next interval. In other words, we need to go 46/64ths of the distance through the length of the interval which in this case is 5. We can write this as follows:

$$C_{50} = 29.5 + \frac{46}{64}(5)$$

$$= 29.5 + \frac{230}{64}$$

$$= 29.5 + 3.59$$

$$= 33.1$$

This can be checked by coming down from the top:

$$C_{50} = 34.5 - \frac{18}{64}(5)$$

$$= 34.5 - \frac{90}{64}$$

$$= 34.5 - 1.4$$

$$= 33.1$$

Suppose we wish to find C_{12} for the same data. First we take 12 percent of 376 which is 45.12 cases. We can count 42 cases from the bottom which brings up to the top of the interval, 19.5. At this point we must interpolate:

$$C_{12} = 19.5 + \frac{45.12 - 42}{42}(5)$$

$$= 19.5 + \frac{3.12}{42}(5)$$

$$= 19.5 + \frac{15.60}{42}$$

$$= 19.5 + .37$$

$$= 19.9$$

Next we shall compute C_{88}. We could start out by taking 88 percent of N and counting up from the bottom as we did for C_{12}. However, we can make our work much easier by taking 12 percent of N and coming down from the top. For example,

$$12\% \text{ of } N = 45.12$$

$$C_{88} = 49.5 - \frac{45.12 - 34}{32}(5)$$

$$= 49.5 - \frac{11.12}{32}(5)$$

$$= 49.5 - \frac{55.60}{32}$$

$$= 49.5 - 1.74$$

$$= 47.8$$

Several of the centile points have special names, such as *median* for C_{50}. C_{25} is known as the first quartile and is written as Q_1. Similarly C_{75}, the third quartile, is represented by the symbol Q_3. In addition to these there are 9 decile points that divide the distribution into ten equal parts. For example, C_{10} equals D_1 and C_{20} equals D_2.

When the data are ungrouped, the individual measures can be arranged from low to high and the centile points obtained by counting. This can be illustrated by finding the median in the following examples.

Suppose that we have the following 11 scores:

$$20, 19, 18, 17, 16, 15, 14, 13, 12, 11, 10$$

In this case the score of 15 has five scores on each side of it and hence is the median.

Here is another series:

$$20, 19, 18, 17, 16, 15, 14, 13, 12, 11$$

In this series of 10 scores we count up 5 cases (or down 5). This brings us to the point 15.5, which is the median, half-way between scores of 15 and 16.

The above two cases are easy, since the median can be obtained by inspection. Suppose that our series is as follows:

$$21, 20, 19, 18, 17, 17, 17, 16, 15, 14$$

Again we have 10 measures and again we wish to find the point that has 5 scores on each side of it.   We start from the bottom and count cases 14, 15, and 16, which occupy the first 3 positions.   However, the three 17's make it impossible to finish this problem as we did the first two.   We continue up to the bottom of the number 17 or to the top of 16.   This point is 16.5. Here we have to interpolate.   We have used 3 cases and need 2 more. These three 17's are assumed to be spread equally through the interval 16.5–17.5, and since we want only two of these 17's, we shall take a point that is two-thirds of the way through this interval as the median.   In summary, $C_{50} = 16.5 + \frac{2}{3} = 16.5 + .67 = 17.2$.

Use of Centiles

Centiles are widely used in educational circles in reporting the results of standardized tests.   In their favor, it can be said that they are very easy to understand.   Even if one does not know that a person who has a centile score of 77 is at a point above 77 percent of those upon whom the test was standardized, at least the 77th centile looks like 77 percent, and even the most uninformed teacher can understand what that means.   Since centiles appear to be like percents, there is little difficulty in understanding their meaning.   Also they give an adequate indication of an individual's rank in a group.

Centiles do, however, have serious limitations, and many makers and users of tests no longer bother with them.   If you examine a set of centile norms or a profile sheet based upon such norms, you will note that the centile norms are piled up at the middle of the distribution.   Notice Fig. 3.12.   A raw score of 33 is equivalent to C_{50}, a raw score of 36, to a centile point of 60, and a raw score of 30, to a centile point of 40.   A change in six raw score units is the equivalent to a change in 20 centile units.   There is, then, a piling up of centile points at the center of the distribution, and differences between them at this part of the curve have little meaning.

To state that an individual who is at C_{47} on a certain test differs from the individual who is at C_{51} on the same test is making much ado about nothing. At the center of distribution, the use of centile scores tends to exaggerate differences that are not actually in existence.   Centiles are unequal units of measurement and cannot be treated arithmetically.   That is, there is no justification for averaging them, combining them, or treating them in any mathematical fashion.   As statistics go, they are dead ends.   Nothing should be done with them.   If we wish to manipulate data which have been reduced to centiles, we should convert the data back to raw scores and work with these.   Since centiles are unequal units of measurement, some statistical workers believe that we would be better off without them.   With standardized tests, centiles are becoming less frequently used as a method of reporting norms.   However, in certain circles, they will be with us for a long time to come.

Let us see why centiles pile up at the center of the distribution.   If we go back to the original definition of a centile point as a point in a distribution

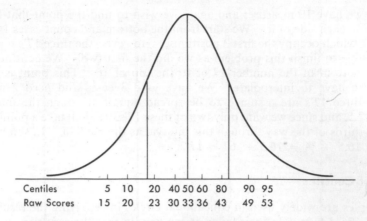

| Centiles | 5 | 10 | 20 | 40 50 60 | 80 | 90 95 |
| Raw Scores | 15 | 20 | 23 | 30 33 36 | 43 | 49 53 |

FIGURE 3.12   **Centile and raw-score equivalents for a set of data.**

with a certain percent of the distribution of the cases below it, it follows that C_{10} is that point in the distribution with 10 percent of the cases below it. To say that 10 percent of the area of a curve falls below C_{10} would be another way of stating this (see Fig. 3.13). If we take C_{20} next, it is by definition that point with 20 percent of the cases in the distribution below it. Ten percent more of the area is added below C_{20} in our figure. This may be continued until all the area or all the cases of a distribution are included. The resulting distribution looks like Fig. 3.13, which, instead of being a normal curve, is a rectangle. The distribution of centiles is described as

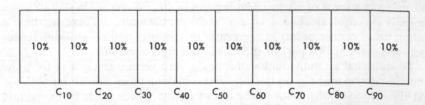

| 10% | 10% | 10% | 10% | 10% | 10% | 10% | 10% | 10% | 10% |

C_{10} C_{20} C_{30} C_{40} C_{50} C_{60} C_{70} C_{80} C_{90}

FIGURE 3.13   **The rectangular distribution of centiles.**

being rectangular. Measurements made in social and biological sciences tend to take the form of the normal curve. Distortions come about when such data are converted to centiles which have a distribution of another shape.

Sometimes confusion arises in the interpretation of tables of centiles. For example, note that Table 3.6 gives a centile value for each interval (cP). However, these centile points correspond to the *upper limit* of each interval. Sometimes tables are prepared which indicate the centile point equivalent to the *midpoint* of each interval. This practice is common in reporting norms for standardized tests.

Exercises

1. What are the exact limits, the midpoints, and the interval sizes for each of the following intervals?
    (a) 2–5
    (b) 15–20
    (c) 0–3
    (d) 5–9
    (e) $(-2)-(-6)$
    (f) $(-3)-(+3)$
    (g) 1.5–2.5
    (h) .50–.75

2. What is the appropriate interval size for each of the following distributions?

	Low Score	High Score
a	0	14
b	30	63
c	0	120
d	2	24
e	−2	+2

3. The following scores were made on a 50-item test:

49	38	31	27	20
48	37	31	26	19
46	37	31	26	18
46	37	30	25	16
45	36	30	24	15
44	35	30	24	
43	35	29	23	
43	34	29	23	
41	33	28	22	
41	33	27	21	
39	32	27	21	
39	31	27	20	

    (a) For the above data set up a frequency distribution starting with a bottom interval of 15–17.
    (b) Make another distribution starting with the interval 14–16.
    (c) Compare the two distributions.
    (d) Construct a frequency polygon for the distribution in (a) above.
    (e) Construct a frequency polygon for the distribution in (b) above.

4. A class was given a spelling test made up of 100 words resulting in the following scores:

46	80	57	59	94	76
48	48	61	65	86	65
64	60	63	68	41	66
76	64	68	67	68	27
78	59	72	71	67	68
54	62	64	72	61	67
39	57	57	75	69	61

    (a) Select an appropriate interval size and set up a frequency distribution for these scores.
    (b) Construct a frequency polygon for these data.
    (c) Construct a histogram for these data on the same axes.
    (d) How do you describe this distribution?

5. Below are the scores of two groups of adolescents on a test of spatial relations.

Scores	Distribution A f	Distribution B f
60–63	2	1
56–59	12	0
52–55	18	2
48–51	36	4
44–47	38	5
40–43	20	8
36–39	18	10
32–35	10	6
28–31	8	4
24–27	6	4
20–23	4	3
16–19	2	3
12–15	0	2
8–11	0	2
4–7	1	1
	175	55

(a) Make a frequency polygon for each of these on the same axis.

(b) How do you describe each distribution?

6. For distribution A in Problem 5, find the following centile points:

C_{10} C_{20} Median Q_3

C_{90} C_{80} Q_1 D_7

7. The following scores were made on tests of psychomotor skills:

(a) 34, 28, 29, 22, 33, 30, 31, 32.

(b) 30, 24, 22, 24, 29, 24, 28, 24.

(c) 34, 28, 29, 30, 32, 35, 33, 22.

(d) 19, 24, 18, 23, 20, 20, 22, 21, 20.

(e) 30, 31, 32, 33, 36, 37, 38, 40.

Calculate the median for each of these.

8. Construct an ogive curve for the data in Problem 5, distribution A. From the curve, read the same centile points that you computed in Problem 6 above. Compare the results.

4

AVERAGES

One of the important ways of describing a group of measurements or scores is by the use of averages.   Usually three averages are considered: the mean, the median, and the mode.   Of these three measures of central tendency, the mean is the most commonly encountered and, as we shall see later, it is this one that is basic to many other statistical computations.   In each of these averages we have a single numerical value which represents a group of individuals.

THE ARITHMETIC MEAN

The mean is another term for arithmetic average.   Everyone who has ever computed an "average" has computed a mean.   Very simply, the mean is the sum of the scores divided by the number of cases.   Suppose that we have five scores: $X_1 = 10$, $X_2 = 12$, $X_3 = 15$, $X_4 = 18$, and $X_5 = 20$. Then the mean ($\bar{X}$), read as "bar X," would be

$$\bar{X} = \frac{X_1 + X_2 + X_3 + X_4 + X_5}{N}$$

$$= \frac{10 + 12 + 15 + 18 + 20}{5}$$

$$= \frac{75}{5} = 15$$

Instead of writing the equation for the mean as above, we shorten it like this

$$\bar{X} = \frac{\Sigma X}{N} \tag{4.1}$$

where $\bar{X}$ = mean
   ΣX = the sum of the scores; Σ is the capital sigma in the Greek alphabet and is customarily used as an abbreviation for sum
   N = the number of cases

37

The Mean for Grouped Data

When the scores have been entered into a frequency table, the mean is computed as is shown in Table 4.1. In this table, the same scores which appear in Table 3.1 are again used. The method illustrated here is that of using an arbitrary reference point. The steps that we go through in finding the mean are outlined below:

TABLE 4.1. Computation of the Mean for Grouped Data

	(1) f	(2) x'	(3) fx'
80–84	1	6	6
75–79	1	5	5
70–74	1	4	4
65–69	4	3	12
60–64	4	2	8
55–59	7	1	7
50–54	6 ←	0	0
45–49	6	−1	−6
40–44	6	−2	−12
35–39	3	−3	−9
30–34	0	−4	0
25–29	1	−5	−5
	$N = 40$		$\Sigma fx' = 10$

1. The frequency table is set up as described in Chapter 3.
2. We take the midpoint of one of the intervals as the arbitrary reference point. As far as the result is concerned, it makes no difference which interval midpoint is used. In the example illustrated, the midpoint of the interval 50–54, 52 is taken as the arbitrary reference point.
3. A second column is set up. This column is labeled x' and can be read as deviations from the arbitrary reference point. Since the interval 50–54 was taken as the interval containing our reference point, there is no deviation, and a zero is placed in column 2 for this interval. The interval of 55–59 deviates one interval from the arbitrary reference point, and a 1 is entered for this interval in column 2. This is continued upward until each interval has a value. We do the same thing for the intervals below the reference point. However, this time we place a minus sign in front of each of our deviations.
4. Next we multiply each f by its x' and enter the product in the third column, labeled fx'.
5. Sum this column.
6. The mean is then computed by substituting in this equation:

$$\bar{X} = M' + \frac{\Sigma fx'}{N} \; (i) \tag{4.2}$$

where M' = arbitrary reference point

i = the size of the class interval and the other symbols are as previously defined

Then for our problem:

$$\bar{X} = 52 + \frac{10}{40}(5)$$

$$= 52 + \frac{50}{40}$$

$$= 52 + 1.25$$

$$= 53.2$$

Suppose that we work the problem over again, this time selecting the midpoint of another interval as the arbitrary reference point. It was noted above that this made no difference in our answer. This time the data are set up in Table 4.2 and the computational work is recorded beneath it. We

TABLE 4.2. Computation of the Mean and Median for Grouped Data

	(1) f		(2) x'	(3) fx'
80–84	1		11	11
75–79	1		10	10
70–74	1		9	9
65–69	4		8	32
60–64	4		7	28
55–59	7	18	6	42
50–54	6	← Mdn	5	30
45–49	6	16	4	24
40–44	6		3	18
35–39	3		2	6
30–34	0		1	0
25–29	1		0	0
	$N = 40$			$\Sigma fx' = 210$

$$\bar{X} = M' + \frac{\Sigma fx'}{N}(i)$$

$$= 27 + \frac{210}{40}(5)$$

$$= 27 + 26.25$$

$$= 53.2$$

begin by selecting the midpoint of the bottom interval as our reference point and placing a 0 for this interval for the x' column. The next interval is given a value of 1, and this is continued up to the top interval, which receives a value of 11. The fx' value is then computed for each interval, and these are summed.   Substitution into formula (4.2) results in a mean of 53.2, which is identical to the value obtained in the first solution.   We could repeat this process ten more times, that is, we could use the midpoint of each of the other intervals as arbitrary reference points.   If our work is done correctly, each solution will result in a mean of 53.2.   When we started with the bottom interval, all of our values were positive, but our x' values became rather large.   Some prefer this method.   However, if no calculating machine is available, it may be more convenient to begin by selecting an interval near the center of the distribution.

It might be noted that the mean obtained here is not identical to that obtained by adding all the scores and dividing by N.   Such differences between the means produced by the two methods are usually very small and of no practical significance.   This difference is brought about by the error of grouping; the concept will be discussed in detail in the next chapter.

A Definition of the Mean

We have previously noted that the mean is the arithmetic average.   This tells us actually very little about what the mean is.   We shall now arrive at a more precise definition of the mean.   Suppose that we have the following very simple distribution:

(1)	(2)	(3)
X	x	x^2
10	4	16
8	2	4
6	0	0
4	−2	4
2	−4	16
$\Sigma X = 30$	$\Sigma x = 0$	$\Sigma x^2 = 40$
$\bar{X} = 6$		

Here we have five measures with a sum of 30 and a mean of 6.   Column 2 is headed by a small x.   This is a new statistic to us and is called a deviation score or measure.   It is defined as $X - \bar{X}$.   Lowercase x is the actual deviation of a score from the mean.   The first score, 10, is four units above the mean.   The second score, 8, deviates by two units, and so it continues for the other measures.

A value of zero is obtained by summing column 2.   This then is the definition of the mean: that point about which the sum of the deviations is zero.   Deviations are sometimes referred to as *moments* and the analogy is made between the mean of a distribution and the fulcrum of a seesaw when the latter is in a state of equilibrium.   The sum of the moments on one side of the fulcrum is equal to the sum of the moments on the opposite side.

In column 3 each deviation has been squared, and the sum of this column taken and found to be 40. This leads to another description of the mean as being that point in a distribution about which the sum of the squares of the deviations is at a minimum. For these data the sum of the squared deviations about any point, other than the mean, would be greater than 40.

AVERAGING MEANS

Often we are given the means of two or more samples and we wish to find the mean of all the measures combined into one group. This is done by computing the weighted mean. Suppose that a test is given to three groups with the following results:

$$\overline{X}_1 = 60 \qquad N_1 = 10$$
$$\overline{X}_2 = 50 \qquad N_2 = 60$$
$$\overline{X}_3 = 40 \qquad N_3 = 30$$

where $\overline{X}$ and N stand for the mean and the number of individuals in groups 1, 2, and 3 respectively. We wish to find the mean of the three groups combined, $\overline{X}_T$.

Previously, we learned that the mean is equal to the sum of the measures divided by the number of cases

$$\overline{X} = \frac{\Sigma X}{N}$$

If we have the mean and the number of cases, we can obtain the sum of the measures by solving the equation for this

$$\Sigma X = \overline{X}(N)$$

This is exactly the procedure followed in obtaining the mean for the total group. We get the sum of the measures for each group and add these, then divide this obtained sum by the total number of cases as follows:

$\overline{X}$	N	ΣX
60	10	600
50	60	3000
40	30	1200
	$\Sigma N = 100$	$\Sigma X = 4800$

$$\overline{X}_T = \frac{4800}{100} = 48$$

It should be noted that this mean cannot be obtained by averaging the three sample means. In this case the average of the three means would be 50. Only when the number in each sample is identical can the means of the samples be averaged directly to obtain the mean of the total group.

Effect on the Mean of Adding a Constant to, or Subtracting One from, Each Measure in a Distribution

Often we are plagued with decimals, rather large numbers, or negative numbers.   Our computational work can be made much easier if we are aware that there are operations that can be performed on measures or scores which do not affect the basic results.   Suppose that we have a group of scores, some of which are negative.   Let us add a constant to each of the scores so that all of the scores will be positive.   Or suppose that we have scores which range from 400 to 780.   This time we reduce these scores by subtracting 400 from each.   The question now is how has the mean of each group been affected.   Such operations are known as coding and are illustrated in Table 4.3.

TABLE 4.3.   Coding Data by Subtraction

X	$X - 500$
750	250
710	210
690	190
680	180
660	160
650	150
620	120
580	80
570	70
550	50
510	10

$$\Sigma X = 6970 \qquad \Sigma(X - 500) = 1470$$
$$\overline{X} = 6970/11 \qquad \overline{X} - 500 = 1470/11 = 133.6$$
$$= 633.6 \qquad \overline{X} = 133.6 + 500$$
$$= 633.6$$

In this table we have 11 scores from each of which a constant of 500 has been subtracted.   Both columns have been summed and the mean of each found.   Note that to the mean of the second column (the coded mean), the constant 500 must be added to obtain the mean of the distribution.   The student must remember that whenever data are coded, the statistics computed are *for the coded data* and such values must frequently be decoded. From this we see that when a constant is subtracted from each score in a distribution, the same constant is subtracted from the mean.   Similarly, the mean is increased by the constant when every score in a distribution has a constant added to it.   The same logic applies to coding by a constant multiplier or divisor.   The mean must be decoded by multiplication if each score has been divided by a common number.

THE MEDIAN

In the previous chapter a description was given of the methods of computing the median for grouped and ungrouped data.   The median was defined as the point in a distribution with an equal number of cases on each side of it. The application of the method discussed in Chapter 3 to the data in Table 4.2 results in a median of 52.8 as summarized:

$$\text{Median} = 49.5 + \frac{4}{6}(5)$$

$$= 49.5 + \frac{20}{6}$$

$$= 49.5 + 3.3$$

$$= 52.8$$

THE MODE

A third average which we shall mention very briefly here is the mode, the symbol of which is Mo. For ungrouped data, the mode is defined as that datum value which occurs most frequently. When the data have been arranged into a frequency table, the mode is defined as the midpoint of the interval containing the largest number of cases. For example, the mode of the data in Table 4.2 is 57, the midpoint of the interval 55–59.

USE OF THE DIFFERENT AVERAGES

Of the three measures of central tendency, the mean is most frequently encountered. However, there are cases when the use of the mean is not justified. If we examine the incomes of a sample of male citizens between the ages of 20 and 60 of any state in the union, we will find that these incomes do not make a normal distribution. The frequency polygon for these data is positively skewed. The lowest value in the distribution is zero and the curve has its frequencies massed at the lower end with a mode in the $5000–$6000 region, and there the tail extends to the right as some incomes may reach into the millions of dollars. A mean for these data would be pulled toward the high salaries, that is, in the direction of the skew.

Suppose that ten individuals make the following contributions to an organization:

$$
\begin{array}{r}
\$10.00 \\
.10 \\
.10 \\
.10 \\
.10 \\
.05 \\
.05 \\
.05 \\
.05 \\
.05 \\
\hline
\Sigma = \$10.65
\end{array}
$$

The mean for these data is $1.06 and the median is $.075 or $.08.   This illustrates that every single measure in a distribution affects the size of the mean.   This is not so of the median.   The top measure could have been a thousand or a million dollars, and the median would still have been 8 cents.

For the above data, the median gives a much more accurate picture of the typical contribution than does the mean.   It then follows that when a distribution is positively or negatively skewed, the best average to be used is the median.   In a positively skewed distribution the mean will be higher than the median, and the latter higher than the mode.   The order of magnitude of the three averages is reversed in a negatively skewed distribution.   In a normal distribution the mean, median, and mode are identical.

The mode is seldom used.   It is very easy to compute, but it suffers from the fact that it is very unstable.   Let us refer to Table 4.2 again.   We noted that the mode for this distribution was 57, the midpoint of the interval 55–59.   Now suppose one of these frequencies is removed from this interval and placed in the interval 45–49.   This interval would now have a frequency of 7, and the mode of the distribution would now be 47.   Then a change in the location of just one case brought about a change in the mode of 10.   A statistic which fluctuates so much is too unstable for any but the crudest of uses.

When data are collected using a nominal scale, the mode would be the appropriate statistic to use as a measure of popularity.   The median is associated with ordinal data.   The mean may be used with interval or ratio data, provided the distribution of the data approximates a normal curve.

When more computational work is to be done later, the mean should be used as an average.   It will be seen that many of our other statistics are determined from the mean.   The median is usually limited to descriptive use in statistical work.   Of these two measures, the mean is more reliable, since it varies less from sample to sample.   This will be discussed later in a chapter on sampling statistics.

OTHER AVERAGES

The student in psychology will infrequently be confronted with data that should have a geometric or harmonic mean used as the average.

The geometric mean of two measures is the square root of their product, of three measures, the cube root of their product, and of n measures, the nth root of their product.   Thus the geometric mean of 2 and 8 is 4:

$$\sqrt{(2)(8)} = \sqrt{16} = 4$$

In general the geometric mean (GM) is equal to:

$$GM = \sqrt[n]{(X_1)(X_2)(X_3) \cdots (X)_n} \tag{4.3}$$

From the above it can be seen that this mean cannot be used when the value of any measure is zero or has a negative sign.   This mean is used in psycho-physics or in other data concerned with measures of rates of change.   We shall refer to it later when we discuss correlation.

A second infrequently encountered mean is known as the harmonic mean and is defined as the reciprocal of the arithmetic mean of the reciprocals of the measures.

$$HM = \frac{1}{1/N(1/X_1 + 1/X_2 + 1/X_3 + \cdots + 1/X_N)} \qquad (4.4)$$

This mean is used in averaging rates.

Exercises

1. The following figures represent the scores of 57 university students on a test in educational measurement.

	f
57–59	1
54–56	1
51–53	5
48–50	9
45–47	5
42–44	8
39–41	10
36–38	6
33–35	4
30–32	7
27–29	0
24–26	1

Compute the three averages for these data.

2. The following distribution of scores was made on a clerical-sales scale of an interest inventory.

Score	f
15	1
14	10
13	10
12	16
11	20
10	15
9	17
8	20
7	14
6	18
5	19
4	15
3	3
	$N = 178$

(a) Compute the three measures of average for these data.

(b) Evaluate each as to applicability to these data.

3. The following scores were obtained by a group of university students on the *Otis Self-administering Test of Mental Ability.*

71	61	54	50
70	60	54	50
69	59	54	49
69	58	54	47
69	58	53	40
64	57	52	39
64	56	52	34
63	55	51	30

(a) Group these data and find the mean, median, and mode.

(b) Draw a frequency polygon for these scores.

4. Below are the salaries of a sample of high school principals:

	f
18,000–and up	5
15,000–17,999	15
14,000–14,999	80
13,000–13,999	40
12,000–12,999	25
11,000–11,999	30
10,000–10,999	18
9000– 9999	10
8000– 8999	6
7000– 7999	6
Below 7000	4

(a) Obtain an appropriate average for these data.

(b) Find Q_3 and Q_1.

5. Below are the number of children of alumni of a certain women's college:

Number of Children	Families
8	1
7	2
6	6
5	8
4	20
3	38
2	60
1	60
0	35

(a) What is the average number of children per family?

(b) Find Q_3 and Q_1 for these data.

6. Scores on a statistics test:

	f
100–104	1
95– 99	2
90– 94	1
85– 89	6
80– 84	7
75– 79	3
70– 74	2
65– 69	1
60– 64	2
55– 59	4
50– 54	0
45– 49	1
	$N = 30$

Compute the mean, median, and mode for the above data.

7. Scores on a reading test:

	f
100–109	12
90– 99	36
80– 89	48
70– 79	72
60– 69	164
50– 59	144
40– 49	120
30– 39	80
20– 29	40
10– 19	33
0– 9	11
	$N = 760$

Compute the mean, median, and mode for these data.

8. For each of the following compute the weighted mean:

(a) $\bar{X}_1 = 60$, $N_1 = 12$, $\bar{X}_2 = 40$, $N_2 = 30$, $\bar{X}_3 = 50$, $N_3 = 60$.

(b) $\bar{X}_1 = 80$, $N_1 = 100$, $\bar{X}_2 = 90$, $N_2 = 50$.

9. The following represent scores on tests of psychomotor skills. For each find the mean, median, and mode.

(a) 24, 18, 19, 12, 23, 20, 21, 22.

(b) 20, 14, 12, 14, 19, 14, 18, 14.

(c) 24, 18, 19, 20, 22, 25, 23, 12.

(d) 9, 14, 8, 13, 10, 10, 11, 12, 10.

10. The Wechsler Intelligence Scale for Children is given to a class of 24 fourth-grade students. Their IQ's are:

98	115	122	99
111	99	113	101
108	103	95	89
100	101	104	107
96	114	116	113
103	90	100	102

(a) What is the mean and median IQ for this class?

(b) Can you tell if the scores are normally distributed, knowing the mean and the median?

5

VARIABILITY

In the previous chapter we were concerned with the computation, meaning, and use of averages. A little thought will soon point up the fact that averages in themselves do not adequately describe a distribution. Averages locate the center of a distribution but tell us nothing about how the scores or measurements are arranged in relation to the center. Let us take two illustrations. Suppose that we have two distributions of scores on the same test, each with a mean of 67. In the first of these the highest score is 72 and the lowest is 62. The second distribution has a high score of 107 and a low score of 25. The range of the first distribution is 11 and that of the second distribution is 83. To give a much better picture of a distribution it follows from this that we need both a measure of central tendency and one of variability or dispersion. In statistical work we would say that the first of our illustrations is a homogeneous group. The individuals within it are very similar in reference to the trait measured. The other group is described as heterogeneous, the variability being great. Both of these terms are widely used in educational, sociological, and psychological work.

MEASURES OF VARIABILITY

The Range

This statistic has already been defined as the high score minus the low score plus one. We used it in the first step in setting up frequency distributions. We will spend little more time on it here, other than to state that, of all the measures of variability, the range is the most unstable. By this we mean that from sample to sample, the range varies more than does any of the others. An illustration will show why this is so. Suppose that we have a distribution of scores, the lowest of which is 30 and the highest is 103. The next score below 103 happens to be 90. By the use of our formula, the range is found to be 74; but 13 of the points making up this range are the result of the large score of 103. The chances are good that the next sample will not contain this high deviate score and hence the range will be much smaller. The range, like the mode, is a very unstable statistic, as it may vary considerably from sample to sample.

The range can be used justifiably when we want a hasty measure of variability and do not have time to compute one of the others. Each of the statistics discussed later in this chapter is a better measure. Of course, in dealing with a population instead of a sample, the range becomes more useful.

The Quartile Deviation

The quartile deviation, symbol Q, is frequently called the semi-interquartile range. In the previous chapter two quartile points were mentioned, Q_1, the equivalent of the twenty-fifth centile, and Q_3, the equivalent of the seventy-fifth centile. The quartile deviation or the semi-interquartile range is half the distance between these two quartile points. In symbols we would write this as follows:

$$Q = \frac{Q_3 - Q_1}{2} \tag{5.1}$$

TABLE 5.1.
Computation of the
Quartile Deviation

	f	
80–84	1	
75–79	1	
70–74	1	
65–69	4	
		7
60–64	4	
55–59	7	
50–54	6	
45–49	6	
		10
40–44	6	
35–39	3	
30–34	0	
25–29	1	
	$N = 40$	

This statistic is easy to calculate. To illustrate we have again set up in Table 5.1 the distribution of geography scores previously used for illustration. We must first calculate Q_1 and Q_3. By definition, Q_1 is the point in this distribution which has 25 percent of the scores below it. Twenty-five

percent of 40 cases is 10 cases.   We start counting cases from the bottom, *Q₁ COUNT DOWN*
and we find that below the lower limit of the interval 45–49 we have exactly *Q₃ COUNT UP*
10 cases.   No interpolation is necessary in this case, and we record that *25% of the*
$Q_1 = 44.5$.   To find Q_3 we repeat this same process except that instead of *cases*
going up 75 percent of the cases, we come down from the top 25 percent
of the cases.   By counting down we find that when we get to 64.5 (the lower
limit of the interval 65–69), we have included 7 cases.   We need 3 more.
Since there are 4 cases in this interval we need to go three-fourths of the
way through the interval.   We can show the operation as follows:

$$Q_3 = 64.5 - \frac{3}{4}(5)$$

$$= 64.5 - \frac{15}{4}$$

$$= 64.5 - 3.75$$

$$= 60.75$$

To find Q we proceed as follows:

$$Q = \frac{Q_3 - Q_1}{2}$$

$$= \frac{60.75 - 44.5}{2}$$

$$= \frac{16.25}{2}$$

$$= 8.125 = 8.12$$

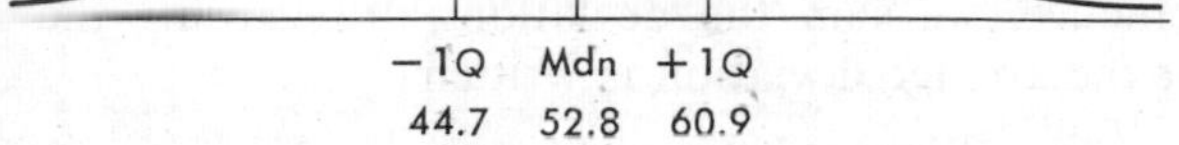

-1Q   Mdn   +1Q
44.7   52.8   60.9

FIGURE 5.1   Relationship of Q to the normal curve.

Interpretation of Q.   In the previous chapter we found that the median
for the data in Table 5.1 was 52.8.   In a normal distribution, if we take the
median and add and subtract one quartile deviation on each side of it, we
will cut off approximately 50 percent of the cases.   That is, for the data at
hand, we would expect to find 50 percent of the cases to fall between 60.9
(the median plus one Q) and 44.7 (the median minus one Q).   This is shown
graphically in Fig. 5.1.

It also happens that if we measure off 4 quartile deviations on each side of the median, we will include practically all the cases. We can state this briefly by saying that 8 Q's approximately cover the range.

When to Use the Quartile Deviation. Since the quartile deviation is associated with the median, it follows that whenever the median is used as a measure of central tendency, the quartile deviation is an appropriate measure of variability. It may be recalled that the median is the statistic to be used as a measure of central tendency when we have a skewed distribution. Even when distributions are skewed, the check using the middle 50 percent of the cases will work.

The Average Deviation

This statistic, also referred to as the mean deviation, is no longer widely used in statistical work, having been replaced by the standard deviation. A brief consideration of it here, however, may make the following material on the standard deviation easier. To begin, we shall again define the symbol x as a deviation of any score from the mean of its distribution. In symbols we can write this as follows:

$$x = X - \bar{X} \tag{5.2}$$

where x = the deviation of a score from the mean
X = a raw score
$\bar{X}$ = the mean

In any distribution the sum of these deviations from the mean is equal to 0. As previously noted, this is an important fact about the mean. About no other point in any distribution is this true. Our definition of the mean is that it is that point about which the sum of the deviations is equal to 0.

Since the sum of the deviations about the mean is equal to 0, it follows that we can obtain no average deviation unless we change our procedure. In actual practice, we sum the deviations disregarding the signs. The equation for the average deviation is written

$$AD = \frac{\Sigma|x|}{N} \tag{5.3}$$

where $|x|$ = the absolute deviations of the scores from the mean, that is, without regard to sign
N = the number of cases

The calculation of the average deviation is shown in Table 5.2. For this distribution then, the scores are, on an average, 6 units from the mean.

TABLE 5.2.   Computation of the
Average Deviation

X	x
26	10
24	8
22	6
20	4
18	2
16	0
14	-2
10	-6
6	-10
4	-12

$\Sigma X = 160$ $\qquad$ $\Sigma x = 0$

$\bar{X} = 16$ $\qquad$ $\Sigma|x| = 60$ $\qquad$ $N = 10$

$$AD = \frac{\Sigma|x|}{N}$$

$$= \frac{60}{10}$$

$$= 6$$

The Standard Deviation

Of all the measures of variability, the standard deviation is by far the most widely encountered, mainly because it is used in so many other statistical operations.   We shall begin by showing how it is computed for both ungrouped and grouped data.   With ungrouped data, the process starts out in the same fashion as does that for the average deviation.   That is, we first compute the mean.   Then we compute the deviation of each score from this mean (see Table 5.3).   Then we square each of these

TABLE 5.3.   Computation of the Standard
Deviation for Ungrouped Data

X	x	x^2
20	7.6	57.76
18	5.6	31.36
16	3.6	12.96
14	1.6	2.56
13	.6 $\Sigma = +19$	.36
11	-1.4	1.96
10	-2.4	5.76
9	-3.4	11.56
8	-4.4	19.36
5	-7.4 $\Sigma = -19$	54.76

$\Sigma X = 124$ $\qquad$ $\Sigma x = 0.0$ $\qquad$ $\Sigma x^2 = 198.40$

$\bar{X} = 12.4$

deviations and add this column. A check on our work would be that the sum of the x column or the sum of the deviations about the mean should be 0. We find that this is true for our problem. To find the standard deviation, we use the following formula and substitute in it as shown.

$$s = \sqrt{\frac{\Sigma x^2}{N}} \tag{5.4}$$

$$= \sqrt{\frac{198.40}{10}}$$

$$= \sqrt{19.840}$$

$$= 4.5$$

If a calculating machine is available, it is much easier to use the so-called raw-score formula for getting the sum of the deviations squared. The sum is usually referred to as the sum of the squares and is one of our most useful statistics. This technique is illustrated in Table 5.4. In this table we copy

TABLE 5.4. Computation of the Standard Deviation Directly from Raw Scores

X	X^2
20	400
18	324
16	256
14	196
13	169
11	121
10	100
9	81
8	64
5	25
$\Sigma X = 124$	$\Sigma X^2 = 1736$

down the scores and label the first column X. The second column is merely the square of each X. (The student should remember that there is a table of squares in the Appendix which indicates the square of any number from 1 to 1000.) Both columns are then summed. It should be pointed out that when a machine is used, it is not necessary to copy the original scores or their squares as shown in Table 5.4. These are entered into the machine one at a time, and as the process goes along, the sum of each is accumulated. At the end, both values may be read directly from the machine.

For this method we obtain the sum of the squares by the following equation:

$$\Sigma x^2 = \Sigma X^2 - \frac{(\Sigma X)^2}{N} \qquad (5.5)$$

$$= 1736 - \frac{(124)^2}{10}$$

$$= 1736 - \frac{15376}{10}$$

$$= 1736 - 1537.6$$

$$= 198.4$$

This value for the sum of the squares is the same as obtained by totalling the deviations of each score from the mean. Even without a calculating machine students may find this method easier than the first. After we obtain the sum of the squares, we next substitute our values into equation (5.4) and solve for the standard deviation.

Instead of using formula (5.4), one may obtain the standard deviation directly by the use of the following formula:

$$s = (1/N)\sqrt{N\Sigma X^2 - (\Sigma X)^2} \qquad (5.6)$$

This is obtained by substituting formula (5.5) into equation (5.4) and simplifying.

TABLE 5.5. Computation of Standard Deviation for Forty Scores on a Statistics Test

(1)	(2) f	(3) x'	(4) fx'	(5) fx'^2	(6) $f(x' + 1)^2$
80–84	1	6	6	36	49
75–79	1	5	5	25	36
70–74	1	4	4	16	25
65–69	4	3	12	36	64
60–64	4	2	8	16	36
55–59	7	1	7	7	28
			+42		
50–54	6	0	0	0	6
45–49	6	−1	−6	6	0
40–44	6	−2	−12	24	6
35–39	3	−3	−9	27	12
30–34	0	−4	0	0	0
25–29	1	−5	−5	25	16
			−32		
	$N = 40$	$\Sigma fx' = 10$		$\Sigma fx'^2 = 218$	$\Sigma f(x' + 1)^2 = 278$

Standard Deviation for Grouped Data. This technique is shown in Table 5.5. The beginning steps are the same as those we went through in calculating the mean for grouped data. Inspection of Table 5.5 shows that the process is identical up to and including column 4. We start out by selecting an arbitrary reference point. In this problem we chose the midpoint of the interval 50–54. Then we gave this interval a deviation value of 0 and set up our x' column (column 3) as shown. We obtain the value in column 4, fx' by multiplying the values in the two previous columns. We obtain the fx'^2 values in column 5 by multiplying the values in the two previous columns. Then we sum the various columns as shown.

To find the standard deviation we again have to find the sum of the squares. For grouped data this is done as follows:

$$\Sigma x^2 = i^2 \left[\Sigma fx'^2 - \frac{(\Sigma fx')^2}{N} \right] \tag{5.7}$$

$$= 5^2 \left[218 - \frac{(10)^2}{40} \right]$$

$$= 25 \left[218 - \frac{100}{40} \right]$$

$$= 25[218 - 2.5]$$

$$= 25[215.5]$$

$$= 5387.5$$

We obtain the standard deviation in the usual fashion by solving as shown below:

$$s = \sqrt{\frac{\Sigma x^2}{N}}$$

$$= \sqrt{\frac{5387.5}{40}}$$

$$= \sqrt{134.69}$$

$$= 11.6$$

We can check the accuracy of the work in several ways. The first of these, called Charlier's check, is a check upon the accuracy of the sums in our fx' and fx'^2 columns. To carry out this check, we set up column 6 as shown in Table 5.5. The heading here tells us to take each x' value, add one to it, square it, and then multiply it by the frequency in the interval. For the top interval this becomes 6 plus 1 which is 7, 7 squared is 49, and this multiplied by the frequency, 1, is still 49. When each interval has been so treated, the values in column 6 are summed. Charlier's check is made by substituting in the following equation:

$$\Sigma f(x' + 1)^2 = \Sigma fx'^2 + 2\Sigma fx' + \Sigma f \tag{5.8}$$

$$278 = 218 + 2(10) + 40$$

$$= 218 + 20 + 40$$

$$= 278$$

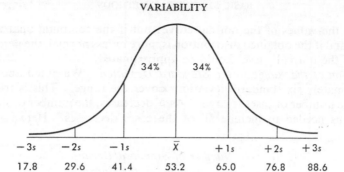

−3s	−2s	−1s	X̄	+1s	+2s	+3s
17.8	29.6	41.4	53.2	65.0	76.8	88.6

FIGURE 5.2 Standard deviation units and the normal curve.

We shall present a second rough check on our computed standard deviation, after we discuss the meaning of a standard deviation.

Interpretation of Standard Deviation. This statistic helps describe the normal curve. When our data take the shape of the normal curve, standard deviation units measured off along the base line, starting from the mean, always cut off certain proportions of the area under the curve. In the problem illustrated in Fig. 5.2, the mean of 53.2 is recorded at the center of the curve. Then one standard deviation unit is added to this mean, 53.2 + 11.6, resulting in a score of 64.8. Similarly, one standard deviation is measured off on the other side of the mean. In a normal curve, these two standard deviation units taken together include approximately 68 percent of the area. We shall in future chapters refer to this as two-thirds the area. If we measure off two standard deviation units on each side of the mean, we include between these two points approximately 95 percent of the area. And when we take three standard deviation units, over 99 percent of the area of the curve is included. Actually, about 13 cases in 10000 are left over on each side of the mean out beyond the plus and minus three standard deviation points. In a later chapter on the normal curve we shall see where these values come from.

Let us return to Table 5.5, and see how our computed standard deviation checks when we count the number of cases included by one standard deviation unit on each side of the mean. As previously noted, the points corresponding to plus and minus one standard deviation are 64.8 and 41.6, respectively. Let us locate 64.8 on Table 5.5. For all practical purposes, we might say that it is the point at the top of the interval 60 64. So we shall start counting down the number of cases between this and 41.6. We have to determine how many of the 6 cases in the interval 40–44 are above 41.6 and are to be included in our sum. The top of this interval is 44.5. The value 41.6 is 2.9 or approximately 3 units below this. Hence we want ³/₅ of the 6 units or approximately 4 of them. So starting from the top (64.8), we add 4 + 7 + 6 + 6 + 4 which equals 27. The number of the cases in this problem is 40. A standard deviation taken on each side of the mean would then include 27/40 of the distribution, which in terms of percents reduces to between 67 and 68 percent. This check may not always come as close to the values of the normal curve; but if the computational work is correct and if the obtained distribution is more or less normal, the percentage areas of the normal curve should be approximated.

Relation of the Range to the Standard Deviation. We noted above that approximately six standard deviations cover the range. This is true only when the number of cases is large. As N decreases, the number of standard deviations needed to include all of the cases decreases. Here is how it looks:[1]

N	Number of Standard Deviations Included in the Range
5	2.3
10	3.1
25	3.9
30	4.1
50	4.5
100	5.0
500	6.1
1000	6.5

Effect of Adding or Subtracting a Constant to Each Measure on the Standard Deviation. Previously we learned that adding or subtracting a constant to, or from each measure in a distribution increased or decreased the mean by the same constant. When measures are so treated, the standard deviation remains the same, as the range of scores is not affected by the addition or subtraction of a constant. This is illustrated below:

X	x	x^2	$X + 10$	x	x^2
20	4	16	30	4	16
18	2	4	28	2	4
16	0	0	26	0	0
14	−2	4	24	−2	4
12	−4	16	22	−4	16
$\Sigma X = 80$		$\Sigma x^2 = 40$	$\Sigma(X + 10) = 130$		$\Sigma x^2 = 40$
$\bar{X} = 16$			$\bar{X} = 26$		

Note that the sum of the squares is similar for both the coded and uncoded data, and hence the standard deviation is in each case $\sqrt{40/5} = \sqrt{8} = 2.8$.

When each measure in a distribution is multiplied or divided by a constant, the standard deviation and the mean are multiplied or divided by the same constant as shown here:

[1] Adapted from L. H. C. Tippett. On the extreme individuals and the range of samples from a normal population. *Biometrika*, 1925, *17*, 386.

X	x	x^2	$2X$	x	x^2
20	4	16	40	8	64
18	2	4	36	4	16
16	0	0	32	0	0
14	−2	4	28	−4	16
12	−4	16	24	−8	64

$\Sigma X = 80$ $\Sigma x^2 = 40$ $\Sigma 2X = 160$ $\Sigma x^2 = 160$
$\bar{X} = 16$ $\bar{X} = 32$

$$s = \sqrt{40/5} = \sqrt{8.0} = 2.83 \qquad s = \sqrt{160/5} = \sqrt{32} = 5.66$$

The standard deviation of the coded data is exactly twice that of the uncoded measures.

Much time and effort can be saved by coding data. Large numbers are made smaller, negative numbers may become positive, and decimals may be converted to whole numbers. We must remember, however, to uncode our final answers so that our statistic will pertain to the original data, not to the coded material.

The Variance. Much of our statistical work is handled by using another statistic to describe variability. This statistic is called the variance and is simply the standard deviation squared.

$$s^2 = \frac{\Sigma x^2}{N} \tag{5.9}$$

The variance (s^2) and other symbols are as previously described. In this textbook we shall have limited use for the variance, but a good share of modern statistics is based upon the manipulation of variances.

The Error of Grouping. In Chapter 4 we noted that when data are grouped, the means computed from such data are not identical with the means computed from the raw scores. We stated that these discrepancies were caused by the error of grouping. We shall now examine this phenomenon more closely.

Suppose that we have a distribution with a range from 30 to 100, and that these scores are set up into a frequency distribution, as shown in Fig. 5.3. Note that all of the data are included within seven class intervals. Let us suppose that the mean is 70. First, we shall consider the interval 70–79. The midpoint of this interval is 74.5. In Fig. 5.3 it is apparent that more of the area of this interval is found below the midpoint than above it. According to chance, we should expect to find more scores between 69.5 and 74.5 than between 74.5 and 79.5. This would be true for all intervals above the mean. The midpoint of each interval is too large when taken as an average of all of the scores in an interval. An inspection of the intervals below the mean shows that for all of these intervals, the reverse is true. The midpoint for these intervals is too small or too low.

In the computation of the mean, these discrepancies are of no major importance. Deviations on the positive side tend to be canceled out by deviations on the negative side, and in the long run, the mean computed by

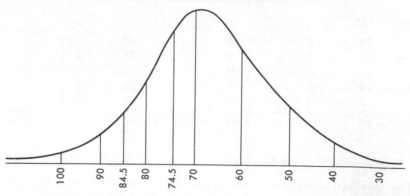

FIGURE 5.3 Frequency distribution and curve for data showing that the mid-point of the interval does not have an equal area on both sides of it.

the group method is very similar to that computed by the raw-score method. This, however, is not true for the standard deviation. The coarser the grouping, the greater the effect of this error of grouping upon the standard deviation. Any distribution which has less than 12 to 14 class intervals can be considered to have coarse groupings, and the standard deviation computed from such frequency distributions should be corrected. The pertinent correction here is known as Sheppard's correction and is given by the following formula:

$$s_c = \sqrt{s^2 - \frac{i^2}{12}} \qquad (5.10)$$

where s_c = the standard deviation corrected for the systematic error brought about by coarse grouping

s^2 = standard deviation squared, or variance, obtained from the coarsely grouped data

i = the size of the interval

Averaging Standard Deviations. In Chapter 4 we learned that if we wished to average two or more means, we could do it by the so-called weighting method. Standard deviations cannot be treated in the same manner. When two or more standard deviations are to be averaged, the following formula taken from McNemar (1962) is to be used:

$$s_T = \sqrt{\frac{N_A(\bar{X}_A{}^2 + s_A{}^2) + N_B(\bar{X}_B{}^2 + s_B{}^2)}{N_A + N_B} - \bar{X}_T{}^2} \qquad (5.11)$$

where s_T = standard deviation of combined groups

N_A, N_B = number of individuals in each of the two groups

$\bar{X}_A, \bar{X}_B$ = means of the two groups

$\bar{X}_T$ = weighted mean of the two groups combined

s_A, s_B = standard deviations of the two groups being combined

If more than two groups are being combined, an additional element is placed in both the numerator and denominator for each additional group.

Summary of the Measures of Variability

At this point we shall briefly summarize the four measures of variability.

1. *The Range.* This is least stable of all four measures. It is of limited use, except when speed is an issue or in simple situations such as in setting up a frequency distribution.

2. *The Quartile Deviation.* This statistic is always associated with the median, and it is used whenever the median is used as a measure of central tendency. This is usually the case in skewed distributions. It is noted here that in a normal distribution the quartile deviation and the standard deviation have a constant relationship. $Q = .6745s$.

3. *The Average Deviation.* This could be used with the mean in a normal distribution. In the past it was a rather widely used statistic, but today it is almost completely replaced by the standard deviation.

4. *The Standard Deviation.* This is the most reliable of all four measures and the one most frequently encountered. It is associated with the mean, and we use it when we are planning to make interpretations associated with the normal curve. As we shall see this statistic has many uses in modern statistics and is one of our most important tools.

MEASURES OF SKEWNESS AND KURTOSIS

Moments

Both of the major statistics already discussed, the average and the standard deviation, are related to a group of statistics known as moments. The first four moments are as follows:

$$m_1 = \frac{\Sigma(X - \bar{X})}{N} = \frac{\Sigma x}{N} = 0$$

$$m_2 = \frac{\Sigma(X - \bar{X})^2}{N} = \frac{\Sigma x^2}{N} = s^2$$

$$m_3 = \frac{\Sigma(X - \bar{X})^3}{N} = \frac{\Sigma x^3}{N}$$

$$m_4 = \frac{\Sigma(X - \bar{X})^4}{N} = \frac{\Sigma x^4}{N}$$

And the nth moment about the mean would be

$$m_n = \frac{\Sigma(X - \bar{X})^n}{N} = \frac{\Sigma x^n}{N}$$

Skewness

The skewness of a distribution (Sk or g_1), as it may be called, is obtained as follows:

$$Sk(g_1) = \frac{m_3}{m_2\sqrt{m_2^2}} = \frac{\Sigma x^3/N}{(\sqrt{\Sigma x^2/N})^3} \qquad (5.12)$$

or the ratio of the mean of the cube of the deviations about the mean to the cube of the standard deviation.   If a distribution of measures is normal in shape, the sum of the cubes of the deviations above the mean will equal the sum of the cubes of deviations below the mean, and the total sum of the cubes of the deviations will be zero and Sk will be O.   If the distribution is positively skewed, the sum of the cubes of the deviations above the mean will be greater than the sum of the deviations below the mean, and Sk will be positive.   Similarly, when conditions are reversed, Sk will be negative in sign.   The larger the value of Sk, the greater the amount of skewness.

Kurtosis

Kurtosis (Ku or g_2) of a distribution is determined by the use of the following formula:

$$Ku(g_2) = \frac{m_4}{m_2^2} - 3 = \frac{\Sigma x^4/N}{(\Sigma x^2/N)^2} - 3 \qquad (5.13)$$

or the ratio of the mean of the fourth power of the deviation about the means to the variance (m_2^2) squared minus 3.

When the value of Ku is zero, the shape of the distribution is mesokurtic, the slope of the normal curve.   When Ku is negative, the curve is platykurtic and, when Ku is positive, the curve is leptokurtic.

Exercises

1. An instructor of a freshman English course in a college administered the *STEP Writing Test* to a class with the following results:

37	35
35	34
43	44
45	43
45	34
35	40
35	38
42	37
40	40
46	38
	36

Use the raw-score formula to compute the standard deviation of these scores.

2. The distribution of scores of 112 high school seniors on the *Cooperative School and College Ability Test* (SCAT) is:

	f		f
90–94	1	55–59	14
85–89	2	50–54	11
80–84	3	45–49	11
75–79	5	40–44	16
70–74	11	35–39	8
65–69	12	30–34	5
60–64	10	25–29	2
		20–24	1

(a) What is the quartile deviation of this distribution?
(b) What is the standard deviation for this distribution?
(c) How would you expect the standard deviation of a national sample of 1500 students to compare with this?

3. On a scale to measure attitudes toward school integration, a senior high school civics class scored as follows:

6	4	8	8
4	9	5	3
8	6	1	7
1	5	7	1
3	2	3	5

(a) What is the quartile deviation?
(b) Is the quartile deviation used appropriately here?

4. The same statistics test was administered to three classes with the following results:

	$\overline{X}$	s	N
Class A	82	10	25
Class B	86	12	35
Class C	88	16	20

Compute the mean and the standard deviation of the three groups combined.

5. A group of university seniors made the following scores on the *Graduate Record Examination*:

602	580
650	601
552	590
402	420
460	449
501	486
550	512
484	498
462	407
544	558
542	550
567	594
560	575
481	476
498	470
422	520

Compute the mean and standard deviation for these data.

6. Calculate the standard deviation for any or all of the problems at the end of Chapter 4 where this statistic is appropriate.

6

STANDARD SCORES
AND THE NORMAL CURVE

STANDARD SCORES

The formula for the standard score is as follows:

$$z = \frac{X - \bar{X}}{s} = \frac{x}{s} \tag{6.1}$$

where X = any raw score or unit of measurement

$\bar{X}, s$ = mean and standard deviation of the distribution of scores

To illustrate the computation and nature of standard scores, let us take the following scores which are a part of a distribution with a mean of 60 and a standard deviation of 10.

X	x	z
70	10	1.00
60	0	.00
50	-10	-1.00
54	-6	$-.60$
46	-14	-1.40

In the first column we have the raw scores (X). The mean is subtracted from each of these, and then this deviation from the mean, or x, is divided by the standard deviation to change the deviation values into standard score values. The raw score of 60 is at the mean. There is no deviation; hence the standard score is 0. A raw score of 70 is one standard deviation above the mean. This results in a z score of 1.00. When we change raw scores to standard scores, we are expressing them in standard deviation units. These standard scores tell us how many standard deviation units any given raw score deviates from the mean.

Since three standard deviations on either side of the mean include

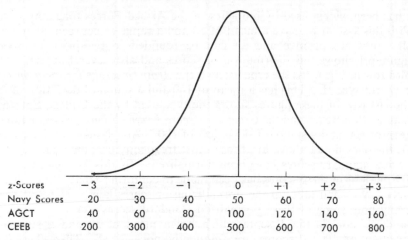

z-Scores	−3	−2	−1	0	+1	+2	+3
Navy Scores	20	30	40	50	60	70	80
AGCT	40	60	80	100	120	140	160
CEEB	200	300	400	500	600	700	800

FIGURE 6.1   Distribution of the various types of standard scores.

practically all of the cases, it follows that the highest z score usually encountered is $+3.00$ and the lowest is -3.00. We can describe the distribution of z scores by saying that they have a mean of 0 and a standard deviation of 1. This is shown in Fig. 6.1. Thus any time we see a standard score, we should be able to place exactly where an individual falls in a distribution. A student with a z score of 2.50 is 2.5 standard deviations above the mean on that test distribution and has a very good score. These standard scores are equal units of measurement and hence can be manipulated mathematically. It should be noted here also that changing a distribution of scores to z scores does not change the shape of the original distribution of scores. If the distribution was positively skewed to begin with, z scores made from such a distribution would be positively skewed.

Since z scores are expressed in decimals and since about half of them are negative, they are rather cumbersome to handle. Many times so-called linear transformations are made. Such transformations consist of making the scale larger, so that negative scores are eliminated, and of using a larger standard deviation, so that decimals are done away with. Transformed scores can be obtained from the following equation:

Standard score = z(new standard deviation) + the new mean

A common form for these transformations is based upon a mean of 50 and a standard deviation of 10. In equation form this becomes

Standard score = $z(10) + 50$

or starting with the raw scores we have

$$\text{Standard score} = \frac{(X - \bar{X})}{s}(10) + 50$$

This system with a mean of 50 and a standard deviation of 10 is very popular.

It has been widely used by branches of the Armed Forces for many years. With this system we have a mean of 50 and a range of between 20 and 80. All scores are positive and all can be rounded to two-place numbers. Figure 6.1 shows this distribution of scores and also several others. The third row in Fig. 6.1 is the type used on the *Army General Classification Test* of World War II. This has a mean of 100 and a standard deviation of 20. The last row of these figures shows the type used by the College Entrance Examination Board and the *Graduate Record Examination*. Here we note a mean of 500 and a standard deviation of 100. Any system can be set up, but the ones noted above are those most frequently encountered.

Some standard scores have been normalized. By this we mean that the distributions of these scores has been made to conform to that of the normal curve. We shall take up the normalizing of scores later. Here we shall briefly note some of these normalized standard scores. A very common standard score is the *T* score which has a mean of 50 and a standard deviation of 10. *T* scores are frequently normalized. Then there are stanines (standard nines) which have a mean of 5 and a standard deviation of approximately 2. Many of the standard scores used in nationwide testing programs have been normalized.

Uses of Standard Scores

Since standard scores are equal units of measurement and since their size is the same from distribution to distribution, they become a very useful tool both in the reporting of test scores and in doing research using test results. When the results of different tests taken by the same individuals are to be compared, this is best done by the use of standard scores. This process is illustrated in Table 6.1.

In part A of Table 6.1 the scores of students on three elementary school tests are presented. Only the scores of three students are shown. At the bottom are shown the mean and standard deviation of each test. If we look at these data in part A of Table 6.1, it should be apparent that, as they stand, they convey little meaning. Which student had the best overall performance? On which test did the different students do best? or worst? None of these questions can be answered as the scores are shown.

Suppose that we now change these scores to standard scores. For this we shall use the system with a mean of 50 and a standard deviation of 10. We shall start with the geography test, and for all of these we shall use this transformation equation:

$$\text{Standard score} = \frac{X - \bar{X}}{s}(10) + 50$$

The standard score in geography for student A in this test is

$$\text{SS} = \frac{60 - 60}{10}(10) + 50$$

$$= 0 + 50 = 50$$

TABLE 6.1. Comparing and Combining Scores
Made on Different Tests by the Use of
Standard Scores

Part A. Raw Scores

Student	Geography	Spelling	Arithmetic
A	60	140	40
B	72	100	36
C	46	110	24
etc.			
Mean	60	100	22
Standard Deviation	10	20	6

Part B. Standard Scores

Student	Geography	Spelling	Arithmetic	Average
A	50	70	80	67
B	62	50	73	62
C	36	55	53	48
etc.				

The geography score for student B becomes

$$SS = \frac{72 - 60}{10} (10) + 50$$

$$= \frac{120}{10} + 50$$

$$= 12 + 50 = 62$$

This is continued until all scores are transformed. The results of trans-
forming the scores in part A of Table 6.1 are shown in part B. This may
seem to be a laborious and time-consuming process. However, if there are
many scores to be transformed, it is most convenient to arrange the scores
from high to low, find the deviation of each from the mean, and since these
are in order, the rest of the process becomes very easy. Scores with a
negative deviation are the same distance below the new mean as the positive
ones with the same deviations above it.

Let us now examine part B of Table 6.1. We now note that student A is
at the mean in geography, two standard deviations above the mean in
spelling, and three standard deviations above the mean in arithmetic. His
average performance on these three tests was 67, 1.7 standard deviations
above the mean. For student A we can then say that his performance is
average in geography, excellent in spelling and superior in arithmetic. In
this manner we can consider the achievement of each of the students on
each of the three tests and we can get an average measure of his performance

on all three tests.   It should be noted that the only justifiable manner to compare scores is to first change the scores to standard scores, and then do the comparing.   Standard scores change the raw scores to equal and comparable units.

Another use of standard scores is in determining final grades for a course. Let us take a course which has three examinations of an hour each during the semester and a final examination 2 hours long.   At the end of the semester the instructor averages the three hour examinations and then combines this average with the final examination in some manner or other. This method is not correct.   Suppose that the means and standard deviations of the three hourly examinations were as follows:

	First Test	Second Test	Third Test	Final Exam
$\bar{X}$	52	87	62	124
s	8	17	11	21

If a student's scores on these three hourly examinations are averaged, each will not contribute equally to the average.   The second test with the largest standard deviation would contribute more to the final average than the other two, and the first examination would contribute least.   The proposed method tends to equalize contributions of hourly examinations to final scores.

In grading situations, if the teacher wants each of a series of tests to contribute equally to the final grade, it follows that the scores of individuals on each test should be changed to standard scores and that these should be averaged.   Then each hourly test is contributing more equally to the final grade.   Suppose now that the instructor wants the final examination to have twice as much weight as each of the other tests in the final grade. These final grades should also be changed to standard scores.   Then for any student his overall average is determined by taking his standard score on each of the first three tests, adding these, then adding to this sum 2 times his standard score on the final examination and dividing the total by 5. In symbols:

$$\frac{z_1 + z_2 + z_3 + z_f(2)}{5}$$

where z_1, z_2, z_3 = the standard scores on the three hourly examinations
$\quad\quad z_f$ = standard score on the final examination
$\quad\quad 2$ = weight final examination is to have

The method above, gives each examination the weight that the instructor desires it to have.   Some teachers convert all scores to standard scores before entering them into their class books.   This is strongly recommended.

Science teachers and some others have special problems with laboratory grades, project grades, and the like.   It is desired that the laboratory grades, for example, contribute a certain amount to the final grade.   This can only be done with any accuracy by changing these to standard scores and giving them the desired weight in the final average as shown above for the combination of hourly examinations and finals.

THE NORMAL CURVE

General Nature of the Normal Curve

For some time we have been talking about the normal curve. Now we shall examine it in detail, discuss its characteristics, its properties, and some of the basic ways in which it can be used. In the eighteenth century gamblers were interested in the chances of beating various gambling games and they asked mathematicians to help them out. DeMoivre (1733) was the first to develop the mathematical equation of the normal curve. Gauss and LaPlace (early nineteenth century) further developed the concept of the curve and probability. It was at about the same time that errors of observation made by astronomers were represented by a curve of this type. Today the normal curve is referred to as the curve of error, the bell-shaped curve, the Gaussian curve, or DeMoivre's curve.

By now the shape of this curve is familiar to all of you. Its maximum height is at the mean. In the language of the curve we say that the maximum ordinate (ordinates are given the symbol y) is at the mean. All other ordinates are shorter than this one. The normal curve is also said to be asymptotic. By this we mean that theoretically the tails never touch the base line but extend to infinity in either direction. In actual practice, however, as we have pointed out before, three standard deviations on either side of the curve will include practically all of the cases. As we have learned previously, the skewness of the normal curve is zero and its peakedness is described as being mesokurtic.

In our educational and psychological work, we assume that certain traits are normally distributed. In actuality, probably no distribution ever takes on the absolute form of the normal distribution. Many of our frequency distributions are very close to the normal one, and we assume that they have a normal distribution. To the extent that our distributions differ from normal, error enters into our work. The normal curve is important not primarily because *scores* are assumed to be normally distributed, but because the *sampling* distributions of various statistics are known or assumed to be normal. Hence the normal curve's importance is primarily in sampling statistics. This will become apparent when the material in Chapters 10 and 11 is studied.

The normal curve is a mathematical entity and is represented by the following formula:

$$y = \frac{n}{\sigma\sqrt{2\pi}} e^{\frac{1}{2}(x/\sigma)^2} \tag{6.2}$$

where n = the number of measures
y = an ordinate taken at any point on the base line
π = 3.1416
e = 2.7183, the base of the system of natural logarithms
σ = the standard deviation of the distribution
x = the deviation of any unit of measurement from the mean

It will be noted in the above equation that we use the symbol σ instead of s, because we are nov' dealing with population values or parameters rather than sample values.

By using formula (6.2) and substituting appropriate values of different points along the base line, we can solve for the ordinates of these points and then draw our curve from the heights of these ordinates. In doing this, we should take enough points along the base line to cover adequately the range and also have enough of these points so the curve will tend to be smooth. For example, we could let the first of the points which we select be the mean. For the mean the deviation value, x, is equal to 0. Since x is equal to 0, the exponent of e is 0, and any quantity raised to the 0 power is equal to 1. Then formula (6.2) becomes

$$y = \frac{1}{\sqrt{2\pi}} = \frac{1}{\sqrt{2(3.1416)}} = \frac{1}{\sqrt{6.2832}} = \frac{1}{2.5066} = .3989$$

Examination of Table II in the Appendix reveals that this value of .3989 is the one recorded for the ordinate of the mean standard score. Other values can then be taken for x, the ordinates computed, and the normal curve drawn using the various y values. Table II is based upon a normal curve with a mean of 0, a standard deviation of 1, and an area reduced to unity. It is referred to as the unity normal curve or the normal curve in standard score units: In actual practice, we do not have to solve equation (6.2) at all. The work has all been done for us, and the results are shown in Table II in the Appendix. Here we find the ordinates and other values of the normal curve for various standard deviation units from the mean.

We must comment here upon how the area under the curve is used. We have already noted that it is reduced to unity. In solving problems, we assume that our cases are spread evenly over this area. Suppose that we have a problem with 500 cases. In solving the problem, we find that .262 of the area of the curve falls above a certain point. To determine the number of cases above this point, we merely multiply our proportion by the number of cases, in this example .262(500). We also use this area of the curve in talking about probability. Suppose that as an illustration we take a raw score which has an equivalent standard score of $+1.88$. By referring to the normal probability table in the Appendix (Table II), we note that approximately .03 of the area of the curve falls above this point. We then say that the probability of obtaining a score equal to or higher than this one of $+1.88$ is .03 or 3 in 100.

Areas Under the Normal Curve

In the chapter in which we discussed standard deviations, we mentioned some of the relationships between standard deviation units and the normal curve. The most important of these relationships are again repeated in Fig. 6.2. To summarize, one standard deviation taken on each side of the mean includes a total area of 68.26 percent of the curve or approximately

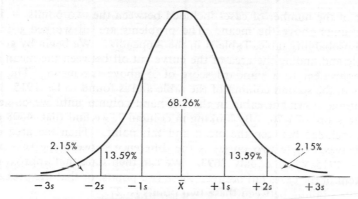

FIGURE 6.2 Percentages under the normal curve at various standard deviation units from the mean.

two-thirds of the cases. In terms of probability, we can state that the chances are about two out of three of a score in any normally distributed sample falling within the area of one standard deviation on each side of the mean. A second standard deviation measured beyond the first one cuts off 13.59 percent of the area. By adding all of the area included by two standard deviation units on both sides of the mean, we have accounted for more than 95 percent of the area or cases. If we continue and measure off another or third standard deviation on each side of the mean, we cut off another piece equal to 2.15 percent of the area. The sum of all of the areas included by these six standard deviation units is equal to 99.74 percent of the total. From this it follows that .26 percent of the cases are beyond three standard deviation units from the mean. This means 26 in 10,000, and dividing this by 2 to distribute these equally on both sides of the mean, we see that on each side we can expect 13 cases in 10,000 to fall beyond three standard deviation units from the mean.

Areas Cut off Between Different Points. Suppose, to begin with, we take the problem illustrated in Fig. 6.3. We wish to find the proportion of the

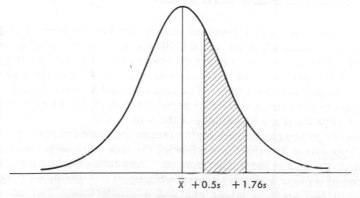

FIGURE 6.3 Percentage of the area of the normal curve between two points on the same side of the mean.

area or of the number of cases included between the two points +.5s and +1.76s units above the mean. The problems are all worked using the normal probability table, Table II in the Appendix. We begin by going to the table and finding the area of the curve cut off between the mean and a point equivalent to a standard score of .5 above the mean. This value appears in the second column of the table and is found to be .1915. Next we continue down the table in the left-hand column until we come to a standard score of 1.76. By looking in column 2, we find that .4608 of the area is included between the mean and this point. Then the area of the curve between these two points is the difference between the two points, .4608 − .1915, which equals .2693. We can then state that approximately 27 percent of the cases fall between these two points, or that the probability of a score's falling between these two points is .27.

In the next illustration, we shall take two points which are on different sides of the mean. This time we wish to determine what proportion of the normal curve falls between a standard score of −.48 and one of +1.5 (Fig. 6.4). There are no values for negative standard scores in Table II.

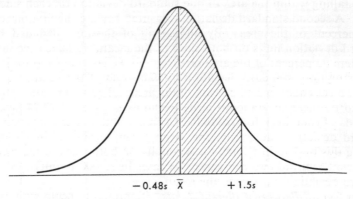

$$-0.48s \quad \overline{X} \qquad +1.5s$$

FIGURE 6.4 Percentage of the area of the normal curve between two points on different sides of the mean.

As far as areas go, equal standard scores, whether positive or negative, include equal areas when taken from the mean. From the table we find that a standard score of −.48 cuts off an area of .1844 between it and the mean. A standard score of +1.5 likewise includes .4332 of the area of the curve between it and the mean. The area included between both points is then equal to the sum of these two areas, .1844 + .4332, which is equal to .6176 or approximately 62 percent of the area.

Before we go any further, we might examine the other columns of Table II in the Appendix. The third one is labeled the area in the larger portion and the fourth, the area in the smaller portion. Any time we take a point on the base line of a curve and erect a perpendicular at this point, we divide the curve into two areas, a larger one and a smaller one. For any given standard score, the sum of these two areas is equal to unity. The last

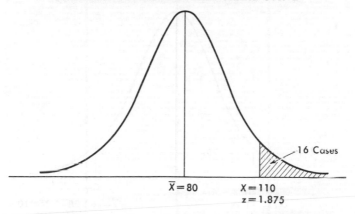

$\overline{X} = 80$ $X = 110$
$z = 1.875$

FIGURE 6.5 Percentages of cases in a normal distribution falling above a certain score.

column of the table, the ordinates, gives the size of the ordinates for the various standard scores.

Here is another type of problem that can be solved using these tables. Suppose that we have a distribution of test scores for which the following statistics have been computed: $\overline{X} = 80$, $s = 16$, $N = 510$. We wish to know what percentage of the scores in this distribution fall above a raw score of 110, assuming a normal distribution (Fig. 6.5). This can, of course, be solved for any score in this distribution. Since the table of the normal curve is in standard units, the first step is to change the raw score of 110 to a standard score as follows:

$$z = \frac{X - \overline{X}}{s} = \frac{110 - 80}{16} = \frac{30}{16} = 1.875$$

Inasmuch as this score is halfway between 1.87 and 1.88, we must interpolate. This time we are interested in the area in the smaller portion of the curve at a given standard score point. The value from the table is half the distance between .0307 and .0301, which equals .0304. Next, we multiply our N by this proportion to find the number of cases above this raw score of 110. We find that 510(.0304) = 15.504 cases. This in round numbers is approximately 16 cases.

Points Above or Below Which Certain Proportions of the Area Fall. Now we are going to reverse the process we have been using. Suppose that we wish to find that point in the distribution which has 10 percent of the cases below it and 90 percent of the cases above it (Fig. 6.6). This point would be the tenth centile. Again we enter the normal probability table and using the fourth column, the area in the smaller portion, we locate the value closest to .10. In the table we find this to be .1003, and reading to the left we find that a standard score of 1.28 divides the area of the curve into the two proportions as desired. Since this standard score is to the left of the mean, it has to have a minus sign in front of it and is correctly written as

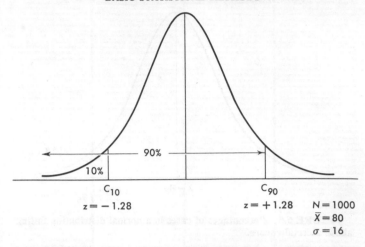

FIGURE 6.6 Points in the normal curve above and below which different percentages of the curve lie.

-1.28. We could have solved this problem just as well by using the third column of the table, the area in the larger portion. We would have gone down this column until we came as close to .90 as possible. This value is .8997 which puts us in the same row as before. The procedure from this point on is identical. If we wanted to find the point in the distribution with 10 percent of the cases above it (C_{90}), the work would be identical to that just completed, except that in the end the value of the standard score would be $+1.28$ because this time our point is to the right of the mean.

NORMALIZING A DISTRIBUTION OF SCORES

In the paragraphs that follow, the process of normalizing a distribution of scores will be demonstrated. From the results, the normal curve for the data will be plotted, this normal curve for any set of data being referred to as the curve of best fit for that set of data. The best-fitting curve for any set of data has the same mean and standard deviation and is based upon the same number of cases as the original data.

This process shall be demonstrated by using the data in Table 6.2. These data are based upon 150 cases with a mean of 63.9 and a standard deviation of 12.2. Column 1 lists the intervals and column 2 shows the observed frequencies, which are labeled this time f_0. After setting up these two columns, we proceed as follows:

1. Determine the upper limit of each interval and record these in column 3.

2. Determine the x values of column 4 by subtracting the mean, 63.9, from each of the upper limits in column 3.

TABLE 6.2. Normalizing a Distribution of Scores

(1)	(2)	(3)	(4)	(5)	(6)	(7)	(8)	(9)
		Upper			Proportion			
	f_o	Limit	x	z	Below	Within	f_e	f_e
90–94	1	94.5	30.6	2.51	.9940	.0119	1.785	1.8
85–89	3	89.5	25.6	2.10	.9821	.0276	4.140	4.1
80–84	8	84.5	20.6	1.69	.9545	.0548	8.220	8.2
75–79	12	79.5	15.6	1.28	.8997	.0919	13.875	13.8
70–74	28	74.5	10.6	.87	.8078	.1306	19.590	19.6
65–69	36	69.5	5.6	.46	.6772	.1573	23.595	23.6
60–64	12	64.5	.6	.05	.5199	.1605	24.075	24.1
55–59	18	59.5	−4.4	−.36	.3594	.1388	20.820	20.8
50–54	10	54.5	−9.4	−.77	.2206	.1016	15.240	15.2
45–49	8	49.5	−14.4	−1.18	.1190	.0631	9.465	9.5
40–44	8	44.5	−19.4	−1.59	.0559	.0331	4.965	5.0
35–39	5	39.5	−24.4	−2.00	.0228	.0148	2.220	2.2
30–34	1	34.5	−29.4	−2.41	.0080	.0080	1.200	1.2

$N = 150$
$\bar{X} = 63.9$
$s = 12.2$

$\Sigma = .9940$ $\Sigma f_e = 149.1$

3. Change each of these x values of column 4 to a standard score, z, by dividing by the standard deviation, 12.2.

4. From the normal probability table in the Appendix (Table II), determine the proportion of the area in the normal curve below each of these standard scores. For the top score, 2.51, we see in the table that .9940 of the area is below this point. These proportions are recorded in column 6.

5. The values in column 7 are determined as follows. The bottom value in column 7 has the same values as that at the bottom of column 6, for the proportion within and below this interval is the same as the proportion below the upper limit of the interval 30–34. The proportion within the second interval is obtained by subtracting .0080, the proportion within the bottom interval, from .0228, the proportion below the upper limit of the second interval. This results in a value of .0148. For the proportion within the third interval, we subtract .0228 from .0559. This process is continued until all the values in column 7 are determined. The sum of this column should be close to 1.00, but it is usually actually a little less than this, for there are always cases in the extremes of the tails of the normal curve that are not taken into account in this process.

6. The values in column 8 are obtained by multiplying the number of cases, 150, by each of the proportions in column 7. Again these add up to slightly less than 150.

7. In column 9 these expected frequencies (f_e) are rounded to the nearest tenth.

In Fig. 6.7, the axes have been set up in the usual manner for constructing a frequency polygon. First the f_o's are plotted and these points connected with a rule as in the usual method for plotting a frequency polygon. Then the values in column 9 are plotted and these are connected by means of a

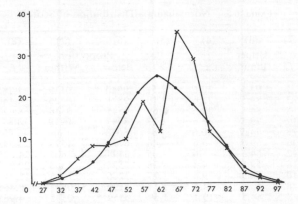

FIGURE 6.7 Frequency polygon and normalized curve for the data in Table 6.3.

smooth curve.   In Fig. 6.7 we have the curve of best fit for these data superimposed upon the frequency polygon for the original data.

The student may now be wondering when he should normalize a curve or even if there is any justification for performing the act.   Later, in Chapter 14 on chi square, we shall see that one of the uses of chi square is to see if a distribution of measures departs from normal.   In order to make a chi-square test, we must be able to set up the expected frequencies for any set of data.   Also there are times when a distribution of a sample of scores is not normal; yet the research worker has a hunch or knows that the distribution of the trait with which he is concerned is normally distributed in the population.   Since he can justify this, he may find it useful to normalize the data in his sample.

Exercises

1. Given a normal distribution with a mean of 26.1 and a standard deviation of 10.7, find the z score equivalents of the following scores in the distribution:
    (a)   5, 18, 30, 39, 46, and 51.
    (b)   Transform each of these z scores to a standard score with a mean of 50 and a standard deviation of 10.
2. Given the following z scores, find the corresponding area from the mean to each standard score.   Assume a normal distribution.

.27	−.65
−2.47	−.05
3.00	.80
1.00	3.20

3. Given an N of 500 and a normally distributed population:
    (a)   How many cases would be expected to exceed each of the z scores in Problem 2?
    (b)   Express each of these z scores in Problem 2 as a centile point.

4. If a frequency polygon were drawn for each of the following, which do you think would approximate a normal curve?
   (a) Income in dollars of 50-year-old males.
   (b) Height of cornstalks (in inches) in a field.
   (c) Height (in inches) of a large sample of adult men.
   (d) Weight (in ounces) of statistics books.
   (e) Means of an infinite number of samples ($N = 10$) drawn from a normally distributed, infinitely large population.
   (f) Errors in the estimation of the speed of an earth satellite.

5. Below are the scores of a sample of 130 students on the *Minnesota Paper-Form Board Test*.

60–62	2
57–59	4
54–56	8
51–53	10
48–50	18
45–47	16
42–44	14
39–41	14
36–38	10
33–35	18
30–32	14
27–29	2

$$N = 130$$
$$\bar{X} = 42.8$$
$$s = 8.2$$

   (a) Assume a normal population distribution and determine what percent of cases you would expect to find between the mean and the following scores in similar samples: 60, 38, 28.
   (b) Find the percentage and number of cases expected to fall between the following pairs of scores: 35 and 45, 50 and 55, 56 and 60.
   (c) How many cases would you expect to find above a raw score of 50? Below a score of 35?

6. Apply the normalizing process to the data of Problem 5 and plot the best-fitting curve for these data. On the same axes, plot the frequency polygon for the original data.

7

CORRELATION—
THE PEARSON *r*

Correlation is basically a measure of relationship between two variables. If we notice some of the common things that we measure, we see that high grades in English tend to be associated with high grades in foreign languages. Both of these tend to be associated with high scores on intelligence tests. In the physical domain, tall people tend to be heavier than short people. The volume of a gas is related to the pressure under which it is kept. In the field of economics, there is a correlation between the price at which products are sold and the amount available for sale. So in all aspects of life, we find that there are relationships of one sort or another. It should be noted here that these relationships do not necessarily imply that one is the cause of the other. This may or may not be the case. In some situations, we find that two variables are related because they are both related to, or caused by, a third variable.

The size of the Pearson product-moment correlation coefficient (*r*) varies from +1 through 0 to −1. Most correlation coefficients tell us two things. First we have an indication of the magnitude of the relationship. It is worth noting at this point that a correlation of −.88 is the same size as one of +.88. The sign has nothing to do with the size of the relationship, but it does give information about the direction of the relationship. When two variables are positively related, as one increases, the other also increases. Intelligence test scores are positively related to academic grades. In general, the higher the intelligence test scores, the higher the grades received in school. Other variables are inversely related. By this we mean that as one increases, the other decreases. Think for a moment of the relationship between the speed of an automobile in high gear and the number of miles per gallon obtained from a gallon of gasoline. The faster that one drives, the worse the gasoline mileage. The absence of a relationship is denoted by a correlation coefficient of .00 or thereabouts.

A Perfect Positive Relationship. Figure 7.1 has been constructed to show the relationship between two variables. Notice how it is constructed.

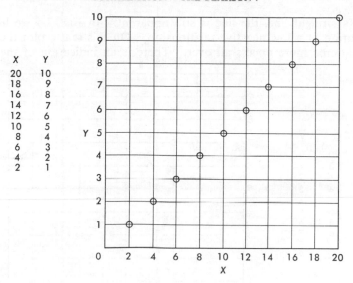

X	Y
20	10
18	9
16	8
14	7
12	6
10	5
8	4
6	3
4	2
2	1

FIGURE 7.1   A perfect positive relationship.

On the abscissa are plotted the X values and on the ordinate, the Y values. Each point on the graph stands for an individual's score on both X and Y. Such a double-entry chart as this is referred to as a scattergram or scatter-plot, and a distribution with two measures on each subject is referred to as a bivariate distribution. It should be emphasized that a scatterplot should be set up every time one is computing a correlation coefficient, no matter what computing technique is being used. The importance of this will be discussed later. To return to Fig. 7.1, notice that for every increase of two units on the X variable, there is a corresponding increase of one unit on the Y variable. This is true for all pairs of the two variables. When pairs of values like these are plotted, they fall along a straight line, and when this straight line runs from the lower left of the scattergram to the upper right, we have an example of a perfect positive relationship. The correlation coefficient is equal to $+1.00$.

A Perfect Negative Relationship. Figure 7.2 is just the opposite of this. Notice that for these data, for every increase of two units on the X axis, there is a corresponding decrease of one unit on the Y axis. Again this relationship is maintained throughout the range. This time our points again fall along a straight line which now runs from the upper left-hand part of the scatterplot to the lower right. This is the example of a perfect negative relationship, a value of -1.00. This means that the individual with the highest score on the X variable had the lowest score on the Y variable. The second highest scorer on the X was second lowest on Y, until at the bottom, the lowest on X was the highest on Y.

Other Relationships. In actual life we usually have situations in which the relationship is not perfect. Figure 7.3 shows the scatterplot of a very high positive correlation. Notice here that while the points do not fall along a straight line, the line is still apparent. In Fig. 7.4 we have the illustration of a low negative relationship. On this scatterplot the points are scattered more or less all over. There is an indication of the points

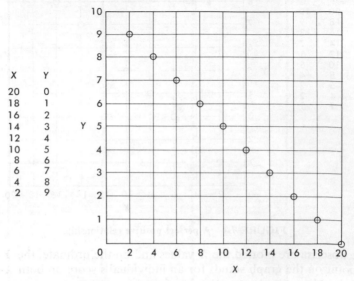

X	Y
20	0
18	1
16	2
14	3
12	4
10	5
8	6
6	7
4	8
2	9

FIGURE 7.2   A perfect negative relationship.

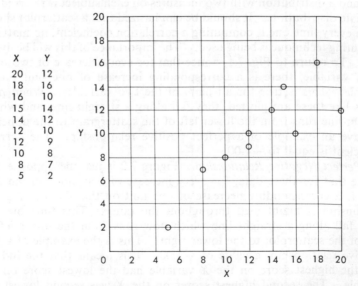

X	Y
20	12
18	16
16	10
15	14
14	12
12	10
12	9
10	8
8	7
5	2

FIGURE 7.3   A high positive relationship (.87).

falling in the general direction from the upper left to the lower right. When the points in the scattergram are spread evenly in all directions, we have an example of no relationship.

By making scatterplots, the student can get an indication of the magnitude of the correlation coefficient and also an indication of the sign of the relationship. This, in part, is a rough check on the computational work.

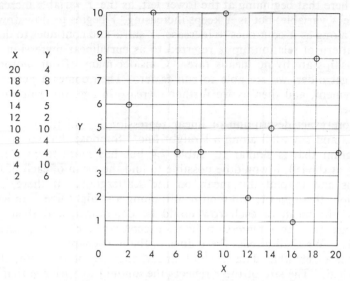

X	Y
20	4
18	8
16	1
14	5
12	2
10	10
8	4
6	4
4	10
2	6

FIGURE 7.4   A low negative relationship (−.31).

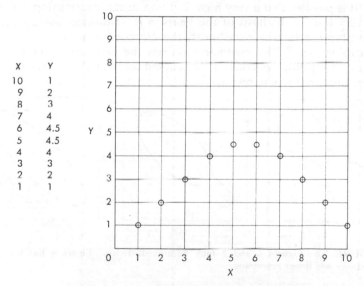

X	Y
10	1
9	2
8	3
7	4
6	4.5
5	4.5
4	4
3	3
2	2
1	1

FIGURE 7.5   An example of curvilinear regression.

Conditions Involved in the Interpretation of r. Before *r* is computed the scatterplot should be examined and sometimes the data tested to see if two conditions exist. The first of these conditions is that we have linear regression (also referred to as rectilinear regression). This means that our points on the scattergram tend to fall along a straight line. This is true of the data picture in Figs. 7.1, 7.2, and 7.3. However, now look at Fig. 7.5. Notice here that beginning at the lower left, as the Y variable increases, so does the X variable; but as X keeps increasing, Y begins to slow down, and further along as X continues to increase, Y starts and continues to decrease. This pattern of relationship is referred to as curvilinear regression. Such relationships are by no means rare. Consider many of our motor skills. As we get older, we are able to run faster. Then comes a period of no improvement, and then as we further increase in age, our running speed decreases.

A more exact description of linear regression is that the means of the columns and rows fall along a straight line. Suppose that you refer to a scattergram that is similar to Table 7.4 but has more frequencies. By starting at the left, it would be possible to find the mean of each of these Y columns and to plot this mean on the scattergram. If there is linear regression, these means will tend to fall along a straight line. In a similar fashion, the mean of each row could be determined and then plotted. There are then two regression lines, except when $r = 1.00$, when they coincide. We shall discuss these lines in the next chapter.

To the extent that data are not linear, the size of the computed r is diminished. The size of the r reflects the amount of variance that can be accounted for by a straight line; whether the data are essentially linear or not. It is possible that a very high, but non-linear, relationship will appear to be very low on the basis of the Pearson r. However, when a bivariate relationship is primarily curvilinear, the *eta* coefficient or the correlation ratio can be used. This coefficient reflects the variance accounted for by the best-fitting line, whether it be curved or straight. This coefficient will be discussed in Chapter 16.

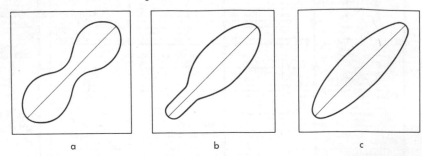

FIGURE 7.6 Figures *a* and *b* lack homoscedasticity. Figure *c* has both homo-scedasticity and linear regression.

The second condition that we should look for is homoscedasticity. By this we mean that the standard deviations (or variances) of the arrays (columns and rows) tend to be equal. In Fig. 7.6 there are three diagrams. In (a) the variance of the columns near the center of the X distribution is smaller than that of the extreme columns. In diagram (b) all of the columns at the left have smaller variances than those at the center and right. Diagram (c) represents the situation when both conditions are met. Note that the points tend to fall in an ellipse about the regression line. When the data are not homoscedastic, the usual methods of evaluating predicted values on the Y axis from the corresponding values on the X axis do not apply. For instance, in diagram (a) it would be possible to make predictions at the center of the X distribution with greater accuracy than at either end.

COMPUTATION OF THE PEARSON PRODUCT-MOMENT CORRELATION COEFFICIENT

Of the various correlation coefficients in current use, the one most frequently encountered is called the Pearson product-moment correlation coefficient, the symbol of which is r. In the pages that follow we shall present various methods for computing this coefficient.

The Pearson r from Standard Scores

In Table 7.1 the scores of ten individuals on two variables, X and Y (columns 1 and 2), are presented. Beneath each of these is the mean. In column 3 is the deviation of each of the X scores from the mean of X, and

TABLE 7.1. Computation of the Pearson Product-Moment Correlation Coefficient by the Use of Deviations from the Means

(1) X	(2) Y	(3) x	(4) y	(5) z_x	(6) z_y	(7) $z_x z_y$	(8) x^2	(9) y^2	(10) xy
20	12	7	2	1.61	.54	.8694	49	4	14
18	16	5	6	1.15	1.62	1.8637	25	36	30
16	10	3	0	.69	.00	.0000	9	0	0
15	14	2	4	.46	1.08	.4968	4	16	8
14	12	1	2	.23	.54	.1242	1	4	2
12	10	-1	0	$-.23$	.00	.0000	1	0	0
12	9	-1	-1	$-.23$	$-.27$	.0621	1	1	1
10	8	-3	-2	$-.69$	$-.54$	.3726	9	4	6
8	7	-5	-3	-1.15	$-.81$	.9315	25	9	15
5	2	-8	-8	-1.84	-2.16	3.9744	64	64	64

$\Sigma X = 130$ $\Sigma Y = 100$ $s_x = 4.34$ $\Sigma z_x z_y$ Σx^2 Σy^2 Σxy $N = 10$
$\overline{X} = 13$ $\overline{Y} = 10$ $s_y = 3.71$ $= 8.6947$ $= 188$ $= 138$ $= 140$

in column 4 we find the deviation of each of the Y scores from the mean of Y. Beneath these two columns are the standard deviations of the columns. In columns 5 and 6 are the standard scores for each of the scores in columns 1 and 2. These were obtained by dividing each score in column 3 by s_x (4.34) and each value in column 4 by s_y (3.71). Here we are using the usual formula for z, $z = x/s$.   Column 7 is the product of the two z scores, the product of the values in columns 5 and 6.   These are summed, and the Pearson r is obtained by the following formula which describes r as the mean z score product:

$$r = \frac{\Sigma z_x z_y}{N} \tag{7.1}$$

By substituting into this formula, we obtain

$$r = \frac{8.6947}{10}$$

$$r = .869 \text{ or } .87$$

Another way of looking at the Pearson r in terms of z score measures is the "difference method for r" mentioned by Peatman (1963).   This formula expresses r as a function of the difference between paired z scores:

$$r = 1 - \frac{\Sigma(z_x - z_y)^2}{2N} \tag{7.2}$$

The expression $\Sigma(z_x - z_y)^2/2N$ increases as the variables become more dissimilar.

The Pearson r from the Deviation from the Means

Since a standard score is defined as the deviation of a score from its mean divided by its standard deviation, we can write

$$z_x = \frac{x}{s_x} \quad \text{and} \quad z_y = \frac{y}{s_y}$$

Then taking formula (7.1) and substituting for z_x and z_y each of the above and solving, we can reduce the formula for r to

$$r = \frac{\Sigma xy}{N s_x s_y} \tag{7.3}$$

which further reduces to

$$r = \frac{\Sigma xy}{\sqrt{(\Sigma x^2)(\Sigma y^2)}} \tag{7.4}$$

since $s_x = \sqrt{\dfrac{\Sigma x^2}{N}} \quad \text{and} \quad s_y = \sqrt{\dfrac{\Sigma y^2}{N}}$

If Σxy, the numerator of equation (7.4), is divided by N, we have a term referred to as the *covariance*. If both factors in the denominator are divided by N, we have the variance of X and the variance of Y. The Pearson r can be described as the ratio of the covariance to the geometric means of the variances.

In column 8, 9, and 10 of Table 7.1 are values for x^2, y^2, and xy and the sum of each is given at the bottom of the table. After substituting these into equation (7.4), we obtain

$$r = \frac{140}{\sqrt{(188)(138)}}$$

$$= \frac{140}{\sqrt{25955}} = \frac{140}{161}$$

$$= .87$$

which is identical with the value obtained previously.

Both of the above methods would be very laborious with an N of any size. We shall pass on next to the two methods most frequently encountered in the computation of r.

The Raw Score or Machine Formula for Computing r from Raw Scores

We shall now go from formula (7.4) to the so-called raw score or machine formula. We have previously written the sum of the squares as

$$\Sigma x^2 = \Sigma X^2 - \frac{(\Sigma X)^2}{N}$$

$$\Sigma y^2 = \Sigma Y^2 - \frac{(\Sigma Y)^2}{N}$$

and it follows by analogy that

$$\Sigma xy = \Sigma XY - \frac{(\Sigma X)(\Sigma Y)}{N}$$

When we insert this formula (7.4) we have

$$r = \frac{\Sigma XY - [(\Sigma X)(\Sigma Y)/N]}{\sqrt{\{\Sigma X^2 - [(\Sigma X)^2/N]\}\{\Sigma Y^2 - [(\Sigma Y^2)/N]\}}}$$

After clearing the above equation of fractions we have

$$r = \frac{N\Sigma XY - (\Sigma X)(\Sigma Y)}{\sqrt{[N\Sigma X^2 - (\Sigma X)^2][N\Sigma Y^2 - (\Sigma Y)^2]}} \tag{7.5}$$

The same data that appear in Table 7.1 have been reproduced in Table 7.2. The original pairs of scores appear in columns 1 and 2. In column 3 are the squares of each of the X scores and in column 4 are the squares of each of the Y scores. Column 5 consists of the cross-products, the product

TABLE 7.2. The Pearson r Computed from Raw Scores

(1) X	(2) Y	(3) X^2	(4) Y^2	(5) XY
20	12	400	144	240
18	16	324	256	288
16	10	256	100	160
15	14	225	196	210
14	12	196	144	168
12	10	144	100	120
12	9	144	81	108
10	8	100	64	80
8	7	64	49	56
5	2	25	4	10
$\Sigma X = 130$	$\Sigma Y = 100$	$\Sigma X^2 = 1878$	$\Sigma Y^2 = 1138$	$\Sigma XY = 1440$

of each X times each Y. All five columns are summed, and we enter formula (7.5) as follows:

$$r = \frac{10(1440) - (130)(100)}{\sqrt{[10(1878) - (130)^2][10(1138) - (100)^2]}}$$

$$= \frac{14400 - 13000}{\sqrt{(18780 - 16900)(11380 - 10000)}}$$

$$= \frac{1400}{\sqrt{(1880)(1380)}}$$

$$= \frac{1400}{\sqrt{2594400}}$$

$$= \frac{1400}{1610}$$

$$= .87$$

which we have obtained twice previously for the same set of data.

If the above formula is used in doing work by hand, a substantial amount of time is saved by using the table of squares in the Appendix. It should also be noted that much time will be saved if the data are coded. Consider the data in Table 7.3. Notice the scores in the first column. They are all large, the smallest is 80 and the highest is 114. If each of these scores is reduced by 80 and the values in the second column by 30 (this would result in one negative score, but would be more convenient than reducing each score by 28, which is the lowest score in this distribution), the correlation coefficient computed from the coded data would be identical to that obtained from the uncoded scores, and the work would be much easier. Even if all of the work is to be done on the calculating machine, many people find that it is time saving to code the scores in the manner indicated. If automatic calculators are available, it is not necessary to go through all of the steps as shown in Table 7.2, as the machine keeps running sums of the sum of the X's, the sum of the Y's, the sum of the X^2's, the sum of the Y^2's, and twice the sum of the XY's as each pair of scores is entered. When the last pair has been put into the machine, the final readings of all five values appear. The work in the solving of the formula is also considerably reduced when done on a desk calculator.

The Scattergram Method

The final method to be taken up consists of tallying all of the scores into a scattergram and solving the correlation from that. It has been recommended that the student always plot his data into a scattergram when he is planning to compute a correlation coefficient.

TABLE 7.3. Scores of Thirty-Five Students on Two Art Judgment Tests

Individual	Meier Art Judgment	Graves Design	Individual	Meier Art Judgment	Graves Design
1	80	61	19	105	86
2	95	28	20	80	63
3	94	74	21	85	31
4	101	46	22	93	57
5	105	44	23	85	70
6	89	38	24	92	43
7	106	72	25	90	70
8	92	41	26	89	54
9	105	49	27	85	51
10	107	69	28	96	58
11	111	82	29	85	63
12	114	76	30	98	73
13	83	39	31	101	71
14	112	64	32	106	76
15	91	77	33	112	76
16	88	50	34	93	59
17	105	55	35	110	71
18	106	59			

In Table 7.3 are the scores of 35 university students on two art judgment tests, the *Meier Art Judgment Test* and the *Graves Design Judgment Test*. We shall compute the Pearson *r* between these two sets of scores by the scattergram method.

In doing this, we go through the following steps:

1. Set up two frequency distributions on the scattergram. We shall enter the Meier scores on the *Y* axis and the Graves scores on the horizontal or *X* axis. These frequency distributions are set up in the usual manner. Notice that the size of the class interval for the data on the *Y* axis is 3; whereas that on the other axis is 5. The size of the class intervals of the two distributions does not have to be the same.

2. Next we tally the scores. We take the first pair, which is a score of 80 on the *Y* axis and 61 on the *X* axis. To enter this, we go up the *Y* axis until we come to the interval containing 80 and then across to the interval containing 61. We enter our tally mark in the cell where these two class intervals meet. We then take the next pair, 95 and 28, and go up the *Y* axis until we come to the interval containing 95 and then over to the interval

TABLE 7.4. Calculation of the Pearson r by the Scattergram Method

X Axis—Graves Design Judgment Test

Y Axis—Meier Art Judgment Test

Marginal totals for the Y Axis (Meier Art Judgment Test):

Meier Art Judgment Test	y' (Q)	f (P)	fy' (R)	fy'^2 (S)	$x'y'$ (T)
114–116	13				
111–113	12	1	12	144	120
108–110	11	3	33	363	308
105–107	10	1	10	100	90
102–104	9	8	72	648	522
99–101	8	0	0	0	0
96–98	7	2	14	98	91
93–95	6	2	12	72	90
90–92	5	4	20	100	105
87–89	4	4	16	64	100
84–86	3	3	9	27	36
81–83	2	4	8	16	44
78–80	1	1	1	1	2
	0	2	0	0	0
		$35 = N$	$\Sigma = 207$	$\Sigma = 1633$	$\Sigma = 1508$

Marginal totals for the X Axis (Graves Design Judgment Test):

	25–29	30–34	35–39	40–44	45–49	50–54	55–59	60–64	65–69	70–74	75–79	80–84	85–90	
(A) f	1	1	2	3	2	3	5	4	1	7	4	1	1	$35 = N$
(B) x'	0	1	2	3	4	5	6	7	8	9	10	11	12	
(C) fx'	0	1	4	9	8	15	30	28	8	63	40	11	12	$\Sigma = 229$
(D) fx'^2	0	1	8	27	32	75	180	196	64	567	400	121	144	$\Sigma = 1815$

containing 28. Again we place the tally mark in the cell where the two intervals meet. We continue this process until all of the pairs of scores are entered. (One is very apt to make mistakes in this plotting, and it is a good idea, if time is available, to replot the two sets of frequencies and compare results before proceeding with the computations.) An inspection of our tally marks leads us to anticipate a moderate size correlation coefficient for these data.

3. Next we go to the bottom of the scatterplot and sum our frequencies, row A. The next three rows should be familiar to the student. Notice that this time the arbitrary reference point for the x variable is taken as the midpoint of the interval 25–29. Rows C and D are then summed.

4. Then we proceed to the right-hand side of the scattergram, and complete columns P, Q, R, and S. This time the arbitrary reference point is taken to be the midpoint of the interval 78–80. Sum columns R and S.

5. Column T is new. Notice that it is labeled $x'y'$, the product of the deviation from the two arbitrary reference points. Since deviations are moments, this could be called the product-moment. Hence the name for this correlational technique. Let us see how the $x'y'$ is obtained. Let us go to the row 114–116. In this row there is one tally and this tally is 10 units from the arbitrary reference point for X and 12 units from the reference point for Y and hence has a product-moment of 120. In the next row, since we have three tallies, we have to find the sum of each $x'y'$. The first one is 77 (7 × 11), the second 110 (10 × 11), and the third 121 (11 × 11). The sum of these three is 308. In the next row there is only one tally with an $x'y'$ of 90. In the next row we have $(3 \times 9) + (4 \times 9) + 2(6 \times 9) + (8 \times 9) + (9 \times 9) + (9 \times 10) + (12 \times 9)$ which is equal to 522. In this manner, all of the $x'y'$ values are obtained. This column is then summed.

6. The value of r is obtained by solving the following formula for r, using coded values:

$$r = \frac{\Sigma x'y' - [(\Sigma fx')(\Sigma fy')/N]}{\sqrt{\{\Sigma fx'^2 - [(\Sigma fx')^2/N]\}\{\Sigma fy'^2 - [(\Sigma fy')^2/N]\}}} \tag{7.6}$$

$$= \frac{1508 - [(229)(207)/35]}{\sqrt{\{1815 - [(229)^2/35]\}\{1633 - [(207)^2/35]\}}}$$

$$= \frac{1508 - 1354.4}{\sqrt{(1815 - 1498.3)(1633 - 1224.3)}}$$

$$= \frac{153.6}{\sqrt{(316.7)(408.7)}}$$

$$= \frac{153.6}{\sqrt{129435.29}}$$

$$= \frac{153.6}{359.7}$$

$$= .427 = .43$$

It is now possible to obtain the means and standard deviations for each of the distributions from the data on the scatterplot. Let us take the variable on the X axis first:

$$\bar{X} = 27 + \frac{\Sigma fx'}{N} \ (i) \qquad \Sigma x^2 = \left[\Sigma fx'^2 - \frac{(\Sigma fx')^2}{N}\right]i^2$$

$$= 27 + \frac{229}{35} \ (5) \qquad\qquad = 316.7(5)^2$$

$$\qquad\qquad\qquad\qquad = 316.7(25)$$

$$= 27 + 32.7 \qquad\qquad\qquad = 7917.5$$

$$= 59.7$$

$$s_X = \sqrt{7917.5/35} = \sqrt{226.21} = 15.0$$

Similarly, the mean and standard deviations of the Y variable are found:

$$\bar{Y} = 79 + \frac{207}{35} \ (3) \qquad \Sigma y^2 = \left[\Sigma fy'^2 - \frac{(\Sigma fy')^2}{N}\right]i^2$$

$$= 79 + 17.7 \qquad\qquad = (408.7)9$$

$$= 96.7 \qquad\qquad\qquad = 3678.3$$

$$s_Y = \sqrt{3678.3/35} = \sqrt{105.09} = 10.3$$

CORRELATION COEFFICIENTS AND THE RANGE

Anyone who uses the correlation coefficient to any extent soon notices that the size of the correlation coefficient is rather directly related to the range in the two variables being correlated. For example, if we were to go into any fourth grade and correlate the height of the children in that grade with their weights, we would probably end up with a rather low coefficient. However, if we were to take a group of children in grades two through seven, we would find a rather high positive correlation between height and weight. Grades in graduate school when correlated with intelligence test scores are likely to result in low coefficients; whereas there is a moderately sized correlation coefficient between these two variables when children in grades three through eight are so studied. In both of these examples we have two situations, one of which has a more restricted range than the other.

Table 7.5 presents the scores of 16 individuals on two tests. In the two right-hand columns are the ranks of the persons on both. An inspection of the data shows that there is a high positive correlation between the two variables. An individual who is high on one variable tends to be about the same on the other. There is little fluctuation of the ranks within the two columns. Suppose that we examine now the scores and ranks of the top five cases. By doing this we are reducing the range rather considerably.

TABLE 7.5.   Data to Illustrate the Effect
of Restricted Range on *r*

Individual	X	Y	R_x	R_y
1	40	19	1	2
2	38	21	2	1
3	36	16	3	5
4	34	18	4	3
5	30	17	5	4
6	29	14	6	6
7	28	13	7	7
8	26	12	8	8
9	25	10	9	11
10	24	11	10	9
11	22	10	11	11
12	20	8	12	14
13	19	9	13	13
14	16	10	14	11
15	15	4	15	15
16	10	2	16	16

SOURCE: Adapted from Reliability and Confidence. *Test Service Bulletin*, No. 44. New York: Psychological Corporation, 1952.

Notice individual 3.   On the first test he has rank 3, on the second rank 5. His rank has changed from 3 to 5, and since there were only 5 ranks, this makes a change of 40 percent.   When the total test is used, his change is 2 out of a possible 15 or about 12 percent.   Thus when we have a restricted group, small changes on one variable may be accompanied with large changes on the other.   These changes lower the size of the *r*.

The fact that it is the range and not the size of the sample which affects the size of the *r* can be demonstrated by selecting five other cases.   Suppose we take individuals 1, 5, 9, 13, and 16.   If we compute a correlation between these five sets of scores, we would find it to be +1.00 when the rank method is used (Chapter 16).

There are times in test work when correlation coefficients have to be corrected for restricted ranges.   Suppose that we consider test work in the Air Force.   To get into pilot training, an individual has to pass a rigorous battery of tests.   The poor and low scorers are not accepted.   Air Cadets are, then, a select group.   After they are selected, they are given further training and testing, and during this process some drop out or are dropped. Finally, we have a more selected group getting commissioned.   If we were to use the group of survivors against which to study our selection tests, we would soon find that our correlation coefficients were very low.   However, there are equations to take care of situations like this, and by using them we can correct the obtained coefficients for restricted range.   These may be found in Guilford (1954), Lindquist (1951), or Gulliksen (1950).

The variability of the group, expressed in terms of either standard deviations or variances, should be reported when correlation coefficients are obtained.   This gives some information on the nature of the group upon whom the data were collected and aids greatly in interpreting such coefficients.

Exercises

1. Give three examples of (a) high positive relationships, (b) moderate positive relationships, (c) negative relationships, (d) curvilinear relationships, (e) two variables related because both are related to a third variable.
2. Explain why the Pearson r is reduced when it is computed for data that depart from linearity.
3. For a group of 40 individuals, the z score product of two variables is 32.40. What is the correlation between the two variables?
4. Ten people are asked to guess the weight of a package to the nearest pound. Two weeks later they are asked to guess the weight of the same package; this time they are told that it contains an object worth $1000.

First Guess	Second Guess
7	9
8	9
7	8
8	9
9	10
6	9
7	9
6	8
7	9
9	10

Compute the Pearson r between the two sets of data.

5. Twenty students are given a test of general ability and an English achievement test with the resulting scores:

Mental Ability	English	Mental Ability (cont.)	English (cont.)
54	203	44	181
53	196	44	175
51	202	44	168
50	186	43	174
48	204	40	162
47	184	38	158
47	196	37	170
46	182	36	144
45	170	34	141
45	178	31	139

(a) Compute r for these data.
(b) Also compute the two means and the two standard deviations.

6. Use the scattergram method to compute *r* for these data.

Sales Attitude Score	Sales Index	Sales Attitude Score (cont.)	Sales Index (cont.)
48	22	32	12
48	19	32	11
47	20	31	17
46	20	30	16
46	17	29	15
43	21	29	15
42	21	28	16
42	19	27	16
41	17	27	13
40	15	27	12
39	18	26	12
38	15	25	15
38	15	25	9
37	20	23	9
37	17	22	13
35	19	21	9
34	15	20	11
34	14	18	11
33	20	17	10
33	13	15	8
32	15		

7. Scores of 18 deaf adolescents on the performance scale of the *Wechsler Adult Intelligence Scale* and four scales of an interest inventory.

	(1) WAIS—P	(2) Janitorial	(3) Clerical	(4) Manual Labor	(5) Paint and Handicraft
1	99	15	33	16	25
2	103	24	20	20	40
3	111	17	37	13	21
4	116	5	42	8	20
5	127	9	40	6	18
6	117	5	48	3	17
7	114	14	34	7	31
8	113	13	33	13	35
9	122	24	20	16	35
10	113	15	32	12	27
11	120	14	43	10	17
12	108	12	36	11	28
13	116	20	31	12	29
14	106	20	19	19	37
15	100	32	22	18	29
16	96	25	21	16	39
17	90	20	31	19	28
18	97	23	16	21	38

Compute correlation coefficients among the above scales as directed.

8. The following scores were made by 30 individuals:

	Minnesota Clerical Numbers	Minnesota Clerical Names	Minnesota Paper Form Board	Otis Quick Scoring Mental Ability
1	68	74	32	42
2	169	167	45	54
3	87	98	45	62
4	93	76	34	45
5	87	65	24	38
6	77	74	27	32
7	154	145	34	36
8	99	69	38	42
9	87	98	64	60
10	110	98	64	60
11	107	104	47	66
12	119	87	45	45
13	67	78	24	42
14	78	100	20	46
15	186	169	57	55
16	113	97	45	47
17	145	159	40	40
18	65	78	20	33
19	106	106	34	48
20	98	105	34	52
21	76	96	49	48
22	119	125	60	54
23	100	109	24	44
24	118	109	36	56
25	154	174	32	42
26	87	88	23	39
27	109	101	41	47
28	88	108	31	48
29	67	76	18	42
30	89	100	47	68

Compute the correlation between any two sets of the above scores using the method directed by the instructor.

8

LINEAR REGRESSION

In Chapter 7 it was noted that one of the basic conditions to be met in using a Pearson product-moment correlation coefficient is that there be a linear relationship between the two variables being studied. In this chapter we shall examine in more detail this phenomenon of regression and the use that is made of regression equations in predicting scores on one variable from scores made on another. For example, grades in a course or a student's grade point index are predicted from a test of mental ability such as the *Scholastic Aptitude Test* of the College Entrance Examination Board. In this example scores on the aptitude test are the predictors, also known as the independent variable. That which is predicted, the grades, is referred to as the dependent variable. By the use of a regression equation, we can predict scores on the dependent variable from those of the independent variable. It is the usual practice to designate the independent variable by the symbol X and the dependent one by Y.

The Equation for a Straight Line

We shall start by presenting the mathematical equation for a straight line:

$$Y = a + bX \qquad (8.1)$$

Let us first find out what a and b in the above equation stand for. To do this we write the equation as $Y = 4 + 2X$. Now we can substitute any value that we wish for X and solve for the corresponding value of Y. A few such values are shown below.

X	Y
0	4
1	6
4	12
8	20

Sets of values like these may be plotted as is illustrated in Fig. 8.1. Since we are dealing with a straight line, and since it takes only two points to determine a straight line, only two sets of these points need to be plotted. Let us examine this line in detail now. Notice that for an increase of one point on the X variable there is an increase of two points on the Y variable. The 2 in this equation is the b coefficient of equation (8.1). The b coefficient gives the relationship between the change in Y in reference to change in X. This ratio of change in one variable to change in another is referred to as the *slope* of the line. In Fig. 8.1 another line has been drawn, $Y = 1 + 2X$. This runs parallel to the first line, because it has the same slope. Theoretically, an infinite number of such lines with a slope of 2 can be drawn on these

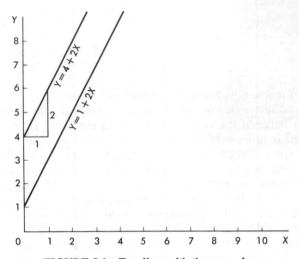

FIGURE 8.1   Two lines with the same slope.

axes. The slope of both of these lines is positive inasmuch as the lines run from the lower left to the upper right on the graph. As was noted previously, a line located like this one is an indication of a positive relationship between the two variables.

Now examine Fig. 8.2. Here we have the equation $Y = 4 - .5X$. By solving for values of Y we have:

X	Y
0	4
1	3.5
2	3
3	2.5
4	2
8	0

This time as X increases from 0 to 1, the corresponding change in Y is from 4 to 3.5. The ratio of the change in Y relative to the change in X is .5

for this example.   But as one variable is increasing, the other is decreasing, and for this case the b coefficient is $-.5$.

As was noted above, there are an infinite number of lines of the same slope which can be drawn on the same set of axes.   Two such lines are shown in Fig. 8.1.   Notice that one of these lines crosses the Y axis at 4 and the other at 1.   These values of 4 and 1 are the a coefficients for the two straight lines. Hence, we might define the a coefficient as the Y intercept, that point where the straight line crosses the Y axis.   The a coefficient identifies one of this infinite number of lines of the same slope.

The straight line used in regression analysis is written on a slightly altered form from that given above:

$$Y' = a + bX \qquad\qquad (8.2)$$

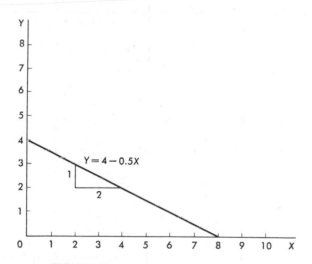

FIGURE 8.2   A line with a negative slope.

where Y' is read as the predicted value of Y. Y' is not usually the same as Y, for the score that is predicted from this equation will not be exactly the same as the one actually obtained.   The values of the predicted Y's will in general be closer to $\bar{Y}$ than are the values of the observed Y's.   Because of this relationship, this phenomenon is referred to as regression and will be discussed later.

Obtaining the *a* and *b* Coefficients

The difference between the obtained score (Y) and the predicted score (Y') is known as the error of prediction.   The regression line, or the line of best fit as it is often called, is that line about which the sum of the squares of these errors of prediction is at a minimum. By starting with equation (8.2), we have

$$Y' = a + bX$$

$$Y - Y' = Y - (a + bX)$$

where the left-hand side is the error of prediction.

These errors of prediction are squared and summed

$$\Sigma(Y - Y')^2 = \Sigma[Y - (a + bX)]^2$$

To obtain values of a and b which minimize the sum of the squares of the errors of prediction, the expression is differentiated by means of the calculus with respect to a and b in turn, and each of the derivatives is equated to zero. This yields

$$b_{yx} = \frac{\Sigma XY - [(\Sigma X)(\Sigma Y)/N]}{\Sigma X^2 - [(\Sigma X)^2/N]} \qquad (8.3)$$

and
$$a_{yx} = \overline{Y} - b_{yx}(\overline{X}) \qquad (8.4)$$

the regression coefficients for predicting Y from X as these subscripts are read.

In the previous chapter we noted that

$$\Sigma x^2 = \Sigma X^2 - \frac{(\Sigma X)^2}{N}$$

and that
$$\Sigma xy = \Sigma XY - \frac{(\Sigma X)(\Sigma Y)}{N}$$

Thus the beta coefficient, b_{yx} [equation (8.3)] may be written as follows in deviation form:

$$b_{yx} = \frac{\Sigma xy}{\Sigma x^2} \qquad (8.5)$$

Since there are two regression lines except when $r = 1.00$, it follows that there is another set of regression coefficients, this time being used to predict X from Y. These are written

$$b_{xy} = \frac{\Sigma xy}{\Sigma y^2} \qquad (8.6)$$

$$a_{xy} = \overline{X} - b_{xy}(\overline{Y}) \qquad (8.7)$$

An Actual Problem. The calculation of the regression coefficients will now be illustrated using the data in Table 7.4 in the previous chapter. For those data, a correlation coefficient was obtained between scores on the *Meier Art Judgment Test* and the *Graves Design Judgment Test*. This was found to be .427. Also for the same data the following statistics were computed:

$$\bar{X} = 59.7 \qquad\qquad \bar{Y} = 96.7$$

$$\Sigma x^2 = 7917.5 \qquad\qquad \Sigma y^2 = 3678.3$$

$$N = 35$$

In addition to the above statistics, we also need Σxy, which is obtained as follows:

$$\Sigma xy = \left[\Sigma x'y' - \frac{(\Sigma fx')(\Sigma fy')}{N}\right] i_x i_y$$

The student should note that this is the numerator of the equation for the Pearson r in the scattergram formula multiplied by the two interval sizes.

$$\Sigma xy = (153.6)(5)(3) = (153.6)15 = 2304$$

First we obtain the b coefficient using equation (8.5).

$$b_{yx} = \frac{\Sigma xy}{\Sigma x^2}$$

$$= \frac{2304}{7917.5}$$

$$= .291$$

We now have the information necessary for the solution of the a coefficient using equation (8.4).

$$a_{yx} = \bar{Y} - \bar{X}(b_{yx})$$

$$= 96.7 - (59.7)(.291)$$

$$= 96.7 - 17.4$$

$$= 79.3$$

Then substituting in the equation for a straight line, $Y' = a + bX$, we have $Y' = 79.3 + .291X$ which is the regression equation for the Y variable on X for these data.

We shall next plot this line. Since two points determine a straight line, we can solve the above regression equation for a couple of points and plot these as shown in Fig. 8.3. Suppose that we take three values of X and by substituting these values in the regression equation obtain the predicted values of Y.

X	Y'
20	85.1
40	90.9
60	96.8

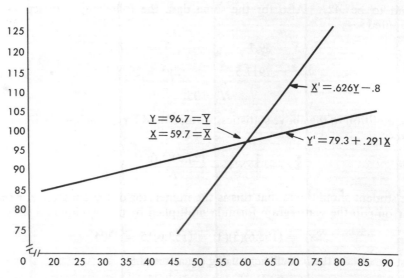

FIGURE 8.3 The two regression lines for the data in Table 7.4.

The plotting of these three sets of values on Fig. 8.3 results in the regression line shown there.

As we have already noted, there are two regression lines unless $r = 1.00$. We shall now proceed to determine the regression line for predicting X from Y. First the b coefficient

$$b_{xy} = \frac{\Sigma xy}{\Sigma y^2}$$

$$= \frac{2304}{3678.3}$$

$$= .626$$

Then the a coefficient

$$a_{xy} = \bar{X} - (\bar{Y})(b_{xy})$$

$$= 59.7 - (96.7)(.626)$$

$$= 59.7 - 60.53$$

$$= -.8$$

The regression equation for predicting X from Y then becomes

$$X' = b_{xy}Y + a_{xy}$$

$$= .626Y - .8$$

Let us again obtain three sets of points and plot this line on the same figure as the other. By substituting in the equation for various values of Y, we obtain and then plot the following:

Y	X'
120	74.3
100	61.8
80	49.3

Checks upon the Work. There are several ways of determining if the calculations are correct. First of all, the product of the two b coefficients should equal r^2:

$$(b_{yx})(b_{xy}) = r^2$$

$$(.291)(.626) = (.427)^2$$

$$.1822 = .1823$$

which checks, disregarding rounding errors.

Secondly, when plotted, the two regression lines should cross at a point equal to the mean of X and the mean of Y. An inspection of Fig. 8.3 shows that this is so. This is the same as saying that when the mean of X is substituted in the equation for predicting Y, the predicted value of Y will be the mean of Y.

By substituting for $\bar{X}$, the mean of X, 59.7, we obtain

$$Y' = 79.3 + (.291)(59.7)$$

$$= 79.3 + 17.4 = 96.7$$

which is the mean of Y. When the mean of Y is substituted in the other regression equation, the predicted value of X will be the mean of X.

The Standard Error of Estimate

It has already been stated that rarely will our obtained Y scores be identical with the predicted Y scores. There is an error in all of our predictions and the extent of this error is measured by a statistic known as the standard error of estimate. When the size of the correlation coefficient between two variables is high, the size of the standard error of estimate is small, and conversely, when the relationship between two variables is low, the size of the standard error of estimate is large. If we have a perfect relationship between X and Y, our obtained Y's will be exactly the same as the predicted ones. This is saying that all of the Y' values will fall on the regression line. Since there is no variation from this line for the various values of X, there is no error in making estimates. When we have the opposite situation, the situation where there is no relationship between the two variables, we have a regression line parallel to the X axis. The solution of the equation for a straight line when b is equal to 0 results in the equation

$Y' = a$. When b is equal to 0, $a = \bar{Y}$. Hence when there is no relationship between two variables, the predicted value of Y is equal to the mean of
Y, $Y' = \bar{Y}$. When this situation prevails the size of the standard error of
estimate is at a maximum. In this case it is the equivalent of the standard
deviation of the Y variable. The size of the standard error of estimate
ranges then from 0 to the size of the standard deviation of the dependent
variable (Y). Most of the situations that are encountered fall between
these two extremes.

Since each obtained score differs from the expected or predicted score,
the discrepancy between each set of these can be obtained, squared, and then
summed. If we divide this by $N - 2$ and then take the square root, the
result is the standard error of estimate.

$$s_{yx} = \sqrt{\frac{\Sigma(Y - Y')^2}{N - 2}} \tag{8.8}$$

A more useful formula is

$$s_{yx} = \sqrt{\frac{\Sigma y^2 - [(\Sigma xy)^2/\Sigma x^2]}{N - 2}} \tag{8.9}$$

We shall now obtain the standard error of estimate for predicting Y from
X for the data of Table 8.4. After substituting in equation (8.9), we obtain

$$s_{yx} = \sqrt{\frac{3678.3 - [(2304)^2/7915.5]}{35 - 2}}$$

$$= \sqrt{\frac{3678.3 - 670.6}{33}}$$

$$= \sqrt{\frac{3007.7}{33}}$$

$$= \sqrt{91.1424}$$

$$= 9.55 = 9.6$$

Similarly, the standard error of estimate associated with predicting X
from Y may be obtained.

An alternate formula for the standard error of estimate is often found in
measurement books,

$$s_{yx} = s_y\sqrt{1 - r_{xy}^2} \tag{8.10}$$

By solving this for these data, we have

$$s_{yx} = 10.3\sqrt{1 - (.427)^2}$$

$$= 10.3\sqrt{.817671}$$

$$= 10.3(.904)$$

$$= 9.31$$

The above formula is appropriately used when the data are based upon large samples. However, as the samples become smaller, less than 50, biases associated with these small samples enter into the work. This is taken into account in formulas (8.8) and (8.9). Formula (8.10) can be corrected for this bias by multiplying the obtained standard error of estimate by $\sqrt{N/(N-2)}$. For this problem this becomes

$$\sqrt{N/(N-2)} = \sqrt{35/33} = \sqrt{1.0606} = 1.029$$

$$(9.31)(1.029) = 9.580 = 9.6$$

which is the same as obtained by the use of formula (8.9).

Interpretation of the Standard Error of Estimate. Let us now take the value of 9.6 for the interpretation of this statistic. In predicting Y from X we can say that for any given value of X, the chances are two out of three that the observed cases will fall within a band which is the predicted value of Y plus and minus one standard error of estimate. When X is equal to 20, we would predict Y at 85.1 (Y'), and about 68 times out of 100 in such predictions the actual values of Y would be between 85.1 $\pm$ 9.6 or between 75.5 and 94.7.

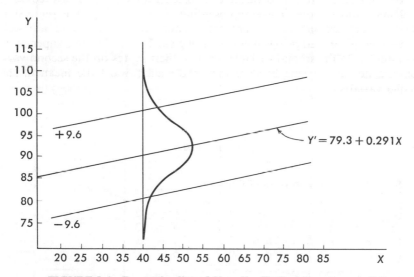

FIGURE 8.4   Regression line of Y on X. Each of the outer parallel lines is one standard error of estimate from the regression line.

This is shown on Fig. 8.4. Since we assume that the standard error of estimate is constant throughout the range, we could measure off 9.6 units on each side of the regression line for any other value of X and then draw two lines parallel to the regression line. Two-thirds of all of the observed scores should fall between these two outer parallel lines. We could set off two lines within which 95 percent of the observed cases should fall by measuring two standard errors of estimate on each side of the regression line. In this kind of interpretation, we are treating the standard error of estimate as a standard deviation. To do this, we must assume that the distributions around the regression line are not only equal in variance (homoscedastic) but also normal.

The Regression Effect

Many years ago Sir Francis Galton noted in studying the relationships between fathers and sons, and mothers and daughters, that the sons of tall fathers tended to be tall, but not as tall as the fathers, and that the sons of short fathers tended to be short but not as short as the fathers; the same applied to mothers and daughters. In other words the offspring of both tall and short parents were regressing toward the mean. If the correlation between the heights of fathers and sons were perfect, there would be no regression, the points representing the height of fathers and sons would all fall along a straight line.

However, since we never have perfect correlation and since many times the correlation between two variables is often rather low, as in predicting academic grades from scores representing mental ability, the regression effect is very frequently encountered. Those individuals who are well above average or well below average on one variable will be less superior or less inferior on the second variable; that is, their scores on the second variable are not as extreme because they regressed toward the mean of the second variable.

Exercises

1. Solve for Y' in each of the following:

   (a) $X =$ 5 $a = -3$ $b =$ 2
   (b) $X = -10$ $a =$ 4 $b = -2$
   (c) $X = -3$ $a =$ 2 $b =$ 3
   (d) $X =$ 7 $a =$ 50 $b = .125$

2. Given the following data, by the use of appropriate formulas find the Y' value corresponding to an X of 20.

X	Y
12	53
14	61
15	73
16	82
17	91
18	98

3. What is the standard error of estimate for Problem 2?
4. Problem 6 of Chapter 7 has already been solved, using the scattergram method for r.
   (a) Set up the regression equation for predicting Y from X from these data.
   (b) Calculate the standard error of estimate for predicting Y from X for these data. Use both formulas for this statistic and compare your results.
5. A small college is doing research in their entrance testing. A mathematics achievement test is given as part of the entrance battery. Scores on this test and mathematics grades are given for 20 freshmen.

Mathematics Test	Mathematics Grade
120	90
112	78
87	61
42	28
56	48
99	71
22	18
50	55
73	81
11	18
63	50
132	96
85	81
93	78
47	45
77	63
61	42
88	73
47	21
75	52

   (a) Plot a scattergram for these data.
   (b) Compute the a and b coefficients for predicting grades from test scores and vice versa.
   (c) Construct the regression lines on the scattergram.
   (d) Compute the standard error of estimate for each of the lines and plot them on the scattergram.
   (e) If 70 is the minimum passing grade, at which test score should candidates be denied admission to this course?
   (f) Do you think the math test is doing a good job?

9

PROBABILITY AND THE
BINOMIAL DISTRIBUTION

In previous chapters we have talked about probability and used the term in interpreting various statistics. In this chapter we shall discuss the laws of probability, the binomial distribution and its relation to probability, and some applications of probability to actual situations. Probability enters into all of our experimental work. Suppose that we have carried out a piece of experimental research to test some hypotheses. We examine the data to see if our hypotheses are supported or not. Procedures like this involve the use of probability for a probability statement is associated with our findings.

Probability enters into much of our daily living. The meteorologist in forecasting weather, the agriculturist in predicting the size of next year's corn crop, the physician making a prognosis about a patient's recovery—each of these uses probability when he makes his official or professional pronouncements. The physician tells the patient that, if he takes these pills, he should feel better in several days. The physician does not say that, if you do as I say, the chances are 90 in 100 that you will recover, but his statements are usually so worded that probability is inferred.

Probability values range from 1 to 0, where a value of 1 stands for absolute certainty and 0, for no chance at all that the event will occur. There are very few things in life about which we can be absolutely certain. One of these is that each of us will someday die. On the other hand the probability of the reader swimming from Seattle to Honolulu or in the course of his lifetime taking a space ship to a remote star is, in each case, zero.

Most things in life, however, have probability values of their occurrence somewhere between 1 and 0. In many predictions of outcomes, such as those of the physician or the weather forecaster, a numerical value is rarely assigned to the probability statement. In our work we shall endeavor to be more specific. Let us begin with a familiar object, a one-cent piece. If we take a new coin which in no way has been mutilated and toss it, we can state that the probability of obtaining a head is one out of two. We write

106

this as $p = \frac{1}{2}$ or .5. It is also true that the probability of obtaining a tail is $\frac{1}{2}$ or .5. In this situation, only one of these two outcomes can occur. The toss will result in a head or in a tail. (We are not interested in the situation where the coin lands in a crack or against an object and stands on edge.) Notice that the sum of the two probabilities is equal to 1. We designate the probability of an event occurring by use of the symbol p and the probability of it not occurring by the symbol q. The sum of $p + q$ is always equal to one. As an additional example, let us take a die and throw it into the air. If this is an accurate and well-made die, the probability of any single side coming up is $\frac{1}{6}$ or .167. That is, when we toss a die, the chance of throwing a six-spot is one in six. There are five in six chances of some other number appearing on the upturned face. In this case, $p = \frac{1}{6}$ and $q = \frac{5}{6}$, and again $p + q = 1$. In test work, the probability of a student getting an answer correct when he knows nothing about the item is, for true-false items, $\frac{1}{2}$ or .5. If we have a five-response multiple-choice item, the probability of getting the correct answer by chance is $\frac{1}{5}$ or .2.

What then is this probability that we have been talking about? It seems that it is related to the laws of chance. When chance operates, we can make statements about the expected outcomes. These statements can be expressed in terms of probability values. Probability, therefore, is the theoretical or expected frequency when the laws of chance are operating.

LAWS OF PROBABILITY

To illustrate these laws, let us return to the tossing of a die. Suppose we toss a die, and this time suppose that we are interested in the appearance of a three-spot on the upturned face. The probability of a three-spot showing is $\frac{1}{6}$. If we toss the same die a second time, the probability of again getting a three-spot is still one in six. What happens the second time is in no way affected by what happened the first time. We say that events like this are independent. Even if we tossed ten three-spots in a row, the probability of obtaining a three-spot on the eleventh toss is still one in six. Suppose instead of tossing one die, we toss two dice. What is the probability of their both being three-spots? The probability of one being a three-spot is $\frac{1}{6}$ and the probability of the other being a three-spot is also $\frac{1}{6}$. The probability of their both being three-spots is $\frac{1}{36}$. This illustrates a first law of probability. *The probability of the simultaneous or successive occurrence of two or more independent events is equal to the product of their separate probabilities.*

Now let us look at the outcome of the die tossing in another manner. The probability of any given side appearing is one in six. Suppose that we ask, what is the probability of getting either a three-spot or a four-spot. Since the probability of the occurrence of either of these is $\frac{1}{6}$, the chances that any given toss of a die will be either a three-spot or a four-spot is $\frac{1}{3}$, the sum of the probability of each. This illustrates a second law of probability.

The probability of the occurrence of any of two (or more) mutually exclusive events is equal to the sum of their separate probabilities.

THE BINOMIAL EXPANSION

If we toss two coins at once, four possibilities may occur. We may find that two heads have come up, a head and a tail, or that both coins show tails. In terms of symbols this may be expressed like this:

First Coin	Second Coin
H	H
H	T
T	H
T	T

From this we see that there are actually four possible outcomes, but two of them are the same in effect, for a head and a tail may be produced in two different ways. Since there are four possible outcomes, we can write that the probability of getting two heads is $\frac{1}{4}$, the probability of getting a head and a tail is $\frac{1}{2}$, and the probability of obtaining both tails is $\frac{1}{4}$. The sum of all these probabilities is again equal to one.

The results obtained above are what we would obtain by squaring a binomial. It may be recalled that the square of the binomial $(x + y)$ is equal to $(x^2 + 2xy + y^2)$. In the tossing of two coins, x is the head or H and y the tail or T. If we multiply $(H + T)$ by itself, we obtain $HH + 2HT + TT$.

Suppose that we have three coins. By using the same symbols as above, we have the possibilities shown below.

Row	First Coin	Second Coin	Third Coin
1	H	H	H
2	H	H	T
3	H	T	H
4	T	H	H
5	H	T	T
6	T	H	T
7	T	T	H
8	T	T	T

Notice that now there are eight possible ways in which these three coins may fall. Inspection shows that rows 2, 3, and 4 are the same as are rows 5, 6, and 7. Actually there are four possible outcomes when three coins are tossed. So the probability of obtaining all heads is $\frac{1}{8}$, of obtaining two heads and one tail is $\frac{3}{8}$, of obtaining one head and two tails is $\frac{3}{8}$, and of all the coins being tails is $\frac{1}{8}$.

When we have only two or three coins, it is fairly easy to see what the probability will be for the various outcomes. But as the number of coins increases, we have to find more efficient ways for obtaining our probability values. We use the binomial theorem, which in its general form looks like this:

$$(p + q)^n = p^n + \frac{n}{1} p^{(n-1)}q + \frac{n(n-1)}{(1)(2)} p^{(n-2)}q^2 + \frac{n(n-1)(n-2)}{(1)(2)(3)} p^{(n-3)}q^3$$

$$+ \frac{n(n-1)(n-2)(n-3)}{(1)(2)(3)(4)} p^{(n-4)}q^4 + \cdots + q^n \qquad (9.1)$$

Suppose that we have eight coins, and that we toss them simultaneously. Let us see how we can use the above equation. In this problem the probability of getting a head on any one coin, p, is $\frac{1}{2}$ and n, the number of coins, is 8. Then by substitution

$$\left(\frac{1}{2} + \frac{1}{2}\right)^8 = \left(\frac{1}{2}\right)^8 + \frac{8}{1}\left(\frac{1}{2}\right)^7\left(\frac{1}{2}\right) + \frac{8(7)}{(1)(2)}\left(\frac{1}{2}\right)^6\left(\frac{1}{2}\right)^2 + \frac{8(7)(6)}{(1)(2)(3)}\left(\frac{1}{2}\right)^5\left(\frac{1}{2}\right)^3$$

$$+ \frac{8(7)(6)(5)}{(1)(2)(3)(4)}\left(\frac{1}{2}\right)^4\left(\frac{1}{2}\right)^4 + \frac{8(7)(6)(5)(4)}{(1)(2)(3)(4)(5)}\left(\frac{1}{2}\right)^3\left(\frac{1}{2}\right)^5$$

$$+ \frac{8(7)(6)(5)(4)(3)}{(1)(2)(3)(4)(5)(6)}\left(\frac{1}{2}\right)^2\left(\frac{1}{2}\right)^6$$

$$+ \frac{8(7)(6)(5)(4)(3)(2)}{(1)(2)(3)(4)(5)(6)(7)}\left(\frac{1}{2}\right)\left(\frac{1}{2}\right)^7 + \left(\frac{1}{2}\right)^8$$

Simplifying, this becomes

$$\left(\frac{1}{2} + \frac{1}{2}\right)^8 = \frac{1}{256} + \frac{8}{256} + \frac{28}{256} + \frac{56}{256} + \frac{70}{256} + \frac{56}{256} + \frac{28}{256} + \frac{8}{256} + \frac{1}{256}$$

Several things should be noted from this problem. In the first place, the sum of all of the values in the numerators must equal the value of the denominator, for the sum of all of the separate probabilities must equal 1. Second, after the middle term was reached, each of the other terms repeats one of the earlier ones in descending order of size. Third, the denominators are all the same. In this case they were all equal to $(\frac{1}{2})^8$. Hence after the first was computed, there was no point in multiplying the rest of the p and q terms. And fourthly, note that there is one more term than n; in this case we have 9 terms in our expansion. Suppose we summarize our results in columnar form, showing the probabilities for the various combinations of heads and tails, as in Table 9.1. From this we see that the probability of getting all heads is .004, about 4 chances in 1000. The probability of getting either 8 heads or 8 tails is .008, the sum of the two separate probabilities. We can also answer other questions, such as the probability of getting at least 6 heads. The probability of this is the sum of the probabilities for 6 heads, 7 heads, and 8 heads—.109 + .031 + .004 which equals .144 or 144 in 1000.

Instead of going through all the work of expanding the binomial as shown above, time may be saved by the use of the so-called Pascal's triangle which

TABLE 9.1.   Probabilities of Obtaining
Various Combinations of Heads and
Tails When Eight Coins Are Tossed

H	T	p	p
8	0	$^1/_{256}$	.004
7	1	$^8/_{256}$	.031
6	2	$^{28}/_{256}$	.109
5	3	$^{56}/_{256}$	.219
4	4	$^{70}/_{256}$	.273
3	5	$^{56}/_{256}$	.219
2	6	$^{28}/_{256}$	.109
1	7	$^8/_{256}$	.031
0	8	$^1/_{256}$	.004
		$^{256}/_{256}$ =	1.000

is shown in Table 9.2.   In the problem used with the binomial we had 8 coins; n is equal to 8.   Going to Table 9.2, we find that for $n = 8$, the same values are obtained for the numerators of our probabilities (Table 9.1) and the column at the right gives the denominator of the probability values, which in this case is 256.   Notice how the triangle is constructed.   A triangle has been drawn upon the table.   When the 6 and 15 at the top of

TABLE 9.2.   Pascal's Triangle

n	Binomial Coefficients									Denominator of p
1					1	1				2
2				1	2	1				4
3			1	3	3	1				8
4		1	4	6	4	1				16
5	1	5	10	10	5	1				32
6	1	6	15	20	15	6	1			64
7	1	7	21	35	35	21	7	1		128
8	1	8	28	56	70	56	28	8	1	256
9	1	9	36	84	126	126	84	36	9	1	512

this small triangle are added, they produce the value 21, which is one of the terms in the row for $n = 7$.   By combining all of the terms in row $n = 6$ in this fashion, all of the values in row $n = 7$ are obtained.   In this manner, the triangle may be expanded indefinitely.   Suppose to illustrate this we compute the values for the next row, that is, when $n = 10$.   The first term would be 1; then the second term, $1 + 9$ or 10; the third term, $9 + 36$ or 45; the fourth term, $36 + 84$, or 120; and the fifth term, $184 + 126$, or 210; the middle term, $126 + 126$, or 252; and the rest of the terms would be the same as the ones already computed in reverse order.

It should be noted that the binomial distribution is symmetrical only when $p = .5$.   So it follows that Pascal's triangle should only be used under this condition.   Suppose that $p = \frac{1}{4}$ and that n equals 5 and $q = \frac{3}{4}$.   The expansion of the binomial gives:

$$\left(\frac{1}{4} + \frac{3}{4}\right)^5 = \frac{1}{1024} + \frac{15}{1024} + \frac{90}{1024} + \frac{270}{1024} + \frac{405}{1024} + \frac{243}{1024}$$

which is a skewed distribution.   Skewness of the binomial distribution may be computed by

$$g_1 = \frac{q - p}{\sqrt{npq}} \tag{9.2}$$

From this it is seen that skewness is zero when $p = q$, that is, when $p = .5$; therefore, the greater the difference between p and q, the greater the skewness.

The Binomial and Normal Distribution

In Fig. 9.1 a histogram is shown representing $(p + q)$; when $p = .5$ and $n = 6$.   As we might expect, there are seven columns; the height of each is in proportion to its probability.   Suppose now that instead of tossing 6 coins we tossed 100 coins.   This time we would have 101 columns in our graph.   Now let us also suppose that for both of these graphs we have the same area and the same base line.   It follows that in the second example the columns will be much narrower than those in Fig. 9.1.   If we have an infinite number, the columns would be very narrow and this binomial distribution would then approximate the normal distribution.   Actually, the binomial distribution is always discontinuous, but as the number of cases gets larger, this binomial curve gets closer and closer to the normal curve; but it never becomes, like the latter, continuous.

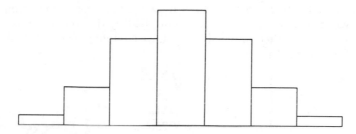

FIGURE 9.1   Curve of the binomial distribution when $n = 6$.

Parameters of the Binomial Distribution

Before we can use this binomial distribution in any problems, we have to learn how to compute several parameters which describe the curve.   Notice now that we are using the term parameter, because we are no longer dealing with samples but with population values.   In Table 9.3 are the results of tossing eight coins at once, or if we wish to deal in educational terms, the

TABLE 9.3.   Worksheet for the Computation of Binomial Parameters

(1) X	(2) f_e	(3) $f_e X$	(4) x	(5) x^2	(6) $f_e x^2$
8	1	8	4	16	16
7	8	56	3	9	72
6	28	168	2	4	112
5	56	280	1	1	56
4	70	280	0	0	0
3	56	168	-1	1	56
2	28	56	-2	4	112
1	8	8	-3	9	72
0	1	0	-4	16	16
Σ's	256	1024			512

chance results of answering eight true-false test items.   In column 1, labeled X, we have all the possible scores or outcomes.   Since we had an n of 8 to begin with, there are 9 values in this column.   In column 2 we have the expected frequencies.   These were obtained by the use of either the binomial theorem or Pascal's triangle.   The third column is obtained by multiplying the values in each of the first two columns row by row.   Column 3 is summed.   If we wish to obtain the mean, we must divide this sum by the number of cases.

$$m = \frac{\Sigma f_e X}{\Sigma f_e}$$

$$= \frac{1024}{256}$$

$$= 4$$

In column 4 we have the deviation of each of the X values in column 1 from this mean of 4.   In column 5 each of these is squared, and in column 6 each of the values in column 5 has been multiplied by the frequency for its row. This last column is then summed.   Next, we compute the standard deviation in the following manner:

$$\sigma = \sqrt{\frac{\Sigma f_e x^2}{\Sigma f_e}}$$

$$= \sqrt{\frac{512}{256}}$$

$$= \sqrt{2}$$

$$= 1.414$$

It should be noticed that we are using different symbols for both mean and standard deviation at this time.

If we are dealing with an actual problem, it is not necessary to go through the work shown in Table 9.3.   Both of these parameters can be obtained by the use of the following formulas:

$$m = np \tag{9.3}$$

where m = the mean of the binomial distribution
p = the probability of the event occurring
n = the number of objects involved, or the exponent of the binomial

For these data we have

$$m = np$$

$$= 8(\tfrac{1}{2})$$

$$= 4$$

which was the value obtained previously. The formula for the standard deviation of the binomial distribution is as follows:

$$\sigma = \sqrt{npq} \tag{9.4}$$

where all symbols are as previously defined.

For our problem, we find the standard deviation as follows:

$$\sigma = \sqrt{8(\tfrac{1}{2})(\tfrac{1}{2})}$$

$$= \sqrt{2}$$

$$= 1.414$$

which is again the same as the value previously computed. These formulas are used when the binomial distribution is taken as an approximation of the normal distribution. This should *only* be done when np or nq (whichever is the smaller) is equal to or greater than 5.

Use of the Formulas of the Binomial Distribution

Suppose that we construct a true-false test consisting of 26 items. We ask the question "What is the probability of getting a score of 20 or higher by chance alone?" that is, by guessing. We must assume that the examinee knows nothing about the material on which he is being tested. First we compute the mean and standard deviation for this distribution Since np is larger than 5, we can use the formulas for the binomial distribution.

$$m = np \qquad\qquad \sigma = \sqrt{npq}$$

$$= 26(\tfrac{1}{2}) \qquad\qquad = \sqrt{26(\tfrac{1}{2})(\tfrac{1}{2})}$$

$$= 13 \qquad\qquad = \sqrt{6.50}$$

$$= 2.55$$

In Fig. 9.2 we have drawn a curve with this mean of 13. Note that we have placed this score of 20 off to the right. The question is exactly how much of the area of the normal curve is above this score of 20. We have

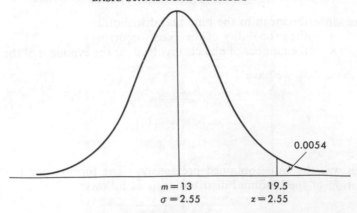

FIGURE 9.2   Finding the probability of obtaining a score of 20 or more on a 26-item true-false test by chance alone.

worked problems like this before.   The first thing that we do is to change the raw score of 20 to a standard or z score as follows:

$$z = \frac{X - m}{\sigma}$$

$$= \frac{20 - 13}{2.55}$$

This standard score formula is based upon a normal curve where the distribution is continuous.   Since we are dealing with a discrete, or non-continuous distribution, we make a correction for the lack of continuity at this point.   This is done by using, instead of the score of 20 in the formula, the lower limit of 20 which is 19.5.   When we make this correction our work is much more accurate.

Then we have

$$z = \frac{19.5 - 13}{2.55}$$

$$= \frac{6.5}{2.55}$$

$$= 2.55$$

In the normal probability table (Table II in the Appendix), we find that .0054 of the area of the curve is above this standard score of 2.55.   Then the chances are 54 in 10000 that an individual can get 20 or more of these items correct by chance alone.

Next let us ask another question.   This time we want to know what is the probability of obtaining a score of exactly 18 on this same true-false test by chance alone.   This time refer to Fig. 9.3.   The lower limit of 18 is 17.5 and the upper limit is 18.5.   We want to find the area of the curve which falls between these two points.   We first change both of these values to

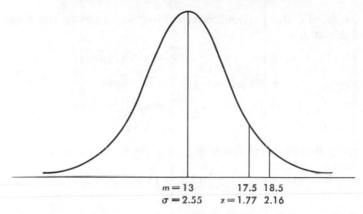

$$m = 13 \qquad 17.5 \quad 18.5$$
$$\sigma = 2.55 \qquad z = 1.77 \quad 2.16$$

FIGURE 9.3   Finding the probability of obtaining a score of 18 on a 26-item true-false test by chance alone.

z scores and then enter the normal probability tables to find the area cut off between the mean and each of these points.   We then subtract the smaller of these areas from the larger.   The remainder will be the area of the curve cut off by the two points.

$$z_1 = \frac{17.5 - 13}{2.55} \qquad\qquad z_2 = \frac{18.5 - 13}{2.55}$$

$$= \frac{4.5}{2.55} \qquad\qquad\qquad = \frac{5.5}{2.55}$$

$$= 1.76 \qquad\qquad\qquad\quad = 2.16$$

In the normal probability table, we find the following areas between the mean and each of these points:

$$z_1 = 1.76 \qquad .4608$$

$$z_2 = 2.16 \qquad .4846$$

The difference between these two areas is .024.   Then we can say that the chances are 24 in 1000 that an individual will obtain a score of exactly 18 on this 26-item true-false test.

In psychological research, the binomial distribution is used to determine the ability of individuals to distinguish between different types of cola drinks, orange juices, cigarettes, oleomargarine and butter, and the like.   This is the way it is done.   Suppose that we have four cola drinks and we have the hypothesis that an individual is unable to separate cola A from the three others.   Suppose that over a period of days we give an individual 60 trials, and we observe that he identifies cola A correctly 20 times.   The question is whether this differs significantly from chance.   We solve this problem exactly as we did the previous ones. First we compute the mean and standard deviations:

$$m = np \qquad\qquad \sigma = \sqrt{60(\tfrac{1}{4})(\tfrac{3}{4})}$$

$$= 60(\tfrac{1}{4}) \qquad\qquad = \sqrt{180/16}$$

$$= 15 \qquad\qquad = \sqrt{11.25}$$

$$\qquad\qquad\qquad = 3.35$$

By changing this observed frequency to a standard score and correcting for continuity we have:

$$z = \frac{19.5 - 15}{3.35}$$

$$= \frac{4.5}{3.35}$$

$$= 1.34$$

The normal probability table indicated that with a standard score of 1.34, we have .0901 of the area of the normal curve which falls to the right of an ordinate erected at this point. The chances then are 9 in 100 that this individual could identify cola A when samples of it are tasted along with three other colas. We shall discuss the real significance of this probability value in a later chapter when we discuss the general problem of testing hypotheses. It might be noted here, however, that it is the usual practice to require a probability value of 5 in 100 or less before we are willing to accept the hypothesis that an individual is doing better than we would expect by chance.

Exercises

1. What is the value of p for the occurrence of each of these events?
    (a) Drawing an ace in one draw from a well-shuffled deck of cards.
    (b) Drawing a heart in one draw from a well-shuffled deck of cards.
    (c) Winning the grand prize of a raffle in which 8000 tickets have been sold.
    (d) Obtaining a head from a tossed coin on the fourth toss when (1) the first three tosses turned up heads and (2) when the first three were tails.
    (e) Drawing a spade from a deck of cards on the fourth draw when the first three draws were spades and were not replaced in the deck.
2. What is the probability of these events?
    (a) Obtaining six consecutive tails when tossing a coin.
    (b) Throwing a twelve (two six-spots) with a pair of dice.
    (c) Throwing an even number with a die.
    (d) One man's drawing of an ace of spades from a deck, this followed by a second man's drawing the king of spades from the same deck with no replacement. Assume that the first man did not draw the king of spades.

3. A box contains seven red and three green balls.
    (a) What is the probability of drawing from this box a red ball, followed by a green ball, with replacement?
    (b) What is the probability of drawing two green balls in succession with replacement?
4. Six coins are tossed.
    (a) What is the probability of getting four or more heads?
    (b) What is the probability that exactly four will be heads?
5. A die is tossed six times.   What is the probability of obtaining four or more four-spots?
6. Smokers claim that they can identify the brand of cigarette which they customarily smoke.   To test this an experiment is planned in which an individual is given four cigarettes to smoke, one of which is his favorite brand.   All cigarettes are of the ordinary type.   Of 110 subjects tested, 32 identify their own brand correctly.   Is this a significantly larger number than would be expected by chance?
7. A 40-item multiple-choice test is made up of five-response items.
    (a) If a person knows nothing about the material tested, what score could we expect by chance?
    (b) What is the probability of getting a score 12 or higher by chance alone?
    (c) What is the probability of getting a score of 12 by chance alone?
8. Bowles and Pronko gave 96 subjects a sample of each of three different cola drinks.[1]   Coca-Cola was correctly identified 39 times; Pepsi-Cola, 36 times.   Is either of these identifications significantly different from what would be expected by chance?
9. Suppose that you were going to take a 30-item true–false test on ancient Greek literature and further suppose that you know nothing about this subject.   You decide to answer the items on the test by tossing a coin.
    (a) What is the probability of your getting a score of 20 correct?
    (b) What is the probability of getting a score of 20 or higher?
    (c) What is the probability of getting all items correct?

[1] *Journal of Applied Psychology*, 1948, *32*, 558–564.

10

SAMPLING

One very important use of statistics is in the making of inferences about larger groups on the basis of information obtained from smaller groups. To state this in other words, we wish to make statements or generalizations about the population on the basis of information obtained from the study of one or more samples. The extent to which we can do this with any accuracy depends on the adequacy of our sample or samples.

KINDS OF SAMPLES

Samples can be broken down into two basic types: nonprobability and probability. In the nonprobability type, there is no way of estimating the probability that each individual or element will be included in the sample. In probability sampling, in the most frequently encountered situations, each individual has an equal chance of becoming a part of the sample.

Nonprobability Sampling

In much of our research, samples of this type are quite common. For example, the American college sophomore who happens to be taking a course in elementary psychology frequently becomes part of the sample in educational or psychological research. He is used because he is convenient. The students in a class may constitute the entire sample because they happen to be in a class whose instructor is interested in doing some research. Such samples as these are called *accidental* or *incidental* samples. Another type of nonprobability sampling is *quota* sampling. In this type of sampling, the proportions of the various subgroups in the population are determined and the sample is drawn (usually not randomly) to have the same percentages in it. For example, if a population has an equal number of males and females in it, so does the sample. Or if the population of a certain state has a certain percentage of farmers, another percentage of small town dwellers, and the rest are urbanites, then a sample drawn to study the inhabitants of this state would be made up of the same percentages of the three groups. This type of sampling is very similar to the stratified random sample described below except for the randomizing (Selltiz, et al., 1959). A third type of nonprobability sampling is known as *purposive* sampling. For example, the counties in the United States that have voted for the winner in a series of past presidential elections could be identified. We could study these counties, and from the voters' preferences in them make a prediction on the outcome of a national election.

The major advantage in the use of samples like those above is that they are convenient and economical. Many students participate in experiments as a part of their work in a course. Hence no expense to the research worker is incurred. As we shall see, the drawing of probability samples is apt to be both expensive and laborious.

Probability Samples

The basic type of probability sample is the *simple random* sample. In a simple random sample, each and every individual in the population has an equal chance of being drawn into the sample. An illustration of this type of sampling took place when the National Selective Service Act was set up. Under the regulations of this act, as each male within the prescribed age range registered with his local draft board, he was given a number which ranged from one to several thousand. Then a series of capsules was set up, each containing one of these numbers. These were then placed in a large goldfish bowl and the Secretary of War, blindfolded, reached in, and drew out a capsule. The number that was drawn first placed all individuals, in the various draft boards holding this number, first in order for induction into the Armed Services. Then a second number was drawn and the process continued until all those registered received an induction number. The system of placing each number in a similar capsule, putting them all in the same bowl, mixing them, and then blindfolding the drawer made this type of sampling truly random. Only when we deal with probability samples can we know the frequency distribution of the sample statistics generated by the sampling procedure repeatedly applied to the same population. It is this knowledge that allows us to infer from a sample to its population. Randomization is essential to probability sampling and, therefore, to statistical inference itself.

When sampling procedures are not carried out like this, the resulting sample is said to be *biased*. Suppose that from a telephone book we select every fiftieth name as the individual to whom we are going to send a questionnaire in a study of attitudes of the citizens of a given city. This sample is biased, because it excludes all those who have no telephone or who have an unlisted number. The sample drawn may approach a random sample of those whose names are listed in the directory, and any inferences would be valid for these individuals but not necessarily for the city as a whole. The famous *Literary Digest Poll* of 1936 which predicted the election of Landon over Franklin Roosevelt sampled those individuals who had registered automobiles or listed telephones. Apparently during the Great Depression many more Republicans were on these lists than were Democrats. Another example of this on the national level was the Dewey-Truman election of 1948. Months before the election, the polls showed that Dewey was going to win by a landslide. A post-mortem of this fiasco showed that there was poor sampling in the lower socio-economic groups, and also that there was a large number of individuals interviewed who stated that they were undecided. In past polls these undecided cases were equally divided among the candidates. Apparently in 1948 a large number of these undecided individuals later voted for Truman instead of Dewey.

A second type of probability sample is the *stratified random* sample. This is very similar to the quota sample except that, after the percentages that are to be in each group are determined, individuals are drawn from each group by random sampling. Suppose that we want a picture of the attitudes of the student body of a large university on a certain campus issue. First, we would determine the number of students in each of the undergraduate classes as well as the number of graduate students. Second, we would obtain the percentage of males and females in each group. If the issue had aspects in which belonging to a fraternity or to a sorority was important, then we should know the proportion of sorority and fraternity members in each class. In another sampling, the school to which the student belonged might be important. Then we would want to know the numbers by sex and class enrolled in the various schools. Our sample should be so drawn that it is made up of the same proportions of the different classes as is the entire student body. Also the proportion of males and females and fraternity and nonfraternity members in our sample should be the same as in the entire student body. The same would be true in drawing a sample when school of enrollment was to be considered.

Next we decide how large the sample is to be. On the basis of our proportions in the university population, we decide, for example, the number of freshmen, male, fraternity men that are needed in our sample. Then this sample is drawn randomly from all freshmen, male, fraternity men. In a similar fashion our sample is drawn from the various other groups. If we wanted to study the attitudes of the citizens of any state, we could get census data from which we could determine the percentage of the population of the state that lived on farms, in small towns, and in cities. After this, we would attempt to apply random sampling within each of the three subgroups. In stratified random sampling it is *not* necessary for the size of each stratum sample to be proportional to the size of the population stratum. It is possible to weight each subsample statistic in proportion to the size of its parent subpopulation. Population estimates are then made from the subsamples combined in proper proportion.

The thoughtful student may conclude that this is a very time-consuming and laborious procedure if the population is very large. In studying the attitudes of a school or university group, it is practical to draw a stratified random sample.   But to attempt this on a national basis would be very difficult and expensive.   A type of sample that is used on such national surveys is referred to as a *cluster* sample.   In stratified random sampling, the population is categorized into groups that are distinctly different from each other on relevant variables.   In *cluster* sampling, the population is viewed as a collection of groups that are much the same.   That is, strata are internally homogeneous, and clusters are internally heterogeneous.   In stratified sampling we select randomly from *within* each stratum.   In cluster sampling, it is the clusters themselves which are randomly selected. In practice, cluster sampling is usually conducted in conjunction with stratified sampling, done in *stages*, or both.   For example, in gathering normative data for the use of a new test on a statewide basis, it would be possible to stratify the school districts of the state on the basis of size and then randomly select districts within each stratum.   In each of the selected school systems, individual schools could be chosen randomly, classes could be similarly selected within each school, and sometimes within each class individual students might be randomly identified for testing.   This type of sampling provides a wide coverage of districts and schools, yet is still economical and efficient in terms of the number of students tested.

We described earlier how a random sample was drawn by placing numbers in a goldfish bowl.   A more usual procedure is to use a table of random numbers such as Table XIV in the Appendix.   Here is how this table is used.   Suppose we have 896 answer sheets, and we wish to study a sample of these.   Assume that we want to draw a random sample of 100 from these 896 papers.   First, we would number each answer sheet, beginning with 001 and continuing to 896.   Then we enter the table of random numbers at any point.   This can be done by moving a pencil over the table without looking and letting the pencil down at any place.   Suppose that we do this and our pencil lands at the junction of column 7 and row 5 of Table XIV.   This becomes our starting place.   In Table XIV we find a 0 at this point.   We can move from this point in any direction; that is, from here we can proceed by taking numbers in threes downward, sideways, or obliquely, for example. When we get to the bottom of a column, we change our direction and proceed as before.   Suppose we decide to start down column 7.   The digits in order are 0, 6, 4.   So the paper with this number becomes the first one drawn for our sample.   The next digits are 0, 0, 8; resulting in paper 8 being the second one drawn for our sample.   The third paper would be 481.   And so we continue until our sample of 100 is drawn.   If we draw the same number twice or draw a number higher than our last paper, such as 909, we disregard the draw and continue the process.

There may be occasions on which we study an entire group.   It may be recalled that we have previously described a *population* or *universe* as an arbitrarily defined group.   Suppose that we define our population as all of the seniors majoring in home economics in a university.   Since this group is likely to be fairly small, we may use all the individuals in the group in the study.   There is no sampling problem here.

SAMPLING DISTRIBUTION OF THE MEAN

Suppose that we consider a large population such as all ten-year-olds in the United States.   With a population of this size and of this nature we can select sample after sample and study them.   Suppose also that we take a group of 30 of these ten-year-olds in a certain school and give them an intelligence test for which we compute the mean and standard deviation. Then we draw another sample of the same size and compute its mean and standard deviation.   We continue this until 5000 samples of size 30 are drawn and we have 5000 means and 5000 standard deviations.   A distribution of these 5000 means is referred to as a sampling *distribution*.   The mean of these 5000 means is a good estimate of the parameter mean.   The variability of this sampling distribution of means is measured by *the standard error of the mean*.

A distribution of the means of samples of equal size, as described above, when taken in large numbers from an infinite population will form a normal distribution.   This is an example of the *central limit theorem*.   If the random samples are large enough, and if there is a large number of samples, the mean of the sample means will equal the mean of the population, and the standard deviation of these sample means about the parameter mean will be equal to the standard deviation of the population divided by the square root of N.

$$\sigma_m = \frac{\sigma}{\sqrt{N}} \tag{10.1}$$

Thus for this application of the *central limit theorem*:

If a population distribution (it need not be normal) has a mean m and a standard deviation σ, then the distribution of random sample means drawn from this population approaches a normal distribution with a mean of m and a standard deviation of σ/√N as the sample size N increases.

When the sample size N is less than about 30 the sampling distribution of means is not accurately represented by the normal curve table (Table II). Instead, Table III (Distribution of t Probability) is used when working with small samples.

Actually this standard deviation of the mean, which is commonly referred to as the standard error of the mean, cannot be obtained from the above equation since the standard deviation of the population is usually not known.   The best that we can do is use the sample standard deviation as an estimate of the parameter value.

Correcting the Sample Standard Deviation for Bias

The sample standard deviation is considered to be a biased estimate of the parameter standard deviation.   If we select a small sample, say with N

equal to 15, from a very large population, the chances are good that the members of our sample will tend to come from the center of the distribution, and hence the range of the sample will be less than the range of the population. It follows that the standard deviation of the sample will also be smaller than the standard deviation of the population. The bias is that sample standard deviations tend to be smaller than the parameter standard deviation. As the size of the sample increases, the chances increase of getting scores from the extremes of the distribution. The sample standard deviation becomes closer and closer to the parameter value. The sample standard deviation, as an estimate of the population value, with a correction for this bias is given by the formula

$$s = \sqrt{\frac{\Sigma x^2}{N-1}} \tag{10.2}$$

If we substitute the above in equation (10.1) we have

$$s_{\bar{X}} = \sqrt{\frac{\Sigma x^2}{N(N-1)}} \tag{10.3}$$

which gives the standard error of the mean directly from the sum of the squares. A more widely used formula for the standard error of the mean is

$$s_{\bar{X}} = \frac{s}{\sqrt{N-1}} \tag{10.4}$$

in which the $N-1$ in the denominator corrects for the bias in the standard deviation in the numerator.

Suppose that we have a sample with a standard deviation of 15.6 based upon an N of 145. The standard error of the mean of this sample is as follows:

$$s_{\bar{X}} = \frac{s}{\sqrt{N-1}}$$

$$= \frac{15.6}{\sqrt{145-1}}$$

$$= \frac{15.6}{\sqrt{144}}$$

$$= \frac{15.6}{12}$$

$$= 1.3$$

An inspection of formula (10.4) reveals a very important characteristic of standard errors, that is, the larger the sample, the smaller the size of the standard error. This makes sense, for we would expect samples based upon larger samples to be more reliable than those based upon smaller ones.

To be more exact, we can say that the size of the standard error of the mean is inversely proportional to the square root of the number of cases in the sample and directly proportional to the standard deviation. This is what we see in formula (10.4). We can generalize from this and say that the size of the standard error of any statistic is inversely proportional to the number of cases in the sample upon which the statistic was computed.

The sample mean is usually described as being an unbiased estimate of the population mean. That is to say, any given sample mean may be higher or lower than the population mean. If we take enough of these samples and average them out, the result will be an unbiased estimate of the population; in other words, this result will tend to be systematically neither too large nor too small when compared with the parameter mean. This is in contrast with the sample standard deviation which we have shown to be a biased estimate of the parameter standard deviation.

All statistics have sampling distributions, and hence all have standard errors. Each of these gives an indication of the reliability of the statistic. When the size of the standard error is small in relation to the units of measurement, it follows that our statistics will tend to vary less from sample to sample and thus we can have more confidence in our results.

The Standard Error of the Median. The standard error of the median is obtained by the following formula:

$$s_{\text{Mdn}} = \frac{1.253s}{\sqrt{N}} \tag{10.5}$$

where all terms are as previously defined. When this formula is compared with that for the standard error of the mean, we see that the standard error of the median is about 25 percent larger than that of the mean. It may be recalled that it was stated in an early chapter that the mean is the most reliable average. By this we meant that it has the smallest standard error of the various measures of central tendency.

Standard Error of a Proportion. This is estimated by the following formula:

$$s_p = \sqrt{\frac{pq}{N}} \tag{10.6}$$

where $q = 1 - p$. The use and limitations of this formula will be discussed in Chapter 12.

Standard Error of a Percentage. Since a percentage is a 100 times a proportion we can write the formula for estimating the standard error of a percentage as follows in terms of proportions:

$$s_P = 100\sqrt{\frac{pq}{N}} \tag{10.7}$$

or like this in terms of percents:

$$s_P = \sqrt{\frac{PQ}{N}} \tag{10.8}$$

where $Q = 100 - P$.

Other Standard Errors. Two remaining standard errors are—*the standard error of a standard deviation*:

$$s_s = \frac{s}{\sqrt{2N}} \tag{10.9}$$

and the standard error of a frequency:

$$s_f = \sqrt{Npq} \tag{10.10}$$

where p is the proportion that responds in a certain way or answers a test item correctly, and q is as previously defined.

ESTIMATING PARAMETER VALUES

There are two aspects to statistical inference, the first estimating parameter values and the second hypothesis testing. In the remainder of this chapter, we will be concerned with estimation of parameter values, and the next three chapters will be devoted mostly to the testing of hypotheses.

Suppose that we have drawn a sample of 145 vocational high school students and have administered a test of mechanical ability to them. We have computed both the mean and the standard deviation for our sample, these being 82 and 14 respectively. From these statistics, we now wish to make statements or inferences about the parameter value of the mean.

Neither the population mean nor standard deviation is known. However, we have pointed out that the sample mean was an unbiased estimate of the population mean and that the sample standard deviation was a biased estimate of the parameter standard deviation, this bias, however, being taken into account in equation (10.4). By using equation (10.4), we obtain the standard error of the mean as estimated from this sample:

$$s_{\bar{X}} = \frac{s}{\sqrt{N-1}}$$

$$= \frac{14}{\sqrt{145-1}} = \frac{14}{\sqrt{144}} = \frac{14}{12}$$

$$= 1.17$$

If we were to continue to draw samples of the same size from this population, we know that the distribution of these sample means would be normal and that this distribution would have an estimated standard deviation of 1.17. According to Table II, we would expect two-thirds of sample means of samples with an N of 145 drawn from this population to fall within 1.17 points of the parameter mean. If we took two standard errors of the mean $(s_{\bar{X}})$, we would have a band in which we would expect to find approximately 95 percent of the sample means with repeated random sampling. After referring to Table II, we see that to be more precise a z score of 1.96 rather than 2 taken on both sides of the mean includes 95 percent of the sample means. Since our standard error of the mean is 1.17, we would expect about 95 in 100 of our sample means to fall within 2.29 units of the parameter mean, that is 1.96×1.17 units.

Previously, we noted that the mean of this sample was 82. Now we can state that the probability is .95 that this sample mean is within 2.29 units of the parameter mean. This can be summarized as follows:

$$95\% \text{ confidence interval} = \bar{X} \pm (1.96)s_{\bar{X}} \qquad (10.11)$$

$$= 82 \pm (1.96)1.17$$

$$= 82 \pm 2.29$$

$$= 79.71 - 84.29$$

In a similar fashion, the 99 percent confidence interval is established. If we consult the normal probability table, Table II, we find that a z score of 2.58 cuts off .005 of the area in the smaller portion. When this is doubled to include the area cut off by a deviation of the same size on both sides of the mean, the result includes 1 percent of the area of the curve. This procedure is similar to that above, except that 2.58 is used instead of 1.96

$$99\% \text{ confidence interval} = \bar{X} \pm (2.58)s_{\bar{X}} \qquad (10.12)$$

$$= 82 \pm (2.58)1.17$$

$$= 82 \pm 3.02$$

$$= 78.98 - 85.02$$

We have an unbiased estimate of the population mean m from the sample mean $\bar{X}$ (82). We can state that with repeated random samples of the same size, the chances are 99 in 100 that the sample means will fall within a band limited by 78.98 and 85.02. As one might expect, this band is wider than that for the 95 percent confidence interval.

In the above fashion confidence intervals can be set up for proportions, percentages, Pearson r's, and so forth. The technique above is for large samples. As we shall see in the next chapter, when we have small samples, we substitute for the z values a statistic called t and proceed as above.

It can be seen that the size of the confidence interval determines the usefulness of the parameter estimate. Suppose that we have two statements, the first that the chances are 99/100 that means of random samples of the same size will fall within the band from 80 to 120 and a second for which the 99 percent confidence interval was 98 to 102. Obviously, the second is much more precise than the first in practical work. Also the probability level has to be considered. If statements are made at the 90 percent, 95 percent, and 99 percent levels, the research worker or the consumer of research should place more confidence in the last one, as it is statistically the strongest statement.

From all of this, we can see that the smaller the standard error, the more confidence we can have in our statistic. We say that our statistics are more reliable, and by this we mean that our statistics tend to vary less from sample to sample. It should be kept in mind that the size of any standard error is a function of the size of the sample. As sample sizes increase, the size of the standard errors decrease; it follows that large samples produce more reliable statistics than those obtained from small samples.

Exercises

1. Which of the following selection techniques will result in random samples?
   (a) Population: all the residents of a given city.
   Sampling technique: for one week stopping every third person who passes by a busy downtown street corner.
   (b) Population: all the students in a large primary school.
   Sampling technique: selecting the first 75 students reporting to school on a Monday morning.
   (c) Population: all tomato plants in a field.
   Sampling technique: selecting one plant, blindfolded, from each square yard.
2. Suppose there are 1300 fifth-grade students in a school system. You are given the task of estimating their arithmetic achievement.
   (a) Define precisely the population.
   (b) How would you sample this population?
   (c) Would your sampling cost less than the population measure?
   (d) It has been said that an investigator can learn more from a sample than from a universe. In a practical situation, does this make sense? Why?
3. What is a sampling distribution?
   (a) What is plotted on the vertical axis of a sampling distribution?
   (b) What is plotted on the horizontal axis?
4. On a *Watson-Glaser Critical Thinking Appraisal*, 36 Ph.D. candidates in education achieve a mean score of 65. The standard deviation of the sample is 12.0.
   (a) What is the standard error of the mean?
   (b) What are the chances of drawing another similar sample with a mean of 69 or greater?
5. The scores of five chimpanzees on a finger dexterity test are as follows: 12, 14, 26, 9, 15.
   (a) What is the standard error of the median?
   (b) In this group, 80 percent of the chimpanzees achieved a score higher than 10. What is the standard error of this percentage? Is this standard error meaningful?
6. Given a distribution with a mean of 80, a standard deviation of 12, and based upon an N of 626, set up the 95 percent and 99 percent confidence intervals for the mean.

11

TESTING HYPOTHESES,
THE DIFFERENCES
BETWEEN MEANS

In this chapter and the next two, we shall consider various methods of testing the differences between two or more statistics. What we are basically interested in is whether or not the difference between two statistics is a real difference or whether it is merely a chance variation. We would expect the real difference to appear in future samples. These tests are referred to as tests of the significance of differences.

MAKING A STATISTICAL TEST

The starting point in all statistical tests is the statement of one or more hypotheses. The type of hypothesis used is called a *null hypothesis*. Such an hypothesis is a statement of no difference. To state that there is no difference between the population mean of A (m_A) and the population mean of B (m_B) is to state a null hypothesis. Another way of stating this hypothesis is that the mean of A is equal to the mean of B. Statements like these merely say that as far as the trait being measured is concerned, the two samples come from the same population; we will assume normal population distributions and equal standard deviations for A and B. Mathematically speaking, two normal distributions with equal means and standard deviations are identical. Note that we *do not* hypothesize that the two sample means ($\bar{X}_A$ and $\bar{X}_B$) are equal. Except in rare coincidences, we know by inspection that the sample means are different. We want to test the significance of these differences.

The null hypothesis is stated so that it can be tested. Suppose, in an experiment, a research worker collects data on his experimental and control groups, and then computes the means and standard deviations of each. His null hypothesis of no significant difference between the two groups, if it can be rejected, will make it possible for him to make probability statements about the success of his experiment.

It is customary for the research worker to state ahead of time the level at which he is going to test his hypothesis. For example, he might decide to use the .05 or 5 percent level of significance. This is called the *alpha level* at which he is working. Another worker might decide to use a more stringent test, such as the 1 percent level. As we shall see soon, *z* scores are used in making tests of significance. We know that a *z* score of 1.96 taken at each end of the normal curve cuts off 5 percent of the total area and a *z* score of 2.58 similarly taken cuts off 1 percent of the area. Any time that we obtain a *z* score between these two points, we reject our null hypothesis at the 5 percent level. If the computed *z* is greater than 2.58, we reject our null hypothesis at the 1 percent level of significance.

Suppose that we set our alpha level at the .05 significance level, and that we obtain a *z* of 2.27. On the basis of our information about the normal curve, we would reject the null hypothesis at the 5 percent level, since the obtained *z* falls between 1.96 and 2.58. If we had set our alpha at the .01 level, we would have been unable to reject the null hypothesis, since the obtained *z* is less than 2.58. In this case we would let the null hypothesis stand, which is the same as saying that there is no significant difference between the two means. Any apparent difference between the two means is attributed to chance.

When we reject a null hypothesis at the 5 percent level, there are 5 chances in 100 that we are wrong, that we are rejecting the null hypothesis when it is actually true. This is known as a *type I error*. Errors of this type may be reduced by making a more rigorous test, such as putting the alpha value at the 1 percent level. Then there would be only 1 chance in 100 of being wrong. If we so desire, we can further reduce our chances by going to the .1 percent level, and so on. But as we reduce our chances of making a type I error, we are increasing our chances of making a *type II error*. This error consists of *not* rejecting the null hypothesis when it should be rejected. So as we decrease the possibility of making one type of error, we increase the possibility of making the other type. Most workers prefer to be cautious, and they try to limit the probability of making a type I error.

The fact that a research worker always rejects an hypothesis with a certain probability of being wrong should lead him to be extremely cautious about any claims that he makes concerning results that are significant. The least that he should do is to run the experiment again. The literature is filled with experimental results that cannot be replicated. Perhaps it would be a good idea if journal editors accepted only experimental reports that had been replicated. Along these lines, McNemar (1962) notes that psychologists who argue for the .05 level quote Fisher as their authority, but they fail to mention that all of Fisher's work was done in agriculture or biology where sampling is better controlled than in the social sciences. We have seen students who, in striving for significance in their research, begin talking about the 15, 20, or 25 percent level of significance. For many years a z score of 3.00 (critical ratio), as it was then called, was arbitrarily used as a test of significance. This has a p of approximately .003 associated with it.

Very frequently, the student finds that he must make several hundred or more tests of significance, such as when he is evaluating the significance of indices of discrimination (Chapter 17). Now suppose that a student has made 200 such evaluations with his alpha level at .05. He finds that 11 of his items are significant at this level or beyond. By chance alone, he would expect 10 of these indices to be significant, that is, 5 percent of 200. All that he has demonstrated is the working of chance. If he selected the 11 items that appeared to be significant and built a short test with them, he would probably find the test worthless.

This discussion might lead one to believe that we are always interested in the rejection of the null hypothesis. While this is the usual case in experimental work, there are occasions when we hope to demonstrate that two groups are the same so that we can combine them. In such cases we would be interested in having the null hypothesis stand.

It cannot be overemphasized that we never make definite or absolute statements when testing hypotheses. When we reject a hypothesis at the 1 percent level, we are saying that the chances are 99 in 100 that it is false. There is still that one chance in 100 that the hypothesis is true.

Two-Tailed Tests

The preceding discussion about testing hypotheses has been concerned with using the area at both ends of the normal curve. The null hypothesis (H_0) that we start with is a simple statement of no difference between population means. We are merely trying to find out if there is a significant difference between the two sample means that we are evaluating. Whether the first mean is larger or smaller than the second is of no concern. All that we are interested in is a difference. The use of a two-tailed test is shown in Fig. 11.1. In making such a test, a negative z score is interpreted in the same manner as a positive one. When we reject a null hypothesis using a two-tailed test, we should say that we have rejected the hypothesis at the 5 or 1 percent *level*. This distinguishes this type of test from the following.

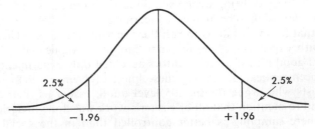

2.5%   2.5%

-1.96 $+1.96$

FIGURE 11.1   Two-tailed test at the 5 percent level.

One-Tailed or Directional Tests

There are times when we are able to make what is called a one-tailed test. Suppose that we plan an experiment using a new reading technique. We have two groups: the control group, which is taught by one of the conventional reading methods, and the experimental group, which is taught by the new method. We have reason to believe that the experimental group will score higher on the reading test which is given at the end of the semester. Our directional hypothesis is that the population experimental group has a mean achievement score which is equal to or less than that of the population control group. If this hypothesis can be rejected, then it follows that we can make a probability statement about the alternative hypothesis, that the mean achievement score of the population experimental group is higher than that of the population control group. This time we are concerned only with one end of the curve, as is shown in Fig. 11.2. At the 5 percent level, we have 5 percent of the area all in one tail rather than having it equally divided into two tails. From the normal probability table, we find that a z score of 1.64 cuts off 5 percent of the area in the smaller part, and a standard score of 2.33 cuts off 1 percent of the area.

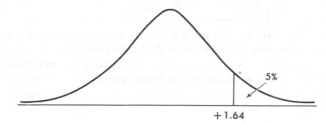

$+1.64$

FIGURE 11.2   One-tailed test at the 5 percent point.

If we had reason to believe that the experimental group would score ower than the control group, we could set up a directional hypothesis that the mean of the experimental group is equal to or greater than that of the control group. Rejecting this would leave us with the hypothesis that the experimental mean was less than that of the control mean. This time the area of the curve in which we are interested is the 5 or 1 percent of the area in the left-hand tail of the curve only. Some authors (Peatman, 1963) refer to a directional hypothesis as a *delta* hypothesis, H_Δ.

In notational form the null hypothesis can be expressed:

$$H_0: \quad m_1 = m_2, \qquad \text{or} \qquad m_1 - m_2 = 0$$

and the directional or delta hypothesis is expressed:

$$H_\Delta: \quad m_1 \geq m_2$$

When we were dealing with a two-tailed or nondirectional test, we noted that we rejected hypotheses at the 1 or 5 percent *levels*. To distinguish directional tests from these, we say, when we reject a hypothesis using a one-tailed test, that we are rejecting at the 1 or 5 percent *points*.

DIFFERENCES BETWEEN MEANS— UNCORRELATED DATA

We shall start with one of the simpler situations in which we have two samples based upon a large N, and in which there is no correlation between the two sets of data.   Let us suppose that we have computed the following statistics for the two samples:

$$\bar{X}_1 = 58.6 \qquad \bar{X}_2 = 56$$
$$N_1 = 95 \qquad N_2 = 101$$
$$s_1 = 8.3 \qquad s_2 = 6.2$$

We begin by stating a null hypothesis about these two population means. We state that the difference between these two means is 0 ($H_0: m_1 - m_2 = 0$). We are saying that this difference between means, $58.6 - 56$, or 2.6, is merely a chance deviation when the population value for the difference is 0. In other words, we now have set up a situation with a mean of 0 and a deviation of 2.6.   Is this deviation too large to be accounted for by chance? By now the student should be familiar with the solution to this question by the use of the standard score z.   In this problem z is the ratio of the difference between the means to the standard error of the difference between the means. The standard error of the difference between the means ($s_{D\bar{X}}$) is the standard deviation of a sampling distribution of $D_{\bar{X}}$ (difference between sample means) when $m_1 = m_2$, and when the samples are randomly and independently selected from normal populations of equal variability.   For the standard error of the difference between the means, we use the following for un-correlated data:

$$s_{D\bar{X}} = \sqrt{s_{\bar{X}_1}{}^2 + s_{\bar{X}_2}{}^2} \qquad (11.1)$$

where $s_{D\bar{X}}$ = the standard error of the difference between two means for uncorrelated data

$s_{\bar{X}_1}, s_{\bar{X}_2}$ = the standard errors of the two sample means

In solving this problem, we first compute the standard error of each sample mean.   This is done as follows:

$$s_{\bar{X}_1} = \frac{s_1}{\sqrt{N_1 - 1}} \qquad\qquad s_{\bar{X}_2} = \frac{s_2}{\sqrt{N_2 - 1}}$$

$$= \frac{8.3}{\sqrt{94}} \qquad\qquad = \frac{6.2}{\sqrt{100}}$$

$$= \frac{8.3}{9.70} \qquad\qquad = \frac{6.2}{10}$$

$$= .856 \qquad\qquad = .620$$

Then using equation (11.1), we have

$$s_{D\bar{X}} = \sqrt{s_{\bar{X}_1}{}^2 + s_{\bar{X}_2}{}^2}$$

$$= \sqrt{.856^2 + .620^2}$$

$$= \sqrt{.732736 + .384400}$$

$$= \sqrt{1.117136}$$

$$= 1.06$$

Next we change our deviation into standard score units as follows:

$$z = \frac{D_{\bar{X}}}{s_{D\bar{X}}} \qquad (11.2)$$

where $D_{\bar{X}}$ = the difference between the two means
$\quad s_{D\bar{X}}$ = the standard error of the difference between the two means

$$z = \frac{\bar{X}_1 - \bar{X}_2}{s_{D\bar{X}}}$$

$$= \frac{58.6 - 56}{1.06}$$

$$= \frac{2.6}{1.06}$$

$$= 2.45$$

Suppose that for this problem we had decided to set alpha at .05. Since our z score is between the values of 1.96 and 2.58, we reject the null hypothesis at the 5 percent level of significance. We can now state that the chances are 95 in 100 that there is a significant difference between these two sample means.

DIFFERENCES BETWEEN MEANS—CORRELATED DATA

We shall next consider the case in which the two sets of data are correlated. We say that data are correlated when they consist of two sets of measurements on the same individuals, repeated measurements of the same individuals with the same scale, or measures made upon twins or siblings. For example, suppose that we had two groups made up of brothers and sisters, the boys comprising one group and the girls the other. An intelligence test is administered to each group. These two sets of scores will be correlated. If data are correlated, such correlations have to be taken into account when tests of significance are being made; because the condition of *independent* samples no longer exists.

TABLE 11.1.　Scores on Two Variables for Twenty Individuals

X	Y	X^2	Y^2	XY
18	20	324	400	360
16	22	256	484	352
18	24	324	576	342
12	10	144	100	120
20	25	400	625	500
17	19	289	361	323
18	20	324	400	360
20	21	400	441	420
22	23	484	529	506
20	20	400	400	400
10	10	100	100	100
8	12	64	144	96
20	22	400	484	440
12	14	144	196	168
16	12	256	144	192
16	20	256	400	320
18	22	324	484	396
20	24	400	576	480
18	23	324	529	414
21	17	441	289	357
$\Sigma X = 340$	$\Sigma Y = 380$	$\Sigma X^2 = 6054$	$\Sigma Y^2 = 7662$	$\Sigma XY = 6736$
$\bar{X} = 17$	$\bar{Y} = 19$			

In Table 11.1 are two sets of measurements (X and Y) on each of 20 individuals. At the bottom of the table are the two means and the rest of the table consists of the information necessary for the computation of the Pearson product-moment correlation coefficient by the use of raw scores. If we substitute into the equation for r,

$$r = \frac{N\Sigma XY - (\Sigma X)(\Sigma Y)}{\sqrt{[N\Sigma X^2(\Sigma X)^2][N\Sigma Y^2 - (\Sigma Y)^2]}}$$

$$= \frac{20(6736) - (340)(380)}{\sqrt{[20(6054) - (340)^2][(20)7662 - (380)^2]}}$$

$$= \frac{5520}{\sqrt{(5480)(8840)}}$$

$$= \frac{5520}{6960}$$

$$= .793$$

The procedure with this problem is basically the same as that for uncorrelated data. We again set up a null hypothesis of no difference between the two population means ($m_x = m_y$), treat the difference between the two sample means as a deviation, and test whether a deviation as large as we have is significant.   In this problem we use the following formula for the standard error of difference between the two means:

$$s_{D\bar{X}} = \sqrt{s_{\bar{X}_1}^2 + s_{\bar{X}_2}^2 - 2(r)(s_{\bar{X}_1})(s_{\bar{X}_2})} \qquad (11.3)$$

The student should be aware that this formula is the same as formula (11.1), the standard error of the difference of the means for uncorrelated data. When data are uncorrelated, r is 0, and the large third term under the radical sign disappears.   The above formula may be considered the basic formula for the standard error of the difference between the means.

Next we shall compute the standard error of the difference between the means for our problem.

The first thing to do is to compute the standard deviation for each distribution and then to use each of these in calculating the standard error of each mean.

$$\Sigma x^2 = 6054 - \frac{(340)^2}{20} \qquad\qquad \Sigma y^2 = 7662 - \frac{(380)^2}{20}$$

$$= 274 \qquad\qquad\qquad\qquad = 442$$

$$s_X = \sqrt{\frac{\Sigma x^2}{N}} \qquad\qquad\qquad s_Y = \sqrt{\frac{\Sigma y^2}{N}}$$

$$= \sqrt{\frac{274}{20}} \qquad\qquad\qquad = \sqrt{\frac{442}{20}}$$

$$= \sqrt{13.70} \qquad\qquad\qquad = \sqrt{22.10}$$

$$= 3.70 \qquad\qquad\qquad\qquad = 4.7$$

Then the standard error of each mean follows:

$$s_{\bar{X}} = \frac{s_x}{\sqrt{N-1}} \qquad\qquad s_{\bar{Y}} = \frac{s_y}{\sqrt{N-1}}$$

$$= \frac{3.70}{\sqrt{19}} \qquad\qquad\qquad = \frac{4.70}{\sqrt{19}}$$

$$= \frac{3.70}{4.3588} \qquad\qquad\qquad = \frac{4.7}{4.3588}$$

$$= .849 \qquad\qquad\qquad\qquad = 1.078$$

After substituting into the formula for the standard error of the difference between means, we have

$$s_{D\bar{X}} = \sqrt{(.849)^2 + (1.078)^2 - 2(.793)(.849)(1.078)}$$

$$= \sqrt{.720801 + 1.162084 - 1.451542}$$

$$= \sqrt{1.882885 - 1.451542}$$

$$= \sqrt{.431343}$$

$$= .657$$

The last step is to compute the z score as follows:

$$z = \frac{\overline{X} - \overline{Y}}{s_{D\overline{X}}}$$

$$= \frac{17 - 19}{.657}$$

$$= \frac{-2}{.657}$$

$$= -3.04$$

A value of this magnitude with a two-tailed test allows us to reject the null hypothesis of no difference between the population means at the 1 percent level.

Suppose that we did not wish to calculate the correlation coefficient but to determine the size of the standard error of the difference between the means directly and thus shorten the work. In Table 11.2 the same set of

TABLE 11.2.   Testing the Significance of
the Difference Between Means When
Data Are Correlated

(1) X	(2) Y	(3) D	(4) D^2
18	20	2	4
16	22	6	36
18	24	6	36
12	10	−2	4
20	25	5	25
17	19	2	4
18	20	2	4
20	21	1	1
22	23	1	1
20	20	0	0
10	10	0	0
8	12	4	16
20	22	2	4
12	14	2	4
16	12	−4	16
16	20	4	16
18	22	4	16
20	24	4	16
18	23	5	25
21	17	−4	16

$$\Sigma D = 40 \qquad \Sigma D^2 = 244$$

scores that appeared in Table 11.1 is again reproduced.   With this method we go through the following steps:

1. Set up column 3 which is the difference between column 1 and column 2.   It makes no difference which way these are subtracted except that the direction started must be continued throughout the entire process.

2. Sum this column of differences.   Add the negative values and then subtract this sum from the sum of the positive values.   Divide this sum by the number of pairs to compute the mean difference.   For these data the mean difference is equal to 40 ÷ 20 which is 2.   It should be noted that this mean difference is identical to the difference between the means which we have previously computed.

3. We are now going to take this mean difference, compute its standard error, and make the usual z test.   We first need, however, the sum of the squares for D and then the standard deviation for D.

4. Square all of the values in column 3.   Then sum these values in column 4.

5. Compute the sum of the squares for D.

$$\Sigma d^2 = \Sigma D^2 - \frac{(\Sigma D)^2}{N}$$

$$= 244 - \frac{(40)^2}{20}$$

$$= 244 - 80$$

$$= 164$$

6. Find the standard deviation of these differences.

$$s_D = \sqrt{\frac{\Sigma d^2}{N}}$$

$$= \sqrt{\frac{164}{20}}$$

$$= \sqrt{8.20}$$

$$= 2.863$$

7. Then the standard error of the mean difference is found.

$$s_{\bar{D}} = \frac{s_D}{\sqrt{N-1}}$$

$$= \frac{2.863}{\sqrt{19}}$$

$$= \frac{2.863}{4.3588}$$

$$= .657$$

8. Then the usual z score is computed.

$$z = \frac{\text{Mean difference}}{\text{Standard error of mean difference}}$$

$$= \frac{2}{.657}$$

$$= 3.04$$

This value of 3.04 agrees with that computed by the use of the correlation coefficient using formula (11.3)[1] There is no question that this second method is easier and faster.

It is to the advantage of the research worker that he use the correct formula when testing differences between the means. Examination of the formula for the standard error of the difference between two means (11.3) shows that when the data are correlated, the size of the standard error is reduced, depending upon the size of the correlation coefficient. When the standard error of the difference decreases, the size of the z score computed is larger, with the same value remaining in the numerator. Thus the student who uses the formula for uncorrelated data when he actually has correlated data is applying an unnecessarily stringent test to his data.

DIFFERENCES BETWEEN MEANS IN SMALL SAMPLES

In the work so far we have paid no attention to the size of the sample. However, in actual practice this is something that cannot be overlooked. When the sample size is large, we use the standard score, z, as the ratio of the difference between the means to the standard error of this difference. We interpret this z score by the use of the normal probability tables. When the size of the sample is small, especially when it is less than 30, a different statistic is used in interpreting the results.

The t Ratio or Student's t

When the number of cases is small, we use the t ratio or Student's t instead of the normal probability tables in interpreting our ratios. These ratios were published by W. S. Gosset in papers which were signed only "Student." An inspection of the t table in the Appendix (Table III) shows that when degrees of freedom (df) is large,[2] the size of the 1 percent and 5 percent values of the t are the same as that for z. By the time that (df) has decreased to 60, the 1 percent value is 2.660 and the 5 percent is 2.000. From this point on down there is considerable difference between the values of t and those of z. In the discussion of the *central limit theorem* (Chapter 10), it was explained that the nature of sampling distributions changes when small N's are used.

The t ratio is defined in the same fashion as z. In other words, it is a deviation divided by a standard deviation; the difference between the means is the deviation, and the standard error of the difference between the means is the standard deviation. It follows that it is not the computation of our

[1] If we had subtracted scores in column 2 from those in column 1, the mean difference would have been negative and hence our z score would have been negative.

[2] This is explained in the following section.

work that must change when we use small samples but the interpretation of our results. This is so because this t statistic is not normally distributed when N is small. As the number of cases decreases, the sampling distribution of t has the extremes of the tails lifted from the base line, allowing for more cases in the tails. Because of this we need different sampling distributions for the different sample sizes.

Degrees of Freedom

Notice that Table III in the Appendix is entered not with the size of the sample but with the number of degrees of freedom (df). Degrees of freedom means freedom to vary. Suppose we have six scores, and the mean of these six scores is to be 10. This sixth score makes adjustments in the variation brought about by the first five scores and assures that the mean of the scores will be 10. For example, suppose we have five scores 10, 12, 18, 16, and 4. In order for the mean to be equal to 10, a sixth score must be 0. In another series, 2, 8, 4, 6, and 10, the sixth score must this time be 30 if the mean of the six scores is to be 10. In each of these cases we have 5 degrees of freedom. Five of the scores in the series may have any value, but the size of the sixth is determined, because the mean in each case is 10.

Suppose we take a case of 44 scores. First we compute the mean, and then we take the deviation of each score from the mean and compute the standard deviation of the sample. In computing this mean, we have used up 1 degree of freedom. We had 44 degrees of freedom to begin with, but now after computing the mean we have ($N - 1$) or 43 degrees of freedom.

When data are paired, as they are in Table 11.2, the number of degrees of freedom is equal to one less than the number of pairs. In Table 11.2 we then have 19 df. Going to the t table we find that the 5 and 1 percent values are 2.093 and 2.861, respectively. For the data in Table 11.2 we obtained a z of 3.04. Because of the size of N we really should have been working with t's here, but the small sample was used to make the illustration compact enough to fit into one table.

Setting up Confidence Intervals for Small Samples

We have previously discussed the method for setting up confidence intervals for a large sample. To do this for the 95 percent level, the confidence interval of the mean was obtained as follows:

$$(\bar{X} \pm (1.96)(s_{\bar{X}})$$

Suppose now that we have the following statistics for a set of data: $\bar{X} = 40$, $s = 6$, $N = 26$. We wish to set up the 95 percent confidence interval for this mean. We would compute the standard error of this mean, which is

$6/\sqrt{25}$, which equals 1.20.   Instead of using 1.96 for the 5 percent value of z, we enter the t table with the appropriate number of degrees of freedom, 25 in this case, and obtain the t value.   We find this to be 2.06.   So the 95 percent confidence interval for these data becomes

$$40 + (2.06)(1.20)$$

$$40 \pm 2.47$$

$$37.53 - 42.47$$

The 99 percent confidence interval is set up in the same manner, using a t ratio of 2.79, which is the 1 percent value for $df = 25$.   These confidence intervals are interpreted in a way similar to those for large samples.

Small Sample Techniques for Testing Differences Between Means

When the data are correlated, the usual technique is to set up the data as shown in Table 11.2, make the t test, and then interpret the results using $N - 1$ ($N =$ number of pairs) degrees of freedom.   When the data are uncorrelated, we proceed as follows.   In Table 11.3 are shown the scores of two groups of individuals on a short test.   The third and fourth columns are the squares of the first two columns.   The means and the sums of the squares are shown at the bottom of the table.   The sum of the squares for each distribution was obtained by the use of this formula:

$$\Sigma x^2 = \Sigma X^2 - \frac{(\Sigma X)^2}{N}$$

It is necessary that these sums be computed, because they are used later in the computation.

We start with the usual null hypothesis of no difference between the population means.   This time we are going to use the t test, and this is

TABLE 11.3.   Scores of Two Groups of Individuals on the Same Test

X_1	X_2	$X_1{}^2$	$X_2{}^2$
26	38	676	1444
24	26	576	676
18	24	324	576
17	24	289	576
18	30	324	900
20	22	400	484
18		324	
$\Sigma X_1 = 141$	$\Sigma X_2 = 164$	$\Sigma X_1{}^2 = 2913$	$\Sigma X_2{}^2 = 4656$
$\bar{X}_1 = 20.14$	$\bar{X}_2 = 27.33$		
$\Sigma x_1{}^2 = 73$	$\Sigma x_2{}^2 = 173$		
$N_1 = 7$	$N_2 = 6$		

defined as the ratio of the difference between the means divided by the standard error of the difference:

$$t = \frac{\overline{X}_1 - \overline{X}_2}{s_{D\overline{X}}}$$

Instead of using the formula for the standard error of the difference between the means that we used previously, we use a modification of this which is based upon the pooled variances of the two samples. Rather than use two separate variances from each of the samples as an independent estimate of the population variance, the two sample variances are pooled to give a better estimate of the population variance.

The F Test

In making a test of the significance of the difference between two means, we make two basic assumptions—first, that our samples were randomly drawn and, second, that the variances of our two population groups do not differ. We test the latter by means of an F test which is defined as follows:

$$F = \frac{s_1^2}{s_2^2} \tag{11.4}$$

where s_1^2 = the larger of the two sample variances
$\quad\;\; s_2^2$ = the smaller of the two sample variances

With this F test we are evaluating the null hypothesis of no difference between the two population variances. If the F is not significant, the null hypothesis stands, and we pool the variances. If the F is found to be significant, a procedure that will be discussed later should be used.

For this problem we compute the two variances as follows:

$$s_1^2 = \frac{73}{7} \qquad\qquad s_2^2 = \frac{173}{6}$$

$$s_1^2 = 10.429 \qquad\qquad s_2^2 = 28.833$$

$$F = \frac{28.833}{10.429} = 2.76$$

Entering the F table, Table V in the Appendix, with 5 df for the larger variance (the greater mean square) and 6 df for the smaller variance (the lesser mean square), we find that our F of 2.76 is below the 5 and 1 percent values. Hence the null hypothesis of no difference between the two population variances stands, and we pool the variances. It should be noted that the F test is a one-tailed test, because we are dealing with the part of the F distribution with values greater than 1. When we obtain results that are significant, we say that they are significant at the 1 or 5 percent point. If the table is used for a two-tailed test, an F significant at the .01 point must be interpreted at the .02 level, and F significant at the .05 point at the .10 level.

Pooling the Variances

As pointed out above, in a test of the difference between the means of small samples, we use a pooled or average variance in the place of the separate variances. The pooling of the variances and the formula for the corresponding standard error of the difference is shown below.

We start with formula (11.1):

$$s_{D\bar{X}} = \sqrt{s_{\bar{X}_1}^2 + s_{\bar{X}_2}^2}$$ (11.1)

We know that

$$s_{\bar{X}_1} = \frac{s_1}{\sqrt{N_1}} \quad \text{and} \quad s_{\bar{X}_2} = \frac{s_2}{\sqrt{N_2}}$$

By substituting the above in formula (11.1), we have

$$s_{D\bar{X}} = \sqrt{\frac{s_1^2}{N_1} + \frac{s_2^2}{N_2}}$$ (11.1 a)

The unbiased estimate of the variance is given by

$$s^2 = \frac{\Sigma x^2}{N - 1}$$

If we substitute in (11.1 a),

$$s_{D\bar{X}} = \sqrt{\frac{\Sigma x_1^2/(N_1 - 1)}{N_1} + \frac{\Sigma x_2^2/(N_2 - 1)}{N_2}}$$ (11.1 b)

The pooling of the two variances gives

$$\frac{\Sigma x_1^2 + \Sigma x_2^2}{N_1 + N_2 - 2}$$

When this combination is substituted for each sample variance in (11.1 b),

$$s_{D\bar{X}} = \sqrt{\frac{(\Sigma x_1^2 + \Sigma x_2^2)/(N_1 + N_2 - 2)}{N_1} + \frac{(\Sigma x_1^2 + \Sigma x_2^2)/(N_1 + N_2 - 2)}{N_2}}$$

and factored, the result is the usual formula for the difference between the means for small samples:

$$s_{D\bar{X}} = \sqrt{\frac{\Sigma x_1^2 + \Sigma x_2^2}{N_1 + N_2 - 2}\left(\frac{1}{N_1} + \frac{1}{N_2}\right)}$$ (11.5)

When $N_1 = N_2$, this further reduces to

$$s_{D\bar{X}} = \sqrt{\frac{\Sigma x_1{}^2 + \Sigma x_2{}^2}{N(N-1)}} \qquad (11.6)$$

By substituting the data from Table 11.3 in equation (11.5), we have

$$s_{D\bar{X}} = \sqrt{\frac{73 + 173}{(7 + 6 - 2)} \left(\frac{1}{7} + \frac{1}{6}\right)}$$

$$= \sqrt{\frac{246}{11} \left(\frac{1}{7} + \frac{1}{6}\right)}$$

$$= \sqrt{(22.3636)(.309524)}$$

$$= \sqrt{6.92207}$$

$$= 2.63$$

We proceed with the t test.

$$t = \frac{\bar{X}_1 - \bar{X}_2}{s_{D\bar{X}}}$$

$$= \frac{27.33 - 20.14}{2.63}$$

$$= \frac{7.19}{2.63}$$

$$= 2.73$$

For this problem the number of degrees of freedom is $(N_1 + N_2 - 2)$ or 11. The t table tells us that when $df = 11$, the 5 percent value is 2.201. Hence we can reject our null hypothesis at the 5 percent level.

t Test When the Variances Differ

When the variances differ as shown by an F test, t is computed by the usual formula. However, this t cannot be interpreted by entering the t table in the usual fashion. Cochran and Cox (1950) have developed a formula for testing the significance of the computed t. This formula is (assuming that we are working at the 5 percent level of confidence):

$$t_{.05} = \frac{s_{\bar{X}_1}{}^2(t_1) + s_{\bar{X}_2}{}^2(t_2)}{s_{\bar{X}_1}{}^2 + s_{\bar{X}_2}{}^2} \qquad (11.7)$$

where t_1 is the 5 percent value for t at $N_1 - 1$ degrees of freedom
t_2 is the 5 percent value for t at $N_2 - 1$ degrees of freedom

Suppose that we have the following data:

	Group I		Group II
$\bar{X}_1$	33	$\bar{X}_2$	40.4
s_1^2	144	s_2^2	289
N_1	31	N_2	41

For these data we compute F:

$$F = \frac{289}{144} = 2.01$$

which for these degrees of freedom is significant at the 5 percent point. Next we compute the squared standard errors of the means, or the *variance error* as this is called,

$$s_{\bar{X}_1}^2 = \frac{144}{30} = 4.80 \qquad s_{\bar{X}_2}^2 = \frac{289}{40} = 7.225$$

To substitute into equation (11.7), we first obtain t_1 which is the .05 value of t for $N_1 - 1 = 30$ degrees of freedom. This we find to be 2.021. Similarly, t_2, the .05 value for $N_2 - 1 = 40$ degrees of freedom, is found to be 2.042.

$$t = \frac{(4.80)(2.042) + (7.225)(2.021)}{(4.80 + 7.225)}$$

$$= \frac{24.40332}{12.025}$$

$$= 2.03$$

t computed for these data is:

$$t = \frac{40.4 - 33}{\sqrt{4.80 + 7.225}} = \frac{7.4}{3.47} = 2.13$$

Since our computed value of $t(2.13)$ is greater than 2.03, we reject the null hypothesis at the 5 percent level.

If $N_1 = N_2$, the above can be shortened by computing t in the usual way and entering the t table with one-half the usual number of degrees of freedom.

Exercises

1. Two groups in two schools were given the *Minnesota Paper Formboard* with the following results:

A	B
$\bar{X}_1 = 32$	$\bar{X}_2 = 36$
$s_1 = 6.2$	$s_2 = 7.4$
$N_1 = 145$	$N_2 = 82$

   Is there a significant difference between the two means?

2. A group of students was given a test in addition. Then a state of "anxiety" was induced and the arithmetic test was readministered. The results are

	Pretest	End Test
	$\bar{X} = 70$	$\bar{X} = 67$
	$s = 6$	$s = 5.8$
	$N = 30$	$N = 30$

r between pre- and end-test scores is .82.

(a) Is there a significant difference between the two sets of scores?

(b) Test the hypothesis that the population mean on the end test is significantly lower than the population mean on the pretest.

3. The following sets of scores were made by 16 individuals in a laboratory experiment on perception:

Test 1	Test 2
18	16
12	14
8	8
6	8
3	8
12	10
16	8
7	14
8	2
12	8
15	14
7	4
5	6
12	6
3	0
11	7

Is there a significant difference between the means of the two distributions?

4. A group of 24 seniors in a technical high school achieved the following scores on the *DAT Numerical Ability Test:*

25	17	29	29	26	24
27	33	23	14	21	26
20	27	26	32	20	32
17	23	20	30	26	12

A group of 24 seniors taking the college entrance curriculum in another high school in the same city obtained these scores on the same test:

21	26	28	31	14	27
29	23	18	25	32	23
16	21	17	20	26	23
7	18	29	32	24	17

Suppose that you are interested in knowing if the mean of the technical high-school group is higher than the college entrance group. State the appropriate hypothesis and test it statistically.

5. Given $\bar{X}_1 = 12.8$, $\bar{X}_2 = 16.9$, $N_1 = 11$, $N_2 = 9$, $\Sigma x_1^2 = 61$, $\Sigma x_2^2 = 51$. Assume that these data are uncorrelated and compute t.

6. Given a mean of 17.5, with a standard deviation of 5.2, N being 10. Determine the 99 percent confidence interval for this mean.

12

TESTING DIFFERENCES
BETWEEN PROPORTIONS

We previously noted that the standard error of a proportion is estimated by the formula

$$s_p = \sqrt{\frac{pq}{N}} \qquad (12.1)$$

where $q = 1 - p$.

This formula is limited in its use. The sampling distribution of p is not the same for all values of p. It may be recalled that p can never be larger than 1. Then it follows that if the population values of p are either large or small, that is, in either extreme of the distribution, it is impossible for the sampling distribution to be a normal one. This is shown in Fig. 12.1 where the sampling distributions of values of .10, .50, and .90 are illustrated.

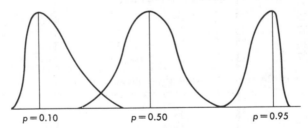

$p = 0.10 \qquad p = 0.50 \qquad p = 0.95$

FIGURE 12.1 Sampling distributions of the various values of p.

From this figure it can be inferred that the closer p is to .50, the more normal is the curve of the sampling distribution. As the size of samples increase, the fact that the curves are cut off at 0 and 1 is of less importance, because the sampling distributions become very narrow and these truncations are of less importance. However, when N is small the departure of the sampling distribution may be very important. It is not recommended that this formula for the standard error of a proportion be used whenever the

146

product of N times p (or Nq, if it is smaller) is less than 10.   McNemar (1962) says 5 instead of 10, but he adds that when the smaller product is between 5 and 10 that a correction for continuity be made by reducing the absolute value of $p_1 - p_2$ by multiplying it by $\frac{1}{2}(1/N_1 + 1/N_2)$.   As we shall see in Chapter 14, when our numbers are small or our proportions extreme, we have another statistic that may be applied to such data in testing significance.

A GENERAL STATEMENT ABOUT TESTS OF SIGNIFICANCE

We have studied in detail some of the ways in which we test the differences between two means.   Now we shall consider specifically differences between proportions and percentages.   Before we do this, however, we should note that there is a general way of testing the differences between two statistics. We use a z or a t test, depending on the size of the sample.   Both of these are defined as the difference between two statistics divided by the standard error of this difference.   In the previous section it was the difference between the means divided by the standard error of the difference between the means. It could just as easily be the difference between two medians or two proportions.   Of course, we have to use the correct formula for the standard error of the different statistics that we are using.   Some of these formulas were presented at the end of Chapter 10.

TESTING THE DIFFERENCE BETWEEN TWO PROPORTIONS OR TWO PERCENTAGES FOR UNCORRELATED DATA

We start with this basic formula as the estimate of (σ_p), the standard error of a proportion.

$$s_p = \sqrt{\frac{pq}{N}}$$

Then our test of significance would be the following:

$$z = \frac{p_1 - p_2}{\sqrt{s_{p_1}^2 + s_{p_2}^2}} \tag{12.2}$$

Before we solve this, we can make the computations easier if we change the denominator as follows:

$$s_{D_p} = \sqrt{s_{p_1}^2 + s_{p_2}^2} \tag{12.3}$$

$$s_{D_p} = \sqrt{\left(\sqrt{\frac{p_1 q_1}{N_1}}\right)^2 + \left(\sqrt{\frac{p_2 q_2}{N_2}}\right)^2}$$

This reduces to

$$s_{D_p} = \sqrt{\frac{p_1 q_1}{N_1} + \frac{p_2 q_2}{N_2}} \qquad (12.4)$$

This latter equation should be used in preference to the denominator of equation (12.2), because we can go into it directly with our p values, and the computation of the two separate standard errors of the proportions is not necessary.

As an illustration, suppose that we have the following data:

$$p_1 = .70 \qquad p_2 = .80$$
$$N_1 = 200 \qquad N_2 = 150 \qquad r_{12} = .00$$

We first compute the standard error of the difference between the two proportions as follows:

$$s_{D_p} = \sqrt{\frac{(.70)(.30)}{200} + \frac{(.80)(.20)}{150}}$$

$$= \sqrt{\frac{.21}{200} + \frac{.16}{150}}$$

$$= \sqrt{.00105 + .00107}$$

$$= .046$$

Then, making our test of significance, we have:

$$z = \frac{p_1 - p_2}{s_{D_p}}$$

$$= \frac{.70 - .80}{.046}$$

$$= \frac{-.10}{.046}$$

$$= -2.17$$

Since this value is larger than the 5 percent level (1.96), we can reject the null hypothesis of no difference between the two population proportions at the 5 percent level.

WHEN SAMPLES ARE SMALL OR PROPORTIONS ARE EXTREME

The above technique works adequately when the N's are above 100. However, if either of the N's is less than 100 and either or both of the p's are extreme, that is, less than .10 or greater than .90, it is better to base the

standard error of the difference on the proportion in the two groups combined. Since we are testing the null hypothesis that the population
proportions are equal (H_0 $p_1 = p_2$), we are justified in doing this.

Here are some more data.

$$p_1 = .90 \qquad p_2 = .80$$
$$N_1 = 40 \qquad N_2 = 30 \qquad r_{12} = .00$$

First we compute p which is the proportion in the two groups combined.
Thus p_1 is made up of 36 individuals (.90 × 40) and p_2 is made up of 24
individuals (.80 × 30). There is a total of 70 individuals (40 + 30). Then
p is equal to

$$\frac{36 + 24}{70} = \frac{60}{70} = .86$$

Then
$$s_{D_p} = \sqrt{\frac{pq}{N_1} + \frac{pq}{N_2}} \qquad (12.5)$$

or
$$s_{D_p} = \sqrt{pq\left(\frac{1}{N_1} + \frac{1}{N_2}\right)} \qquad (12.6)$$

By substituting with the given data we have

$$s_{D_p} = \sqrt{(.86)(.14)\left(\frac{1}{40} + \frac{1}{30}\right)}$$

$$= \sqrt{(.1204)(.025 + .033)}$$

$$= \sqrt{(.1204)(.058)}$$

$$= \sqrt{.0069832}$$

$$= .084$$

Then
$$t = \frac{p_1 - p_2}{s_{D_p}}$$

$$= \frac{.90 - .80}{.084}$$

$$= \frac{.10}{.084}$$

$$= 1.19$$

This is not significant at the 5 percent level, and hence our null hypothesis of
no difference between the two population proportions stands.

The above technique can be used with large samples as well as with small
ones. With large samples, the difference in the results will be trivial; with
smaller samples, more reliable results are obtained using the last method.

With data like these, the number of degrees of freedom is equal to the
sum of the number of degrees of freedom in each of the samples. For

example, in the last problem, $df = (N_1 - 1) + (N_2 - 1)$ or $39 + 29$ which equals 68.

In certain types of work, we find that we have to make a large number of tests of significance between percentages or proportions.   This is especially

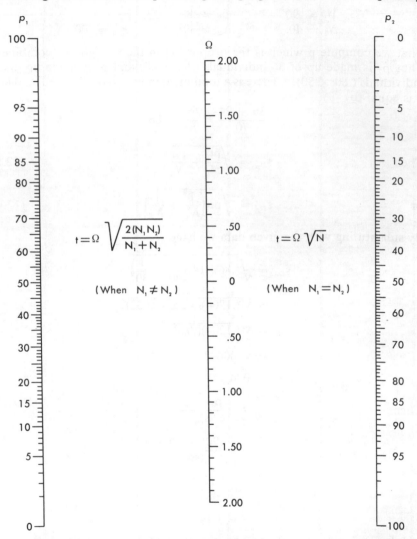

FIGURE 12.2   Lawshe-Baker Nomograph for testing the significance of the differences between two percentages (by permission of Dean C. H. Lawshe).

true in item analysis work (see Chapter 17).   Figure 12.2 which is referred to as the Lawshe-Baker Nomograph was constructed to facilitate such work.

This is very simple to use.   Notice that the right-hand column is p_1 and the left-hand one p_2.   We place a straightedge between p_1 and p_2—the percentages or proportions whose difference is being tested. The center line is the omega value (ω). Notice that there are two t's presented, one to be used when $N_1 = N_2$ and the other when $N_1 \neq N_2$. Suppose we had a series of tests, all of which were based upon 100 in each group. We would first solve the equation for $t = \omega\sqrt{N}$ for the 5 percent level of significance, that is $1.96 = \omega\sqrt{100}$ or $\omega = .196$. Similarly, the 1 percent value could be obtained by $2.58 = \omega\sqrt{100}$ or $\omega = .258$. By rounding these we would have the 5 percent value of omega at .20 and the 1 percent at .26. As we read our *omega* values from the nomograph, we could immediately determine whether or not each was significant and, if so, at what level.

TESTING THE DIFFERENCE BETWEEN PROPORTIONS FOR CORRELATED DATA

The student should note that the above solutions were for uncorrelated data, $r = .00$. When the data are correlated, the formula for the standard error of the difference between two proportions becomes:

$$s_{D_p} = \sqrt{s_{p_1}{}^2 + s_{p_2}{}^2 - 2(r_{12})(s_{p_1})(s_{p_2})} \tag{12.7}$$

TABLE 12.1. Responses of 120 Individuals to Two Attitude Scale Items

		Item 2		
		No	Yes	
Item 1	Yes	a 33	b 47	80
	No	c 25	d 15	40
		58	62	120

McNemar (1962) has developed a technique for testing the difference between two percentages that does not necessitate the computation of the correlation coefficient between the two variables. The data have to be tabulated into a two-by-two table as shown in Table 12.1. Suppose that we are interested in the differences of the responses that the same group of individuals make to two different attitude scale items. The responses of each individual have to be taken separately, and each one entered into the table. Suppose that the first individual responded "Yes" to the first and second items. A tally would then be placed in the cell labeled b. The next individual responded "No" to the first item and "Yes" to the second one. This tally would be placed in the d cell. In this fashion the responses to all of the items by all of the individuals are tallied. Notice that the tallies placed in the b and c responses are those individuals who responded in the same direction to the two items. Cells a and d represent the individuals who answered the two items differently. In Table 12.1 are shown the responses of 120 individuals to two such items tallied in the manner just described.

The test of significance is made in the following manner:

$$z = \sqrt{\frac{(a-d)^2}{a+d}} \qquad (12.8)$$

$$= \sqrt{\frac{(33-15)^2}{33+15}}$$

$$= \sqrt{\frac{(18)^2}{48}} = \sqrt{\frac{324}{48}}$$

$$= 2.60$$

which is significant at the 1 percent level.

As a concluding note, since proportions and percentages are similar, all techniques applied here to proportions can be used equally well with percentages.

Exercises

1   The following are the responses of 100 students to two items on a test:

	Item 1	Item 2
Right	78	68
Wrong	22	32

(a) Assume that the two items are uncorrelated, and test to see if there is a significant difference in the responses to the two items.

(b) Suppose that the correlation between item 1 and 2 is .32, again test the difference using this information.

2. Thirty-two in a group of 40 and 18 in a group of 50 respond "Yes" to a certain attitude test item. Do the responses of the two groups differ significantly?

3. In the United States Senate, in 1958, there were 11 members of the scholastic honorary society, Phi Beta Kappa. Nine of these were Democrats and two were Republicans. There were 49 Democrats and 47 Republicans in the Senate. Is the difference between the proportions of Phi Beta Kappas statistically significant?

4. In a survey it was found that 60 out of 170 females and 32 out of 128 males preferred a certain TV program over two other programs. Is there a sex difference in the preference for this program?

5. Given the following responses of 100 individuals to 2 items on a personality scale, determine whether there is a significant difference to the responses to the two items.

| | | *Item* 1 | |
		Disagree	Agree
Item 2	Agree	40	20
	Disagree	25	15

13

TESTING THE SIGNIFICANCE
OF THE PEARSON *r*

After a correlation coefficient is computed, the next question is whether or not the *r* is significant.   That is, does it represent a real correlation or is the computed *r* merely brought about by chance?   We ask whether the *r* in question is a chance deviation from a population *R* of zero.   Also there are times when we have two or more *r*'s, and we wish to know if significant differences exist among them.   Both of these questions are answered in this chapter.

The Sampling Distribution of r.   As we have already learned, the Pearson product-moment correlation varies between +1 and −1.   Since this is so,

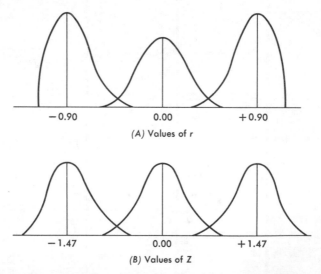

(A) Values of r

(B) Values of Z

FIGURE 13.1   Sampling distribution of *r* when the population values are .00 and ± .90, and the sampling distributions of the *Z* statistics are equivalent to the *r*'s.

the sampling distribution of *r* is usually not normal. Notice the *A* part of Fig. 13.1. As *R* increases in size, the sampling distribution becomes more and more skewed. Suppose that the parameter value of *r* is .90. As samples are drawn from this population, they will vary. However, there is a limit that these sample values can take in an upward direction, 1.00. Downward, there is practically no limit. So the sampling distribution of *r*, when the parameter value (*R*) is .90, is negatively skewed. Similarly, the sampling distribution when *R* is −.90 is positively skewed. The sampling distribution of *r* is normal when the parameter value is .00. As this value approaches median values of *R* (.50), the skewness begins to be considerable. It is also true that the degree of skewness is also a function of the size of the sample, the smaller the sample, the greater the degree of skewness. Since in our work we are usually not interested in *r*'s of zero or thereabouts, this skewness in the sampling distribution has to be taken into account in all of our work in which *r*'s are manipulated.

TESTING THE SIGNIFICANCE OF *r*

Suppose that we compute the Pearson *r* for two sets of data based upon 82 cases and obtain an *r* of .30. We wish to know if this *r* indicates a real relationship between these two variables. We start with the usual null hypothesis that the population *R* is zero. By this we are saying that our obtained *r* is merely a chance deviation in the sampling distribution in which the population *R* is 0 ($H_0: R = 0$). We test this *r* in the usual way by making a *z* or *t* test. Again these are defined as the ratio of a deviation to a standard deviation. The deviation in this case is our obtained *r*; the standard deviation is the standard error of this *r*. We obtain the standard error of the *r* by the use of the following formula:

$$s_{r_0} = \frac{1}{\sqrt{N-1}} \tag{13.1}$$

where s_{r_0} = standard error when *R* is assumed to be 0
    N = number of pairs used in computing *r*

$$s_{r_0} = \frac{1}{\sqrt{82-1}}$$

$$= \frac{1}{\sqrt{81}} = \frac{1}{9} = .11$$

$$z = \frac{.30}{.11}$$

$$= 2.73$$

which with *N* − 2 degrees of freedom is significant at the 1 percent level.

Let us next take a case in which the N is small. Suppose that we have $N = 18$ and $r = .50$. The above technique is suitable when N is large, but when N is less than 30, the standard error of r should be computed by the following formula:

$$t = \frac{r}{\sqrt{1 - r^2}} \sqrt{N - 2} \tag{13.2}$$

then:

$$t = \frac{.50}{\sqrt{1 - (.50)^2}} \sqrt{18 - 2}$$

$$= \frac{.50}{\sqrt{.75}} \sqrt{16}$$

$$= \frac{(.50)(4)}{.866} = \frac{2.00}{.866}$$

$$= 2.31$$

This value with $(N - 2)$ df, or 16 df, is significant at the 5 percent level ($t_{.05} = 2.12$ for $df = 16$).

A table has been developed which makes it unnecessary to go through either of the above procedures. This table (Table VI in the Appendix) is entered with $N - 2$ degrees of freedom, and the sizes of the r's needed to be significant for various degrees of freedom are shown. Suppose that we solve the previous problem by the use of this table. N is 18; hence df is 16. For $df = 16$, we see that the r must be at least equal to .468 to be significant at the 5 percent level and .590 at the 1 percent level. Since the obtained r is .50 and falls between these two table values, we can reject the null hypothesis at the 5 percent level. The obtained r in general is compared with the table values. If it is larger than both, the null hypothesis is rejected at the 1 percent level; if it falls in between the two table values, the null hypothesis is rejected at the 5 percent level; and if it is smaller than both table values, the null hypothesis stands.

The student should check the significance of any r that he is going to use in further computations. For example, in testing the difference between means, the r can rapidly be checked by the use of Table VI, and the appropriate formula can be used in the calculation of the standard error of the difference between the two means.

Fisher's Z Transformation

Fisher has developed a statistic which is a transformation of r. The sampling distribution of this statistic is approximately normal for all values. This is shown in the B part of Fig. 13.1. This statistic is used in problems involving the sampling distribution of r.

The standard error of Z is

$$s_Z = \frac{1}{\sqrt{N - 3}} \tag{13.3}$$

Testing the Difference Between Two Correlation Coefficients for Uncorrelated Data

Suppose that we have the following data:

$$r_{12} = .85 \qquad r_{34} = .75$$
$$N = 103 \qquad N = 147$$

We wish to test the null hypothesis that the two population R's do not differ ($H_0: R_{12} = R_{34}$). The first thing that we do is change each of these into Fisher's Z statistic by the use of Table VII in the Appendix. This gives us

$$r_{12} = .85 = Z = 1.256$$
$$r_{34} = .75 = Z = .973$$

The problem now is one of testing the difference between these two Z's. The standard error of the difference between two Z's is written as shown in equation (13.4), but we simplify it to the form of equation (13.5) before we use it

$$s_{D_Z} = \sqrt{s_{z_1}^2 + s_{z_2}^2} \tag{13.4}$$

$$= \sqrt{\left(\frac{1}{\sqrt{N_1 - 3}}\right)^2 + \left(\frac{1}{\sqrt{N_2 - 3}}\right)^2}$$

$$= \sqrt{\frac{1}{N_1 - 3} + \frac{1}{N_2 - 3}} \tag{13.5}$$

$$= \sqrt{\frac{1}{103 - 3} + \frac{1}{147 - 3}}$$

$$= \sqrt{\frac{1}{100} + \frac{1}{144}}$$

$$= \sqrt{.01 + .0069} = \sqrt{.0169}$$

$$= .13$$

Next we make the usual test of significance.

$$z = \frac{Z_1 - Z_2}{s_{D_z}}$$

$$= \frac{1.256 - .973}{.13}$$

$$= \frac{.283}{.13} = 2.18$$

Since z is more than 1.96, the difference is significant at the 5 percent level. Hence, since there is a difference between the two Z statistics, we conclude that there is significant difference between the two population correlation coefficients at the same level.

If the situation exists in which variable 1 is correlated with variable 2, and variable 1 is also correlated with variable 3, and all measurements are made upon the same sample, the above technique cannot be used, for here the relationship between the pairs of r's has to be taken into account. Once again we are dealing with correlated data. A t test that can be made when this situation occurs follows:

$$t = \frac{(r_{12} - r_{13})\sqrt{(N - 3)(1 + r_{23})}}{\sqrt{2(1 - r_{12}^2 - r_{13}^2 - r_{23}^2 + 2r_{12}r_{13}r_{23})}} \tag{13.6}$$

This is interpreted by going into the t table with $N - 3$ degrees of freedom.

Establishing the Confidence Interval for the Pearson r

This is done by changing the r to Z and by setting up the confidence interval for Z.

$$Z_{95} = Z \pm (1.96)s_Z$$

After the confidence limits have been established for Z, these are translated to r's by the use of Table VII.

Averaging Pearson r's

Since Pearson r's are not equal units of measurement, they should not be added and averaged. To find an average correlation coefficient, change each r to its respective Z using Table VII. Then average these Z's, and using the same table, convert this Z back to an r. This is the average r. For example, see the table below. The sum and mean in the left-hand column are merely inserted to show that there is a difference between the

	r	Z	
	.68	.83	
	.77	1.02	
	.86	1.29	
	.79	1.07	
	.92	1.59	
Sums	4.02	5.80	
Means	.80	1.16	which converts to an r of .82

two techniques. If the r's were all fairly similar in size, little would be gained by using this technique. Also if they were all small, they could be averaged as is, for an inspection of Table VII reveals that up to an r of .25, the values of r and Z are quite similar.

A more precise procedure is to weight each Z by multiplying each by

$N - 3$. These products are summed and, if we were averaging four Z's, this sum would be divided by $(N_1 - 3) + (N_2 - 3) + (N_3 - 3) + (N_4 - 4)$. This weighted Z is then translated to an r using Table VII.

Exercises

1. A student computes an r of .32 with 22 cases. By use of the appropriate formula, test the significance of this r. Check your results by using the tables for testing the significance of an r.
2. $N = 103$. What is the standard error of a Fisher's Z which corresponds to an r of .90?
3. We find r's of $-.60$ and $-.51$, N being 85 in both sets of data. Use the formula for uncorrelated r's, and test the hypothesis of no significant difference between these two r's.
4. The following correlations are found among three variables in the same sample of 103 individuals:

	(1)	(2)	(3)
(1)	—	.76	.93
(2)	—	—	.85
(3)	—	—	—

Is the correlation between 1 and 2 significantly different from the correlation between 1 and 3?

5. On five independent random samples the following r's were obtained: .93, .81, .63, .78, .68. What is the best estimate of the population R?

14

X²—CHI SQUARE

Thus far we have been concerned with three statistics used as tests of significance. These are z, t, and F. While these are all very useful statistics, they are limited in their usage, because they are all based upon the assumption of a normal distribution in the population. They are referred to as parametric statistics, and they are used in testing one difference at a time. In this chapter, we shall consider another statistic used as a test of significance, chi square. This is a very useful test, because no assumptions are necessary about the shape of the parameter distribution, and as we shall see, two or more differences may be evaluated at the same time using this statistic. Such statistics as chi square are known as *nonparametric* or *distribution-free* statistics. As we shall find later (Chapter 18), chi square is but one of a large group of such statistics.

Chi square is used as a test of significance when we have data that are expressed in frequencies or data that are in terms of percentages or proportions and that can be reduced to frequencies. Many of the applications of chi square are with discrete data; however, any continuous data may be reduced to categories and the data so tabulated that chi square may be applied. For example scores on a test of mental ability and a dexterity test could be tabulated as shown below. Scores of these individuals on

Mental Ability Scores	Scores on a Dexterity Test		
	12–20	21–29	30–38
140 and up		/	///
120–139	//	++++	//
100–119	++++	///	/
80–99	///		

another variable such as on another test of ability could be tabled on the other axis, or a trichotomy such as "yes," "undecided," or "no" might be placed there.   Chi square could then be applied to these data to see if there is a significant difference between mental ability scores and scores on the other ability test or on the attitudinal scale.   A certain amount of information about our data is lost when data are so categorized.   But there are times when this has to be tolerated, especially when we are unable to make or to meet assumptions about our data.

USES OF CHI SQUARE

First, chi square is used to determine if a certain distribution differs from some predetermined theoretical distribution.   For example, we may have a distribution based on the tossing of a die or a series of coins.   We can determine whether our observed frequencies differ from the frequencies that we would expect if our distribution followed a stated theoretical distribution.   An application of this is brought about when we test whether a distribution of measures differs from what we would expect if the distribution followed the shape of the normal distribution.   This is an example of testing goodness of fit.   Another use of chi square is in testing null hypotheses of no significant differences between or among the responses of individuals in two or more groups as we noted on p. 160.   The student who studies statistics beyond the introductory level will find that chi square has many more uses than the several basic ones mentioned here.   While the uses of chi square are different, the computation of chi square is the same for all applications.   The differences are in the methods used to obtain the theoretical or expected frequencies.

As a simple illustration, suppose that we toss a fifty-cent piece in the air 100 times and record our results.   We observe that 40 heads and 60 tails appear.   We refer to these frequencies as the observed frequencies.   In a previous chapter we gave these the symbol f_o.   However in this chapter we shall, for the sake of convenience, refer to these observed frequencies with the symbol O.   Next we make the usual null hypothesis that this distribution of 40 heads and 60 tails does not differ from what we would expect by chance, that is, 50 heads and 50 tails.   These frequencies are called the expected, theoretical, or hypothetical frequencies.   In this chapter we shall refer to these using the symbol E.

We can set all these data up in a contingency table like this:

	O	E
Heads	40	50
Tails	60	50
	100	100

Notice that the sum of the observed frequencies equals the sum of the expected frequencies. Also, it is important to note that we use all of the data. We do not consider merely the number of observed heads but also the "non-heads" or tails.

We test our hypothesis by using the general formula for chi square.

$$\chi^2 = \sum \frac{(O - E)^2}{E} \tag{14.1}$$

$$= \frac{(40 - 50)^2}{50} + \frac{(60 - 50)^2}{50}$$

$$= \frac{(10)^2}{50} + \frac{(10)^2}{50}$$

$$= \frac{100}{50} + \frac{100}{50}$$

$$= 2 + 2$$

$$= 4.00$$

Formula (14.1) demands that we take each observed frequency, subtract from it the corresponding expected frequency, square the difference, and divide the result by the expected frequency. The sum of these is chi square.

Table IV in the Appendix is used for the interpretation of chi square. We enter this table with $df = 1$ (this will be explained later) and find that the value of chi square for 1 df is 3.841. Our computed value of 4.00 is larger than this but less than the 2 and 1 percent values; hence we reject our hypothesis of no difference at the 5 percent level of significance. We can be fairly confident that these results are different from those produced by chance alone.

The above problem, or any chi square problem, may also be solved in a tabular form as below. Some prefer this form:

	O	E	$O - E$	$(O - E)^2$	$(O - E)^2/E$
Heads	40	50	10	100	2.00
Tails	60	50	10	100	2.00
					$\Sigma = \overline{4.00} = X^2$

Suppose that we take another example. This time we toss a die 144 times, and we observe that a five-spot appears 36 times. We organize our observations as follows:

	O	E
Five-spots	36	24
Not five-spots	108	120
Total	$\overline{144}$	$\overline{144}$

Since there were 36 five-spots, it follows that there were 108 observations that were not five-spots. Our expected frequencies are based upon chance. Since the probability of tossing a five-spot is $\frac{1}{6}$, we put down our expected frequencies in that proportion, which in this case gives us 24 and 120. It is important to note that, in a chi-square problem, the sum of the observed frequencies has to equal the sum of the expected frequencies. For these data

$$X^2 = \frac{(36 - 24)^2}{24} + \frac{(108 - 120)^2}{120}$$

$$= \frac{12^2}{24} + \frac{12^2}{120} = \frac{144}{24} + \frac{144}{120}$$

$$= 6.0 + 1.2$$

$$= 7.20$$

which with $df = 1$ is significant at the 1 percent level.

An Alternate Formula

Chi square can also be obtained by the formula

$$\chi^2 = \sum \frac{O^2}{E} - (N) \tag{14.2}$$

If we use the above data in our example about the tossing of a die, we have

$$\chi^2 = \left[\frac{(36)^2}{24} + \frac{(108)^2}{120}\right] - 144$$

$$= \left[\frac{1296}{24} + \frac{11664}{120}\right] - 144$$

$$= [54 + 97.2] - 144$$

$$= 151.2 - 144$$

$$= 7.2$$

Chi Square in a 2 × 2 Table

One of the commonest uses of chi square is found in the so-called 2 × 2 table or fourfold table. In Table 14.1 are shown the "Yes-No" responses of two groups to an item on an attitude inventory. The observed frequencies have been entered in the left-hand table. Such a table as this is referred to as a *contingency table*. On the assumption that chance alone is operating, the expected frequencies are set up by assigning half of the "Yes" responses and half of the "No" responses to each of the two groups since the groups are equal in size. It may be noted that it is not necessary

TABLE 14.1.   Chi Square in a 2 × 2 Table

	O				E		
	Yes	No			Yes	No	
Group 1	40	28	68		45	23	68
	a	b	k				
Group 2	50	18	68		45	23	68
	c	d	l				
	90	46	136		90	46	136
	m	n					

to have the groups of equal size for the use of this technique.   Chi square is computed for these data in the same manner as it was for the previous problem, except that now we have four sets of cells to compare.

$$\chi^2 = \frac{(40 - 45)^2}{45} + \frac{(28 - 23)^2}{23} + \frac{(50 - 45)^2}{45} + \frac{(18 - 23)^2}{23}$$

$$= \frac{25}{45} + \frac{25}{23} + \frac{25}{45} + \frac{25}{23}$$

$$= .555 + 1.087 + .555 + 1.087$$

$$= 3.285$$

Degrees of Freedom

In a chi-square problem degrees of freedom are determined generally by the use of the following formula:

$$df = (r - 1)(c - 1) \tag{14.3}$$

where r = the numbers of rows in the contingency table
    c = the number of columns in the contingency table

For the data in Table 14.1, this reduces to

$$df = (2 - 1)(2 - 1) = 1 \times 1 = 1$$

The student will note that as soon as one of the cell values is determined, the marginal values remaining the same, the frequencies of the other cells are then fixed.   For this table, then, there is only 1 df.   Obviously, this formula cannot be applied to the two problems that we worked first, for then we would have 0 df.   In a 2 × 1 table, df is always equal to 1.   By entering the chi square table in the Appendix, we find that for $df = 1$ a chi square of 3.285 is not significant.

Another method for finding the value of chi square in a 2 × 2 table is by the use of the following formula which avoids the computation of the expected frequencies:

$$\chi^2 = \frac{N[(ad) - (bc)]^2}{(k)(l)(m)(n)} \tag{14.4}$$

where the various letters are shown in the left-hand contingency table in Table 14.1 and N is the total number of frequencies. If we combine the data in Table 14.1 and this formula,

$$\chi^2 = \frac{136[(40)(18) - (28)(50)]^2}{(68)(68)(90)(46)}$$

$$= \frac{136(720 - 1400)^2}{19,143,360} = \frac{62,886,400}{19,143,360}$$

$$= 3.285$$

which is identical to the answer computed by the other method.

Obtaining the Expected Frequencies

To illustrate how the expected frequencies are obtained, we shall use the material in Table 14.2. The cell frequencies of this 3×3 contingency table are designated by the letters within the cells. The rows and columns are summed and the total number of frequencies is represented by T. We are going to obtain these expected frequencies by manipulating the margins.

TABLE 14.2. Obtaining the Expected Frequencies

O				E			
a	b	c	R	$\dfrac{MR}{T}$	$\dfrac{NR}{T}$	$\dfrac{PR}{T}$	R
d	e	f	S	$\dfrac{MS}{T}$	$\dfrac{NS}{T}$	$\dfrac{PS}{T}$	S
g	h	i	W	$\dfrac{MW}{T}$	$\dfrac{NW}{T}$	$\dfrac{PW}{T}$	W
M	N	P	T	M	N	P	T

To obtain the expected frequency for the extreme upper-left cell, we multiply M by R and divide this by the total number of cases, T. The E for the cell below this is obtained by multiplying M by S and dividing by T. After we finish the left-hand column of the contingency table, we move to the right, and to obtain the E for the top middle cell we multiply N by R and divide this by T. In this manner, all the expected cell frequencies in the contingency table may be determined. If the student wishes he may go back to Table 14.1 and, if the method just described is applied, he will compute the same expected frequencies as are noted there. This method results in theoretical frequencies that are proportional to both margins.

THE NATURE OF THE CHI-SQUARE DISTRIBUTION

While the origin and development of chi square is beyond the scope of this text, it can be noted that the distribution of chi square is a function of the number of degrees of freedom.   These distributions vary considerably in shape when the number of degrees of freedom is small.   As the degrees of freedom approach 30, the shape of the chi-square distribution approaches that of the normal curve.

Chi Square When Frequencies are Small and $df = 1$

When any one of the expected frequencies is small, say less than 10, the chi square computed is likely to be an overestimate.   With $df = 1$, a correction called Yates' correction for continuity is applied.   This correction is used because the distribution of chi square is discrete, whereas the values obtained by the formulas result in a continuous probability model.   When frequencies are large, this difference is of no importance; but as the frequencies become small, Yates' correction should be applied.   It is noted that some use Yates' correction always with one degree of freedom, regardless of sample size.   When we work the data by formula (14.1), the corrected formula becomes

$$\chi^2 = \sum \frac{(|O - E| - .5)^2}{E} \tag{14.5}$$

In the above formula, what is actually happening is that each O which is larger than E is decreased by .5 and each O which is less than E is increased by .5.

When Yates' correction is applied to formula (14.4), this formula becomes

$$\chi^2 = \frac{N \left(|ad - bc| - \frac{N}{2}\right)^2}{(k)(l)(m)(n)} \tag{14.6}$$

The parallel lines around the $(O - E)$ and the $(ad - bc)$ indicate that the absolute values are to be reduced by .5.   If $(O - E)$ were -3.5, this would be reduced to -3.

TABLE 14.3.   The Use of Yates' Correction in Chi Square

		O				E	
	Yes	No			Yes	No	
Group 1	23	2	25		19	6	25
	a	b	k				
					19	6	25
Group 2	15	10	25				
	c	d	l		38	12	50
	38	12	50				
	m	n	N				

To illustrate the use of Yates' correction, we shall work the data in Table 14.3.   In Table 14.3 are shown the expected frequencies which result in the equations below:[1]

$$\chi^2 = \left[\frac{(23 - 19 - .5)^2}{19} + \frac{(2 - 6 - .5)^2}{6}\right](2)$$

$$= \left[\frac{(3.5)^2}{19} + \frac{(3.5)^2}{6}\right](2)$$

$$= (.6447 + 2.0417)(2)$$

$$= (2.6864)(2)$$

$$= 5.3728$$

which, with $df = 1$, is significant at the 5 percent level.   It might be noted here that the chi square when computed for these data, not using Yates' correction, is 7.017 which is significant at the 1 percent level.

When formula (14.6) is used, this problem is worked as follows:

$$\chi^2 = \frac{50\left(\left|(23)(10) - (15)(2)\right| - \frac{50}{2}\right)^2}{(25)(25)(38)(12)}$$

$$= \frac{50(200 - 25)^2}{285000}$$

$$= \frac{1,531,250}{285,000}$$

$$= 5.37$$

When E values are less than 5, and especially when they are around 2, even Yates' correction for continuity is not too good, and a method known as Fisher's exact method must be used.   This will not be discussed here, but it may be found in McNemar (1962, p. 236).   This method is a complicated one.   The student might find it to his advantage to increase the size of his N rather than be concerned with frequencies of 1 or 2.

Chi Square and z

When $df = 1$, $\chi^2 = z^2$.   This may be illustrated by the following data:

O	E
36	24
108	120
144	144

[1] Since the other two cells would be identical to the first two, we multiply by 2.

Since these data resulted from the toss of a die, the probability that any particular face of the die will appear is $\frac{1}{6}$. By applying the formulas of the binomial distribution (9.3 and 9.4),

$$m = mp \qquad\qquad \sigma = \sqrt{Npq}$$

$$= (144)\frac{1}{6} \qquad\qquad = \sqrt{144(\frac{1}{6})(\frac{5}{6})}$$

$$= 24 \qquad\qquad\quad = \sqrt{720/36}$$

$$= \sqrt{20}$$

$$= 4.472$$

We next consider our observed frequency of 36 five-spots as a deviation from the mean of 24, and we apply a z test to see if our observed frequency of 36 is large enough to be considered a significant one. Also, we correct for lack of continuity by reducing the 36 to 35.5.

$$z = \frac{35.5 - 24}{4.472}$$

$$= \frac{11.5}{4.472}$$

$$= 2.571$$

$$z^2 = 6.61$$

When we apply chi square to these data and also use Yates' correction for the lack of continuity, we have

$$\chi^2 = \frac{[(36 - 24) - .5]^2}{24} + \frac{[(108 - 120) - .5]^2}{120}$$

$$= \frac{11.5^2}{24} + \frac{11.5^2}{120}$$

$$= 5.51 + 1.10$$

$$= 6.61$$

which is the value of z^2 obtained above.

Since this is so, we have a choice in the solving of certain problems. For example, tests of the significance of the difference between proportions for uncorrelated data (Chapter 12) might more easily be solved by the use of chi square in lieu of z or t.

Chi Square a Nondirectional Test

From the above we can get some idea of the nature of the chi-square test. It has been noted that only the right-hand side of Table IV is used and the reader might infer from this that we are to make a one-tailed test. This is not so, as chi square is a nondirectional test. Since the statistic is arrived at by squaring the difference between observed and expected frequencies, it has no sign. Consider the .05 value for one degree of freedom in Table IV. This value is 3.841 and the square root at this is ± 1.96 which is the .05 value of z for a two-tailed test. Similarly, from this same table for the same number of degrees of freedom we find the .01 value of z to be 6.635. The square root of this is ± 2.58, the .01 value of z for a two-tailed test.

As can be seen from the examples that we have worked in this chapter, the usual type of test made with chi square is a two-tailed test. However, there may be cases where chi square is to be used in making a one-tailed test. In this case we double the p value and the 5 percent point becomes 2.706 and the 1 percent point 5.412.

Chi Square in a Table Larger than 2 × 2

Suppose that we have the responses of three groups to a single item of an attitude inventory scale. The responses were recorded as "strongly agree," "agree," "no opinion," "disagree," and "strongly disagree." The frequencies of the responses for the three groups are shown in Table 14.4.

TABLE 14.4. Chi Square in a Large Table

O

	SA	A	NO	D	SD	
Group 1	12	18	4	8	12	54
Group 2	48	22	10	8	10	98
Group 3	10	4	12	10	12	48
	70	44	26	26	34	200

E

	SA	A	NO	D	SD	
Group 1	18.9	11.9	7.0	7.0	9.2	54
Group 2	34.3	21.6	12.7	12.7	16.6	97.9
Group 3	16.8	10.5	6.3	6.3	8.2	48
	70	44	26	26	34	200

$$\chi^2 = \frac{(12 - 18.9)^2}{18.9} + \frac{(48 - 34.3)^2}{34.3} + \ldots + \frac{(12 - 8.2)^{2a}}{8.2}$$

$$= 2.519 + 5.472 + \ldots + 1.761$$

$$= 34.209 \text{ which with } df = 8 \text{ is significant for}$$
$$\chi^2 \text{ with } df = 8, \text{ at the } 1\% \text{ level} = 20.09$$

[a] Twelve of the components are not shown.

There is nothing different in the solution of the chi square for these data than that for the 2 × 2 table, other than the amount of work involved. First the marginal values for the observed frequencies are obtained. Then, using these margins, the expected frequencies are determined. For this problem these were carried to the nearest tenth. The chi-square component for each cell is then determined, these components are summed, the chi-square table in the Appendix is entered with (3 − 1)(5 − 1) or 8 degrees of freedom, and the appropriate conclusion is drawn.

The resulting chi square is large, and we reject the null hypothesis of no significant difference among the three groups at the 1 percent level. We now have strong reason to believe that there is a significant difference among the three groups. But where? Further tests have to be made to see if each group differs from the other or if two of them are similar, both differing from a third. A chi-square test can be made, taking one group at a time versus another group. If the overall chi square had not been significant, we could have stopped at that point. But if we have evidence that differences are present, we should take additional steps to find out where they are.

Small Frequencies in Large Tables

Suppose, using the same terminology as used in Table 14.4, we have the following responses of two groups to an attitude test item:

	SA	A	NO	D	SD
Group 1	2	15	12	18	1
Group 2	1	14	8	13	2

Before we start we should combine the frequencies in the "strongly agree" and "agree" categories and those also in the two "disagree" categories and apply chi square to a contingency table that looks like this:[2]

	A	NO	D
Group 1	17	12	19
Group 2	15	8	15

Another situation like this may arise:

	SA	A	NO	D	SD
Group 1	24	46	2	14	8
Group 2	16	13	3	34	16

[2] A good rule to follow is to combine frequencies when any E is less than 5.

For these data it would be best to discard the "no opinion" category and perform the chi-square test using the other four columns.

The next situation contains the responses of students in five different schools of a university to a five-response attitude test item.

	SA	A	NO	D	SD
Liberal Arts	16	32	12	37	18
Engineering	23	15	7	23	5
Home Economics	6	14	6	13	6
Fine arts	9	23	6	7	8
Education	2	3	4	10	1

In the above contingency table it will be noted that the number of respondents in Education is small. There are three possibilities in handling data like this. First, the education data can be dropped from the analysis. Second, the frequencies of the education group can be combined with those of some other group if there is any logic for such a combination. In this situation education might be combined with liberal arts, for on some campuses these two groups are together. Third, and probably best, more individuals in education should be sampled. Yates' correction is not applied to these larger tables.

Chi-Square Test for Correlated Proportions

In Chapter 12, we made a z test (or a t test) for the difference between two proportions when the data are correlated. The data used in Chapter 12 are reproduced below:

Item 2

		No	Yes
	Yes	a 33	b 47
Item 1			
	No	c 25	d 15

In this table we have the responses of 120 individuals to two test items. The data are arranged in the table by taking into account the agreement and disagreement of the responses of the individuals to the two items.

The formula for chi square for this type of problem is:

$$\chi^2 = \frac{(a - d)^2}{a + d}$$

$$= \frac{(33 - 15)^2}{33 + 15}$$

$$= \frac{(18)^2}{48} = \frac{324}{48}$$

$$= 6.76$$

In Chapter 12, we found a z of 2.60 for this problem. This value squared is equal to 6.76, which it should be, since with 1 df, z^2 is equal to chi square.

Testing Goodness of Fit

Another use of chi square is testing a set of data to see if the data are normally distributed, that is, if they fit the normal distribution. In Chapter 6 we learned how to normalize a set of data. The student who wishes to review at this point is referred to Table 6.2 and the discussion associated with it. In Table 6.2 we set up the expected frequencies for the distribution in the table. Both the observed and expected frequencies from Table 6.2 are reproduced in the first two columns of Table 14.5. It should be apparent by now that any time that we have a set of observed and a set of expected frequencies, we can apply the chi-square test.

TABLE 14.5. Testing Goodness of Fit

	(1) O	(2) E	(3) O	(4) E	(5) $O - E$	(6) $(O - E)^2$	(7) $(O - E)^2/E$
90–94	1	1.8					
85–89	3	4.1					
80–84	8	8.2	12	14.1	2.1	4.41	.313
75–79	12	13.8	12	13.8	1.8	3.24	.235
70–74	28	19.6	28	19.6	8.4	70.56	3.600
65–69	36	23.6	36	23.6	12.4	153.76	6.515
60–64	12	24.1	12	24.1	12.1	146.41	6.075
55–59	18	20.8	18	20.8	2.8	7.84	.377
50–54	10	15.2	10	15.2	5.2	27.04	1.779
45–49	8	9.5	8	9.2	1.5	2.25	.237
40–44	8	5.0	14	8.4	5.6	31.36	3.733
35–39	5	2.2					
30–34	1	1.2					
	$\Sigma = 150$	$\Sigma = 149.1$					$\chi^2 = 22.864$

In columns 1 and 2 of Table 14.5, we have the observed and expected frequencies. In columns 3 and 4 are the same frequencies, this time with the frequencies in the extreme class intervals combined so that none of the expected frequencies is less than 5. In column 5 are shown the differences between each O and E, in column 6 the square of these differences, and in column 7 the square of the differences divided by the expected frequencies. These are then summed, and a chi square of 22.864 results.

The null hypothesis that we have here is that the distribution of observed scores is a chance variation from a normal population. Basically, the number of degrees of freedom for this situation is the number of intervals minus three. We placed three restrictions upon our data when we normalized them. We noted that the best-fitting normal curve for a set of data has the same mean, standard deviation, and number of cases as the original data. One degree of freedom was lost for each of these restrictions. In our problem we reduced the number of class intervals to 9, when we combined those in the tails having small frequencies. For these data it follows that $df = 6$, that is, 9 categories minus 3. In the chi-square table we find for $df = 6$ that the 1 percent value of chi square is 16.812. Since our chi-square value is larger than this, we reject the null hypothesis at the 1 percent level. In other words, differences this large would be expected 1 time in 100 with repeated sampling from a normal curve. We do not believe this *is* that once in a hundred occurence and, therefore, choose to believe that the population from which this sample was drawn is not normal. It might be noted from Table IV that this chi square of 22.864 is actually significant slightly beyond the .001 level.

Exercises

1. A student responds to a 70-item true-false test by guessing the responses to every item. He obtains a score of 45. Does this differ significantly from what would be expected by chance?

2. One hundred cards were pulled from a well-shuffled deck of ordinary playing cards, each card being replaced after being drawn and the deck then reshuffled. Do the following results deviate from what we would expect by chance?

Red card	38
Black card	62
	100

King, Queen, or Jack	16
Numbered card or ace	84
	100

3. A job information test was given to attendants in a mental hospital. Below are the responses to two items of attendants rated "good" and "poor" by their supervisors. Do the responses to the two items differ significantly?

	Yes	No
Item 1:		
Rated good	72	28
Rated poor	22	4
Item 2:		
Rated good	12	88
Rated poor	12	14

4. Seven dimes were tossed 128 times, with the following results:

$x^2 = 3.48$

7 heads, 0 tails	2
6 heads, 1 tail	8
5 heads, 2 tails	18
4 heads, 3 tails	32
3 heads, 4 tails	41
2 heads, 5 tails	17
1 head, 6 tails	10
0 heads, 7 tails	0

Are these results different from what would be expected by chance?

5. Two hundred subjects of both sexes were given tests of margarine and butter and asked to name the one that they preferred. Do the preferences of the two sexes differ significantly in respect to these staples?

EXAMPLE OF D.F. = 1

YATES' CORRECTION? necessary

	First Choice	
	Margarine	Butter
Males	34	46
Females	72	48

6. A nation-wide sample of 2000 high school students was asked to agree or to disagree with the statement: "People should not be allowed to vote unless they are intelligent and educated." The responses of the two sexes were tabulated separately.

	Agree	Disagree
Boys	360	640
Girls	290	710

Do the opinions of these boys and girls differ significantly?

7. Solve Problems 1–5 at the end of Chapter 12 by the use of chi square.

8. Two hundred boys, some of whose mothers were college graduates and some of whom were not, were asked whether they agreed or disagreed about an aspect of teenage behavior. The results follow:

	Agree	Disagree
Mother college graduate	38	12
Mother not college graduate	84	66

Is the attitude of these mothers related to college graduation?

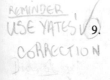

REMINDER
USE YATES'
CORRECTION

9. Two lots of 14 rats each were subjects in an experiment related to the effectiveness of a drug. All rats were inoculated with the causative organism, but only one lot was previously given a preventive serum. The results follow.

	Serum	No Serum
Recovered	12	6
Died	2	8

Can anything be said of the effectiveness of the serum?

10. In another survey this question was posed: "Do you think that some racial and religious groups should be prevented from living in certain sections of cities?" When the responses were tabulated by region, the following frequencies were observed:

	Agree	Undecided	Disagree
East	89	79	297
Midwest	118	130	350
South	241	140	248
West	37	59	197

(a) Compute the expected frequencies.

(b) How many degrees of freedom are there for this problem?

(e) Do the responses of eastern students differ significantly from those of western students on this question?

(d) Compare the responses of midwestern students with those of southern students.

15

ANALYSIS OF VARIANCE
AND COVARIANCE

In the previous chapter, we were concerned with the z and t tests for testing differences between two groups. In actual practice, however, it often happens that more than two groups are involved in a study. For instance, one of the authors carried on a study involving a series of tests given to students in five different colleges of a large university. He was interested in differences in performance of the students in the different colleges on these different tests. By means of the z test, he could have taken the colleges two at a time and tested for differences between each two, but for the five different colleges this would have amounted to ten different z tests. Frequently, there are more than five groups in a research study, and the number of comparisons that would have to be made to cover all possible tests would be too cumbersome to carry out. The general formula for determining the number of combinations to be made, taking the groups two at a time, is $N(N - 1)/2$, where N is the number of groups. For example, if there are 15 groups, we would have to run 105 separate z tests.

In addition to the nearly prohibitive number of calculations involved in comparing subsamples one by one, there is another, and more important, limitation. When we analyze our data this way, we ignore the fact that these subsamples exist in a set. The elements of such sets are known to *interact*. This interaction should be taken into account in our analysis. Analysis of variance does not ignore interaction. In more complex statistical designs than we will be able to discuss here, estimates of variance due to interaction are made. These estimates often prove to be extremely important in the interpretation of the statistical analysis.

To avoid these limitations, statisticians have designed the so-called analysis of variance techniques in which all of the data are treated at once and a general null hypothesis of no difference among the means of the various groups is tested. In this simple type of analysis of variance, we are concerned with two types of variation.

Suppose that we have IQ scores on five samples of adults. The mean and variance (s^2) of each group is

Groups

	(1)	(2)	(3)	(4)	(5)
$\overline{X}$	102	123	100	108	112
s^2	15	12	12	14	10

We can see that the means of the groups vary. This variation of group means from the total or grand mean of all groups is referred to as "between groups" variance. The average variability of the scores *within* each group is called "within groups" variance.

Now let us suppose that we throw all the IQ scores into one big pot and mix thoroughly. We can forget for the moment which scores belong in which groups. These scores will vary. The variation of these individual scores is called "total" variance.

The heart of analysis of variance lies in the following fact: If the groups are random samples from the same population, the two variances, *within* and *between*, are unbiased estimates of the same population variance. We can test for the significance of the difference of the two types by use of the F test.

ASSUMPTIONS UNDERLYING THE USE OF THE ANALYSIS OF VARIANCE

When the analysis of variance technique is used, the following assumptions should be met:

1. The individuals in the various subgroups should be selected on the basis of random sampling from normally distributed populations.

2. The variance of the subgroups should be homogeneous (H_0: $\sigma_1^2 = \sigma_2^2 = \cdots = \sigma_5^2$). This assumption of homogeneity of subgroup variance should be tested by Bartlett's test (or some other) whenever analysis of variance is to be used [see Bartlett (1937) or Edwards (1954, 1960)].

3. The samples comprising the groups should be *independent*. Unless the samples are independent, and thereby yield independent variance estimates, the ratio of *between* to *within* variances will not have the F distribution.

MEETING THE ASSUMPTIONS

The logic of analysis of variance requires all three assumptions. In use, however, the assumptions are not equally critical. It has been demonstrated that the distribution within each of the subgroups can be skewed to a rather high degree without affecting the significance test (Cochran, 1947).

The first and third assumptions depend upon the adequacy of the experimental design. This emphasizes the necessity for careful planning prior to the execution of statistical tests.

The second assumption, that of homogeneity of variance, is very important and is almost always tested before the analysis of variance is made. The most frequently used test of this assumption is one devised by Bartlett (1937). The computational method for performing this test is included in the model worksheet shown later as Table 15.5. Bartlett's test yields a chi square. If the chi square is significant with number of groups minus 1 degree of freedom, we have reason to believe that the second assumption has not been met. Other methods have been developed for testing samples with significantly different variances.

In this chapter we shall discuss only the very simplest application of the analysis of variance. Usually a good share of a second and third course in statistics is devoted to the many uses and ramifications of this technique.

TESTING THE DIFFERENCES AMONG SEVERAL MEANS

We shall illustrate the basic solution of an analysis of variance problem by using the three sets of data in Table 15.1. Here we have the scores of 7 individuals in three groups, A, B, and C, to a short test. In the three columns at the right, we have the squares of each of these scores.

TABLE 15.1. Example of Single Classification Analysis of Variance

Group A X	Group B X	Group C X	Group A X^2	Group B X^2	Group C X^2
12	18	6	144	324	36
18	17	10	324	289	100
16	16	18	256	256	324
8	18	4	64	324	16
6	12	6	36	144	36
12	17	12	144	289	144
10	10	14	100	100	196
$\Sigma X = 82$	108	70	$\Sigma X^2 = 1068$	1726	852
$\bar{X} = 11.71$	15.43	10			
$\bar{X}_T = 12.38$					

The Total Sum of Squares

The total sum of squares could be obtained by finding the mean of the 21 scores, taking the deviation of each score from this mean, and squaring and summing these squared deviations. It may be recalled that we can obtain the sum of the squares by the use of the following equation:

$$\Sigma x^2 = \Sigma X^2 - \frac{(\Sigma X)^2}{N} \qquad (15.1)$$

This would mean

$$[(12)^2 + (18)^2 + (16)^2 + \cdots + (12)^2 + (14)^2] - \frac{(260)^2}{21}$$

Or from the data in Table 15.1

$$\Sigma x^2 = 1068 + 1726 + 852 - \frac{(82 + 108 + 70)^2}{21}$$

$$= 3646 - \frac{(260)^2}{21}$$

$$= 3646 - \frac{67600}{21}$$

$$= 3646 - 3219$$

$$= 427$$

The "Between" Sum of Squares

The sum of the squares between the various groups can be found by taking the mean of each group, getting its deviation from the total mean, squaring this deviation, and then multiplying each of these by the number of individuals in each group (n), as follows:

$$\Sigma x^2 = \Sigma(\bar{X} - \bar{X}_T)^2 n \qquad (15.2)$$

$$= (11.71 - 12.38)^2(7) + (15.43 - 12.38)^2(7) + (10 - 12.38)^2(7)$$

$$= (-.67)^2(7) + (3.05)^2(7) + (-2.38)^2(7)$$

$$= (.4489)(7) + (9.3025)(7) + (5.6644)(7)$$

$$= 3.1423 + 65.1175 + 39.6508$$

$$= 107.9$$

A more direct method of obtaining the so-called "between" sum of squares is as follows:

$$\Sigma x^2 = \left[\Sigma \frac{(\Sigma X)^2}{n}\right] - \frac{(\Sigma X_T)^2}{N} \qquad (15.3)$$

$$= \left[\frac{(82)^2}{7} + \frac{(108)^2}{7} + \frac{(70)^2}{7}\right] - \frac{(260)^2}{21}$$

$$= \frac{6724}{7} + \frac{11664}{7} + \frac{4900}{7} - \frac{67600}{21}$$

$$= (960.6 + 1666.3 + 700) - 3219$$

$$= 3326.9 - 3219$$

$$= 107.9$$

The "Within" Sum of Squares

To obtain the "within" sum of squares we could, group by group, take each score, subtract it from the mean of the group, square each score, and sum.

Group A: $(12 - 12.38)^2 + (18 - 12.38)^2 + \cdots + (10 - 12.38)^2$

This is repeated for the other two groups, and then the three sums are summed. However, this is a rather tedious method, and we obtain the identical results as follows:

For group A
$$\Sigma x^2 = \Sigma X^2 - \frac{(\Sigma X)^2}{n} \qquad (15.4)$$

$$= 1068 - \frac{(82)^2}{7}$$

$$= 1068 - 960.6$$

$$= 107.4$$

For group B
$$\Sigma x^2 = 1726 - \frac{(108)^2}{7}$$

$$= 1726 - 1666.3$$

$$= 59.7$$

For group C
$$\Sigma x^2 = 852 - \frac{(70)^2}{7}$$

$$= 852 - 700$$

$$= 152$$

Summing for all three groups

$$\Sigma x^2 = 107.4 + 59.7 + 152$$

$$= 319.1$$

The "within" sum of squares added to the "between" sum of squares should total the "total" sum of squares.

$$319.1 + 107.9 = 427$$

It follows that the "within" sum of squares can be obtained directly by subtracting the "between" sum of squares directly from the sum of squares of the total, instead of going through the process described above.

Degrees of Freedom

Since there are 21 cases in the problem that we are working, we have $N - 1$ or 20 df. In group A there are 7 cases; hence there are 6 df for this group, and since in this problem the number of cases is the same in each problem, there are 6 df in each of the other groups. So far we have accounted for 18 of the total number of degrees of freedom.   We have three groups.   Then it follows that there are 2 *df* for the groups.   To generalize:

df for total groups = number of cases in total (N) minus 1
df for groups "between" = number of groups (k) minus 1
df for groups "within" = sum of the number of cases within each subgroup (n) minus 1.

$$(n_1 - 1) + (n_2 - 1) + \cdots + (n_k - 1)$$

The Analysis of Variance

The usual technique at this point is to set up a table similar to Table 15.2. Into this table we place, in the appropriate column, the number of degrees

TABLE 15.2.   Analysis of Variance for the Data in Table 15.1

Source of Variation	df	Sum of Squares	Mean Square
"Between" Groups	2	107.9	53.95
"Within" Groups	18	319.1	17.73
Total	20	427	

of freedom, the sum of the squares for each of the three categories, and in the last column the so-called mean-square values.   These mean squares are obtained by dividing each of the sum of squares by its respective number of degrees of freedom.   Such a ratio or division results in a variance.   The "between" and the "within" mean squares are then two estimates of the population variance.

The *F* Test

We made an *F* test previously when testing the difference between two variances to see whether or not we should pool them.   The analysis of variance table is evaluated by making the following *F* test:

$$F = \frac{\text{mean square for "between" groups}}{\text{mean square for "within" groups}} \qquad (15.5)$$

$$= \frac{53.95}{17.73}$$

$$= 3.04$$

F ratios are interpreted by use of the *F* table (Table V of the Appendix). This table is entered with the number of degrees of freedom for the greater mean square across the top and with the number of degrees of freedom in the lesser mean square on the left-hand side.   For this problem, we go over to 2 and down to 18.   In that location we observe that the value of *F* needed for significance at the 5 percent point is 3.55.   Since our obtained

F ratio is lower than this, we do not reject the null hypothesis. It is important to remember that though our test is a ratio of variances, the null hypothesis is that the means of the populations from which the samples are selected are equal (H_0: $m_A = m_B = m_C$).

There are times when the value of the F ratio will be less than 1. There is no point in solving for the value of such a ratio as all such ratios are not significant.

THE ANALYSIS OF VARIANCE WITH ONLY TWO GROUPS

The analysis of variance may be applied to only two groups. When this is done, a relationship of the F ratio and the t ratio becomes apparent. In Table 15.3 are two sets of scores representing the responses of two groups

TABLE 15.3.   Analysis of Variance for Two Groups

X	X_1	X^2	X_1^2
22	12	484	144
18	16	324	256
24	10	576	100
22	10	484	100
16	4	256	16
18	6	324	36
13	17	169	289
18	14	324	196
19	14	361	196
22	10	484	100
$\Sigma X = 192$	113	$\Sigma = 3786$	1433
$\bar{X} = 19.2$	11.3		

to a short test. In the table we are shown the various sums and means. The sum of the squares is computed as follows:

Sum of squares for total

$$\Sigma x^2 = 5219 - \frac{(305)^2}{20}$$

$$= 5219 - 4651.25$$

$$= 567.75$$

The "between" sum of squares

$$\Sigma x^2 = \frac{(192)^2}{10} + \frac{(113)^2}{10} - \frac{(305)^2}{20}$$

$$= (3686.4 + 1276.9) - 4651.25$$

$$= 4963.3 - 4651.25$$

$$= 312.05$$

The "within" sum of squares

Within sum of squares = (total sum of squares)

− (between sum of squares)

$$\Sigma x^2 = 567.75 - 312.05 = 255.7$$

The analysis of variance table is organized as shown in Table 15.4 and the F test is made. This time we find that the F ratio is equal to 21.96.

TABLE 15.4. Analysis of Variance for the Data in Table 15.3

Source of Variation	df	Sum of Squares	Mean Square
"Between" groups	1	312.05	312.05
"Within" groups	18	255.7	14.21
Total	19	567.75	

Suppose that we next compute a t ratio for the above data. We shall use the following formula for t, the formula for small samples:

$$t = \frac{\bar{X} - \bar{X}_1}{\sqrt{\frac{\Sigma x^2 + \Sigma x_1^2}{(N_1 + N_2) - 2}\left(\frac{1}{N_1} + \frac{1}{N_2}\right)}}$$

$$= \frac{19.2 - 11.3}{\sqrt{\frac{99.6 + 156.1}{(10 + 10) - 2}\left(\frac{1}{10} + \frac{1}{10}\right)}}$$

$$= \frac{7.9}{\sqrt{\frac{255.7}{18}[(.1) + (.1)]}}$$

$$= \frac{7.9}{\sqrt{(14.20)(.2)}}$$

$$= \frac{7.9}{\sqrt{2.84}}$$

$$= \frac{7.9}{1.685}$$

$$= 4.69$$

Both this F of 21.96 and the t of 4.69 are significant beyond the 1 percent level of significance.   Both techniques lead to the same conclusion.   It may be noted that when df for "between" groups $= 1$, $\sqrt{F} = t$ or, putting it the other way around, $t^2 = F$.

$$\sqrt{21.96} = 4.69 = t$$

t Tests Made after F Tests

In the problem worked first in this chapter no significant differences were found among the three groups when the F test was applied to the data. Suppose that this F had been significant.   Should we then proceed and make a series of t tests to see just what groups differ from each other?   In general, it appears that it is best not to.   One might look at the various means and carry on further research using the observed differences that appear to be large enough to be significant.

Tukey (1949) has come up with an exact answer to this problem of testing the differences between individual means when the F is significant.   It involves making three tests, one for the "significant gap," one for the "straggler," and one for "excessive variability."   These three tests are not difficult, but they are rather long.   The student who is interested is referred to Tukey (1949) or Edwards (1954).

A COMPUTATIONAL FORM

A worksheet for computing single classification analysis of variance is shown in Table 15.5.   This form includes Bartlett's test for the homogeneity of variance assumption.

In this table the scores on a measure of social class among 971 high school students are tested against the following responses of the students to the question "How do you feel about going to college?"

1.   It would be a waste of time.
2.   I don't have the ability.
3.   I would go chiefly to gain more earning power in terms of pay.
4.   I would go chiefly to enjoy social contacts in college and have a good time.
5.   I would go chiefly to prepare for more advanced training such as law and medicine.
6.   I would go to gain knowledge for its own sake.

Computations from the raw scores are entered in the table in columns a, c, and d.   Then, by merely filling in the remaining blanks, as the headings indicate, the analysis is completed.

First, the Bartlett test of homogeneity of variance is made.   The constant, 2.3026, multiplied by the entries from the table yields a chi square.

TABLE 15.5. Worksheet for Computing Single Classification Analysis of Variance

	a	b	c	d	e	f	g	h	i
	n	$n-1$	ΣX	ΣX^2	$\dfrac{c^2}{a}$	$d-e$	$\dfrac{f}{b}$	$\log g$	bh
Waste of time	63	62	375	3,079	2,232	847	13.661	1.13548	70.39976
Don't have ability	116	115	557	4,009	2,675	1,334	11.600	1.06446	122.41290
More earning power	196	195	999	6,805	5,092	1,713	8.785	0.94374	184.02930
Social contacts	49	48	295	2,459	1,776	683	14.229	1.15317	55.35216
Prepare for more training	300	299	1,808	14,402	10,896	3,506	11.726	1.06915	319.67585
Gain knowledge	247	246	1,460	11,226	8,630	2,596	10.553	1.02337	251.74902
Total	971	965	5,494	41,980	31,301	10,679	70.554		1003.61899

Other Computations

j	$(\Sigma c)^2$	30,184,036
k	$\dfrac{j}{\Sigma a}$	31,086
l	$\dfrac{\Sigma f}{\Sigma b}$	11.0663
m	$\log l$	1.04400

Bartlett: $\chi^2 = 2.3026\,[(\Sigma b)\,m - \Sigma i)] = 8.844$

		SS	df	MS	F
Total	$\Sigma d - k$	10,894			
"Within"	$\Sigma d - \Sigma e$	10,679	965	11.07	
"Between"	$\Sigma e - k$	215	5	43.00	3.88

In this example, the chi square of 8.844 is not significant. This means that variances of the social-class scores of students choosing the alternatives can be assumed to have come from the same population distribution.

We can now legitimately make the F test. The sums of squares and degrees of freedom are entered into the final table as the headings show us. The "within mean square" and "between mean square" are found by dividing their corresponding sum of squares by their degrees of freedom. Finally, the value of F, the ratio of the two mean squares, is computed. In this example, this ratio equals 3.88. By comparing this value with the F table (Table V in Appendix), we find that the F is significant. This allows us to conclude that the students choosing different alternatives have significantly different social-class scores.

ANALYSIS OF COVARIANCE

It sometimes happens that the experimenter cannot completely control all the variables relevant to his research. For example, he might randomly assign high-school physics students to each of two types of instruction—one with films and the other without the use of such aids. Even though student assignment has been random, it may be that the two groups of students differ significantly in academic ability. To test for the significance of any difference in physics achievement, it is necessary to account for the influence of differences in prior ability.

A method is available for testing the significance of differences among means which have been influenced by one or more uncontrolled variables. This method is called *analysis of covariance*. In effect, analysis of covariance adjusts the means for the effect of the uncontrolled variable (academic ability in our example) and makes the necessary modifications in sampling error. The corrected sampling error is then used to test for the significance of differences among adjusted means.

As might have been anticipated, the adjustments made in analysis of covariance are based on the application of regression analysis to the data. Several assumptions beyond those necessary for analysis of variance must be met, depending on the experimental design. These assumptions, the various types of covariance analysis, and their computational procedures will be found in more advanced texts (e.g., Edwards, 1960).

Exercises

1. Below are the scores of 10 individuals on test X and 10 others on Y.

X	Y	X	Y
40	29	22	27
46	38	20	45
35	20	31	17
17	27	18	26
11	28	22	29

(a) Use an F test and test the difference between the means of groups X and Y.

(b) Test the significance of the difference between these two means using a t test.

2. The following data represent the scores of ten students in each of five schools of a university on the *Ohio Psychological Examination*. By means of analysis of variance, test the difference between the means.

Liberal Arts	Business Administration	Home Economics	Fine Arts	Engineering
106	79	133	50	109
120	91	78	60	129
81	105	113	112	111
92	127	40	97	77
102	71	103	80	102
121	115	80	62	130
86	95	113	116	125
131	115	90	134	75
62	62	84	98	93
122	52	113	112	82

3. If the F test in a single classification analysis of variance is not significant, can we say that the means of the population from which the samples were drawn are equal?

4. What do we call the risk we take of being wrong in rejecting a null hypothesis?

5. The enrollment of the grades in an elementary school is as follows:

First	75	Fifth	61
Second	86	Sixth	58
Third	72	Seventh	53
Fourth	68	Eighth	43

(a) Can we test the significance of the difference between the enrollments by analysis of variance?

(b) Can we test by other means?

6. Given the following four random samples, test the hypothesis that they are from the same population.

Sample A	Sample B	Sample C	Sample D
15	24	20	25
20	22	22	18
26	20	30	16
26	21	27	32
24	34		24
	18		

7. Three types of advertising were tested for their effectiveness. Their "effectivity" mean scores were

$$M_1 = 80 \qquad M_2 = 45 \qquad M_3 = 63$$

An analysis of variance was performed and the means were found to differ significantly.

(a) Do we know that type 1 is better than type 2? Type 1 is better than type 3?

(b) If you are the advertiser and type 1 costs one-third more than type 3, what would you do?

(c) How might you use sales records?

16

OTHER CORRELATIONAL TECHNIQUES

In Chapter 7, the entire chapter was devoted to the most widely used correlation coefficient, the Pearson r. When the data that we wish to correlate meet the assumptions basic to certain interpretations of the Pearson r, and when the two variables are continuous, it is the best statistic to use. However, there are times when the relationship between two variables is not linear, when one or both of the variables are not continuous, or when the number of pairs of measurements is too small, or when certain assumptions cannot be made about the distribution of the trait in the population so that certain deductions from the Pearson r are not applicable. In this chapter, we shall study some of the special correlational techniques which may be applied to some of the situations just described. For convenience, we shall divide them into parametric and nonparametric statistics.

PARAMETRIC CORRELATIONAL TECHNIQUES

The Point-Biserial r_{pb}

There are circumstances, especially in the field of test construction and test validation, where one of the variables is continuous, and the other is conceived of as a dichotomy. In the usual scoring of items, the procedure is to mark the item either right or wrong. This right-wrong scoring is regarded as being a true dichotomy. In item analysis work (see Chapter 17) the test-maker is usually concerned with how well the item is separating the good students from the poor ones. The ability of an item to discriminate between the two groups is frequently measured by a correlation coefficient. Dichotomously scored items may be correlated with a continuous total score or with a continuous outside criterion such as academic grade-point indexes or other measures of achievements.

189

This is done by setting up a table like Table 16.1. In the first column appears an interval grouping for the total test scores. Then the papers are taken one by one and the first item on the test is examined to see whether or not the subject answered it correctly. Suppose that the first paper has a score of 73 and that this student answered the item correctly. Then a tally is placed in the "Right" column, column 2. Each paper is taken, and

TABLE 16.1.   Worksheet for the Point-Biserial and Biserial r

(1)	(2) f_p Right	(3) f_w Wrong	(4) f_t	(5) x'	(6) $f_t x'$	(7) $f_t x'^2$	(8) $f_p x'$
70–74	3	0	3	5	15	75	15
65–69	6	1	7	4	28	112	24
60–64	6	2	8	3	24	72	18
55–59	5	4	9	2	18	36	10
50–54	6	2	8	1	8	8	6
45–49	7	6	13	0	0	0	0
40–44	6	8	14	−1	−14	14	−6
35–39	3	6	9	−2	−18	36	−6
30–34	3	9	12	−3	−36	108	−9
25–29	1	4	5	−4	−20	80	−4
20–24	0	12	12	−5	−60	300	0
	$\Sigma = 46$	$\Sigma = 54$	$\Sigma = 100$		$\Sigma = -55$	$\Sigma = 841$	$\Sigma = 48$

the response of the first item is tallied into either column 2 or 3. Actually, we have a scatterplot with the variable on the Y axis continuous, just as with the Pearson r, but with the variable on the X axis reduced to two categories.

Column 4 is the total number of frequencies falling in each of the intervals. The sum of this column is 100, which is the sum of the number who responded correctly and the number who responded incorrectly to the item. We now proceed to compute the mean and standard deviation of the total scores. Columns 5, 6, and 7 are set up in the usual way and columns 6 and 7 are summed. We also need the mean of the individuals getting the item correct. For this we set up column 8 which contains the products of the values in columns 2 and 5.

A formula for the point biserial is as follows:

$$r_{pb} = \frac{\bar{X}_p - \bar{X}_t}{s_t} \sqrt{\frac{p}{q}} \tag{16.1}$$

where $\bar{X}_p$ = the mean score of those answering the item correctly
$\bar{X}_t$ = the mean of the total test scores
s_t = the standard deviation of the test
p = the proportion of the total group answering the item correctly
$q = 1 - p$

We first solve for the two means.

$$\bar{X}_p = 47 + \frac{48}{46}(5) \qquad \bar{X}_t = 47 + \frac{-55}{100}(5)$$

$$= 47 + 5.2 \qquad\qquad = 47 + (-2.75)$$

$$= 52.2 \qquad\qquad = 44.2$$

The standard deviation must also be computed.

First, the Σx^2:
$$\Sigma x^2 = \left[841 - \frac{(-55)^2}{100}\right](5)^2$$

$$= (841 - 30.25)(25)$$

$$= 20268.75$$

Then s_t:
$$s_t = \sqrt{\frac{20268.75}{100}}$$

$$= \sqrt{202.69}$$

$$= 14.2$$

$$p = \frac{46}{100} = .46$$

By substituting these values in equation (16.1), we have

$$r_{pb} = \frac{52.2 - 44.2}{14.2}\sqrt{\frac{.46}{.54}}$$

$$= \frac{8}{14.2}\sqrt{.851851}$$

$$= .563(.923)$$

$$= .52$$

This coefficient is a product-moment correlation coefficient and is used and interpreted just as the Pearson r is. If the test being analyzed contains a large number of items, the use of this computation is almost prohibitive from the point of view of time. There are data processing aids and short-cut methods which will facilitate such computations. In test validation work, the criterion may be "pass" or "fail," "obtained his wings," "did not obtain his wings," "on probation," or "not on probation," and the like.

Reliability of the Point Biserial. The significance of the point-biserial correlation coefficient may be tested by the use of the following t test and entering the t table with $N - 2$ degrees of freedom.

$$t = \frac{r_{pb}\sqrt{N - 2}}{\sqrt{1 - r_{pb}^2}} \qquad (16.2)$$

For these data:
$$t = \frac{.52\sqrt{98}}{\sqrt{1 - (.52)^2}}$$

$$= \frac{(.52)(9.8995)}{\sqrt{1 - .2704}}$$

$$= \frac{5.1477}{.854}$$

$$= 6.03$$

which with $df = 98$ is significant.

This coefficient could more easily be tested by entering Table VI with $N - 2$ degrees of freedom, which in this case is 98 df. From this we see that the coefficient is significant well beyond the .001 level.

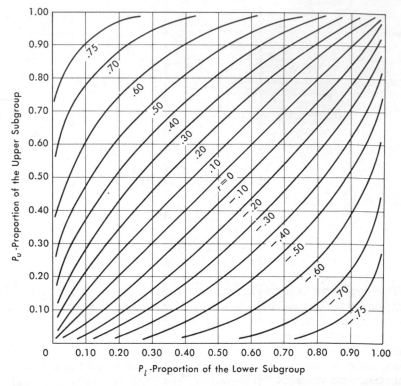

FIGURE 16.1   An abac for estimates of the point-biserial r when one variable is divided at the median of the distribution.   (Prepared by Harvey F. Dingman.)   Source: J. P. Guilford. *Psychometric Methods*.   New York: McGraw-Hill, 1954.   Reprinted by permission of the publisher.

A quick and efficient method of estimating the point-biserial r is to use an abac prepared by Dingman (Fig. 16.1).   This abac can be used when one variable is divided at the median.   The proportion of subjects in the upper criterion group who pass a given item is found on the ordinate. The corresponding proportion from the "low" group is found on the abscissa. The estimated point-biserial r is found at the perpendicular intersection of these values.

The Biserial Correlation Coefficient

Another statistic widely used in item analysis work is the biserial $r(r_b)$. We use this statistic when we have one continuous variable and another which is actually continuous but which has been forced into a dichotomy. Passing or failing is an example of a forced dichotomy. Achievement may be thought of as a continuum ranging from those who pass with exceedingly high honors down to those who fail miserably. Passing is made up of groups of individuals from the honor students down to the borderline cases, and failure includes all those who just barely failed down to the utter failures. We reduce this continuum to a pass-fail dichotomy, and as this is the usual procedure in test scoring, the biserial r may be used as a measure of the discrimination index of an item.

To find the value of the biserial r, one of the easiest formulas is

$$r_b = \frac{\bar{X}_p - \bar{X}_t}{s_t} \left(\frac{p}{y}\right) \tag{16.3}$$

All symbols are the same as those defined for the point-biserial r except y, which is the ordinate obtained from the normal probability table, cutting off above it an area equal to p.

We shall take the data in Table 16.1 and this time solve for the biserial r.

$$r_b = \frac{52.2 - 44.2}{14.2} \left(\frac{.46}{.3969}\right)$$

$$= \frac{8}{14.2} (1.159)$$

$$= .563(1.159)$$

$$= .65$$

The biserial r is an estimation of the product-moment correlation coefficient. The standard error of the biserial r may be estimated by the following equation:

$$s_{r_b} = \frac{(\sqrt{p_1 p_2}/y) - r_b{}^2}{\sqrt{N}} \tag{16.4}$$

where p_1 and p_2 are the proportions in each of the two categories, and the other terms are the same as in equation (16.3).

For this problem,

$$s_{r_b} = \frac{[\sqrt{(.46)(.54)}/.3969] - (.65)^2}{\sqrt{100}}$$

$$= \frac{1.2547 - .4225}{10}$$

$$= .083$$

The significance of a biserial r can be tested using the null hypothesis of no difference between the estimated population biserial and zero with a formula similar to equation (13.1). This is done by dropping the r_b^2 in formula (16.4). Thus

$$s_{r_b} = \frac{\sqrt{p_1 p_2}}{y} \left(\frac{1}{\sqrt{N}} \right)$$

$$= \frac{1.255}{10} = .1255$$

Then $t = \dfrac{.65}{.1255} = 5.18$, which is significant beyond the .001 level.

From formula (16.4) it can be demonstrated that the standard error of the biserial r is large when p_1 and p_2 are extreme splits, for example, .90–.10 and .95–.05. In such cases one of the means is computed on a small number of cases and is less reliable than the other mean. Both this statistic and the one previously discussed are thus most reliable when the point of dichotomy is somewhat close to the center of the distribution. As noted, the biserial r is an estimate of the Pearson product-moment r. But we cannot manipulate it as we did the Pearson r. For instance, there is no Z transformation for the biserial which could be used to avoid the skewed sampling distributions associated with high r's. Also, it is not used in regression equations or in the standard error of estimate. Another peculiarity of the biserial r is that sometimes it may be larger than 1 as computed. Such errors are brought about either by departures from normality in the continuous or dichotomized variable, or both.

Flanagan's abac provides an efficient method for estimating r_b (Fig. 16.2). This device is designed for use when the "upper" and "lower" groups have each been selected to contain approximately 27 percent of the total distribution (see Chapter 17).

The Triserial r

Very often we find that data are reduced to a trichotomy rather than to a dichotomy. For example, in the classification of airmen in the United States Air Force we might make a trichotomy of a sample of men on the basis of their education as follows: work beyond high school, high school graduate only, non-high school graduate. The other variable considered would be a continuous variable. Jaspen (1946) developed the following formula for the triserial r:

$$r_{tri} = \frac{y_h(\bar{X}_h) + (y_c - y_h)\bar{X}_c - y_c \bar{X}_l}{s_t [y_h^2/p_h + (y_c - y_h)^2/p_c + y_c^2/p_l]} \tag{16.5}$$

where $\bar{X}_h$, $\bar{X}_c$, $\bar{X}_l$ are the means of the three categories, high, center, and low
p_h, p_c, p_l are the proportions in the three categories
y_h, y_c, y_l are the ordinates of the normal curve cutting off $-p_h$, p_c, and p_l
s_t is the standard deviation of the entire combined distribution

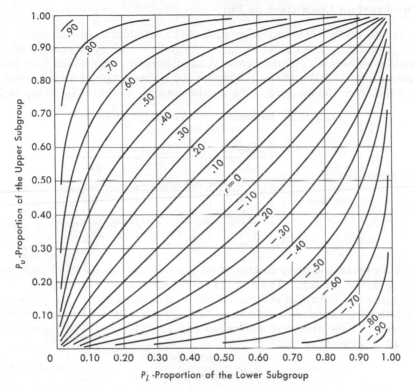

FIGURE 16.2 An abac for estimating biserial coefficients of correlation between item and total score when the sample has been restricted to the highest and lowest 27 percent of the total-score distribution. The proportion of examinees passing the item in the upper criterion group P_u is found on the ordinate, and the corresponding proportion from the lower criterion group P_l is found on the abscissa. The coefficient r_b is found at the intersection of perpendiculars at these values. Thus with P_u equal to .75 and P_l equal to .45, $r_b = .31$. (Adapted from a similar abac by J. C. Flanagan, with his permission.) Source: J. P. Guilford. *Psychometric Methods.* New York: McGraw-Hill, 1954. Reprinted by permission of the publisher.

Jenkins (1956) showed that when the numbers in both the high and low groups did not differ by more than .10, r_{tri} could be estimated as follows:

$$r_{tri} = \frac{\overline{X}_h - \overline{X}_l}{s_t} \left[\frac{(p_h + p_l)/2}{2y_{h \text{ and } l}} \right] \tag{16.6}$$

where $y_{h \text{ and } l}$ is the ordinate that cuts off the average area of p_h and p_l, and all others terms are as previously described.

Jaspen also developed formulas for 4, 5, 6, and a general number of classes. However, as the number of classes increases, the possibility that the Pearson r can be used becomes greater, especially if the assumptions related to the Pearson r are met.

The Fourfold Coefficient or Phi

The phi coefficient is used when each of the variables is a dichotomy. To illustrate this technique, let us suppose that we are making an analysis of the relation between an opinion item and an information item which have been administered to 200 students. Suppose 100 students agree with the opinion and the other 100 disagree. We set the data up as shown in Table 16.2,

TABLE 16.2. Responses of the Two Hundred Students to Test Items

	Right	Wrong	
Agree	70 a	30 b	100 k
Disagree	30 c	70 d	100 l
	100 m	100 n	200 N

with the agree and disagree groups on the side and the scores of right and wrong across the top. The number in the agree and disagree groups that answered the information item correctly and the number that answered incorrectly are entered in the cells. Note that the cells are lettered and that marginal values have been computed and given letters. The formula for the phi coefficient is

$$\Phi = \frac{(ad - bc)}{\sqrt{(k)(l)(m)(n)}} \qquad (16.7)$$

where the various letters are the frequencies as shown in Table 16.2.

Solving for these data, we have

$$\Phi = \frac{(70)(70) - (30)(30)}{\sqrt{(100)(100)(100)(100)}}$$

$$= \frac{4900 - 900}{10000}$$

$$= \frac{4000}{10000}$$

$$= .40$$

Guilford (1954) has shown that when there is an equal number in both parts of the splits, phi can be obtained by the following formula:

$$\Phi = \frac{p_u - p_l}{2\sqrt{pq}} \qquad (16.8)$$

where p_u = proportion in the agree group answering the item correctly
p_l = proportion in the disagree group answering the item correctly
p = proportion in the two groups responding correctly to the item
$q = 1 - p$

If we use this formula for these data, we have

$$\Phi = \frac{.70 - .30}{2\sqrt{(.50)(.50)}}$$

$$= \frac{.40}{2(.5)} = \frac{.40}{1} = .40$$

Guilford also presents an abac for graphic estimation of the phi coefficient when one variable has an even division of cases in two categories. This abac is presented in Fig. 16.3.

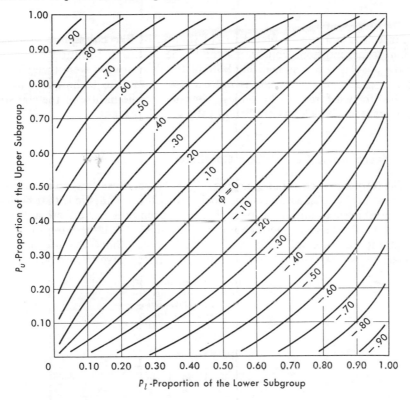

FIGURE 16.3 An abac for graphic estimates of the phi coefficient when one variable has an even division of cases in two categories. Used similarly to the abac in Fig. 16.1. Source: J. P. Guilford. *Psychometric Methods.* New York: McGraw-Hill, 1954. Reprinted by permission of the publisher.

Testing the Significance of Phi. The student has probably been struck by the similarity of equation (16.7) with the equation for chi square when data are set up into a fourfold table. The two equations are very similar, and the relationship between these two statistics can be given by

$$\chi^2 = N\Phi^2 \qquad (16.9)$$

Because of this relationship, the phi coefficient may be tested for significance by the use of chi square. For any number in two groups, we can set up the 1 percent and 5 percent values of phi and use these to evaluate the significance of the phi coefficients for the items of the test being analyzed. After obtaining the 1 percent and 5 percent values of chi square for $df = 1$ from the chi square table, we have:

$$\chi^2 = N\Phi^2 \qquad\qquad \chi^2 = N\Phi^2$$
$$6.635 = 200\Phi^2 \qquad\qquad 3.841 = 200\Phi^2$$
$$\Phi^2 = .03318 \qquad\qquad \Phi^2 = .019205$$
$$\Phi = .18 \qquad\qquad \Phi = .14$$

Since this statistic is related to chi square, it, like chi square, is based upon no assumptions concerning the shape of the distribution of scores. In the past, it was assumed that both of the dichotomies were true dichotomies. Such an assumption is not necessary, and the technique may be applied to two forced dichotomies. Because of the nature of the statistic, it favors items which have difficulty values of 50 percent.

The Tetrachoric Correlation Coefficient

The tetrachoric correlation coefficient also involves setting up data into a fourfold table. An assumption associated with this statistic is that both of the variables are continuous ones that have been both forced into a dichotomy. In the past, the tetrachoric coefficient was obtained by solving a quadratic equation of the second power for r_t. Since the use of these equations is laborious, various computing devices have been developed to

TABLE 16.3. Responses of One Hundred Individuals to a Test Item, the Data Being Arranged for the Solution of the Tetrachoric Correlation Coefficient

	Right	Wrong	
Upper 50	20 a	30 b	50
Lower 50	10 c	40 d	50
	30	70	100

aid in the computation of the statistic. The one that we shall demonstrate here is that proposed by Davidoff and Goheen (Table VIII in the Appendix).

Suppose that we have the responses of 100 individuals to a test item. A table such as that shown in Table 16.3 is set up, and the values in the various cells are tabulated. Our papers were divided into the top 50 and the bottom 50, and then the right and wrong answers for each group were counted.

Notice again that the cells are lettered in the usual fashion. Davidoff and Goheen's table (Table VIII in the Appendix) is entered with the value ad/bc, and from the table the estimation of the tetrachoric coefficient is obtained. For these data:

$$\frac{(20)(40)}{(30)(10)} = \frac{800}{300} = 2.67$$

When we refer to the tables with a value of 2.67, we find an r_t of .37. The equation solved for these data resulted in an r_t or .36. Both of these, however, are approximations, for this quadratic equation is only solved for r_t to the second power, all higher powers being ignored.

If ad is less than bc, we use the ratio bc/ad for entering the tables. The larger of the two products is always placed in the numerator. This table works best when both variables have been dichotomized on the basis of a fifty-fifty split. As a statistic r_t is less reliable than the Pearson r, but since its standard error is complicated, it will not be discussed here.

NONLINEAR RELATIONSHIPS

It frequently happens that the relationship between two sets of variables is not linear. When such a relationship occurs, the Pearson r and variations of this r as described in this chapter are inappropriate as measures of relationship. When a relationship is curvilinear, something like this happens: as one variable increases, the other may increase up to a point and then begin to decrease, as the first variable continues to increase. Examples of this were noted in the chapter on correlation. When r is used as a measure of relationship with data that are nonlinear, the r calculated is always an underestimate of the true relationship between the two variables. Sometimes this relationship is actually very high, but the resulting r approaches zero. Since it is difficult to tell whether or not data are linear by looking at them, a scatterplot should always be made. If a deviation from linearity is apparent or even suggested on the scattergram, then the Pearson r should not be used.

The correct coefficient to use when the relationship between two sets of data is curvilinear is the correlation ratio or the *eta* coefficient. We shall illustrate the computation of this coefficient, using the data in Table 16.4. These data consist of measures of 200 individuals on two scales: age and scores on an information test.

Computation of Eta

In solving for eta, we first set up a scatterplot as in Table 16.4. Here we have chronological age on the X axis and scores on the information test on the Y axis. After the tallies have been entered, values for the Y variable on the right-hand side of the scatterplot are obtained.

TABLE 16.4. Scatterplot for Scores on a General Information Test and Ages for Two Hundred Individuals

Y Axis: Scores	X Axis: Age														
	(15–19)	(20–24)	(25–29)	(30–34)	(35–39)	(40–44)	(45–49)	(50–54)	(55–59)	(60–64)	(65–69)	(70–74)	f	fy'	$f(y')^2$
85–89				1									1	16	256
80–84				1									1	15	225
75–79		2	3										2	28	392
70–74		4	3	3	1	1							9	117	1521
65–69		3	3	5	3								14	168	2016
60–64		3	3	4	5	2		1					20	220	2420
55–59			1	3	6	4	3						23	230	2300
50–54	1	1	1	4	4	3	3	3	5	2		1	25	225	2025
45–49	1	1	2	2	5	3	3	7	7	2			29	232	1856
40–44	1	2	2	3	3	2	4			2	2	3	20	140	980
35–39	1	2	1	2	2	3	3			3	2	3	22	132	792
30–34	2	2		1	1	2	2			1	1	2	11	55	275
25–29	1	3						1		2	1		10	40	160
20–24	2	2								1	1		7	21	63
15–19	2	2								1	1		4	8	16
10–14	1											1	1	1	1
5–9	0												0	0	0
f	9	15	20	23	18	30	18	15	24	11	7	10	$N = 200$	$\Sigma = 1648$	$\Sigma = 15298$
x'	0	1	2	3	4	5	6	7	8	9	10	11			

The most direct approach to the computation of eta is to define eta squared as the ratio of the sum of the squares of the "between" columns for variable Y to the total sum of squares for variable Y:

$$\eta_{yx}^2 = \frac{\Sigma y_b^2}{\Sigma y_t^2} \tag{16.10}$$

and eta is

$$\eta_{yx} = \sqrt{\frac{\Sigma y_b^2}{\Sigma y_t^2}} \tag{16.11}$$

The total sum of squares for Y is readily available from the data on the scatterplot:

$$\Sigma y_t^2 = \Sigma f(y')^2 - \frac{(\Sigma fy')^2}{N}$$

$$= 15298 - \frac{(1648)^2}{200}$$

$$= 15298 - 13579.52$$

$$= 1718.48$$

The calculation of the "between" sum of squares for Y is shown in Table 16.5. This between sum of squares is determined from the means of

TABLE 16.5. Calculation of the "Between" Sum of Squares for the Data in Table 16.4

(1) Column	(2) f_x	(3) y'	(4) $(\Sigma y')^2$	(5) $(\Sigma y')^2/f_x$
0	9	42	1764	196.00
1	15	73	5329	355.27
2	20	202	40804	2040.20
3	23	244	59536	2588.52
4	18	196	38416	2134.22
5	30	278	77284	2576.13
6	18	159	25281	1404.50
7	15	123	15129	1008.60
8	24	173	29929	1427.04
9	11	65	4225	384.09
10	7	43	1849	264.14
11	10	50	2500	240.00
	$\Sigma f_x = 200$	$\Sigma y' = 1648$		$\Sigma(\Sigma y')^2/f_x =$ 14448.71

the columns taken from the means of the entire distribution. The first column in Table 16.5 identifies the columns. It consists of x' values from the bottom of the scatterplot. Column 2 is made up of the frequencies of the various columns. In column 3, we find the sum of the y' (deviation from the arbitrary reference point for y) for the frequencies of each of the columns. Column 0 has 9 frequencies with y' values of 1, 3, 3, 4, 5, 5, 6, 7, and 8 which sum to 42. In this way, all of the values in column 3 are obtained. Each of the values in column 3 is then squared, the square placed in column 4, and then each of these squares is divided by the appropriate column frequency. These are summed, and the sum of the squares for "between" columns is found as follows:

$$\Sigma y_b{}^2 = \Sigma \left[\frac{(\Sigma y')^2}{f_x} \right] - \frac{[\Sigma(\Sigma y')]^2}{N}$$

$$= 14448.71 - \frac{(1648)^2}{200}$$

$$= 14448.71 - 13579.52$$

$$= 869.19$$

For these data,

$$\eta_{yx} = \sqrt{\frac{869.19}{1718.48}}$$

$$= \sqrt{.505784}$$

$$= .711$$

This can all be combined into one formula for eta squared

$$\eta_{yx}{}^2 = \frac{\Sigma[(\Sigma y')^2/f_x] - \{[\Sigma(\Sigma y')]^2/N\}}{\Sigma f y'^2 - [(\Sigma f y')^2/N]} \tag{16.12}$$

When we were dealing with the correlation coefficient, we noted that the correlation between X and Y was the same as that between Y and X and that only one needed to be computed. With the correlation ratio there are two coefficients, one between X and Y and the other between Y and X. We could obtain the other eta coefficient by inserting the corresponding values for x in equation (16.12).

Significance of the Correlation Ratio

The significance of the correlation ratio may be evaluated by means of the F test, in which F is the ratio of the "between" mean square divided by the "within" mean square. The mean square between columns is obtained by dividing the sum of the squares for the "between" columns by the number of columns in the scatterplot, minus one.

$$\frac{869.19}{c - 1} = \frac{869.19}{11} = 79.02$$

The "within" sum of squares is obtained as follows:

$$\Sigma y_w{}^2 = \Sigma y_t{}^2 - \Sigma y_b{}^2$$

$$= 1718.48 - 79.02$$

$$= 1639.46$$

The mean square for the "within" columns is obtained by dividing the sum of the squares for "within" columns by the number of pairs in the sample less the number of columns.

$$\frac{1639.46}{N - c} = \frac{1639.46}{200 - 12} = \frac{1639.46}{188} = 8.72$$

Then the F ratio is computed,

$$F = \frac{79.02}{8.72}$$

$$= 9.06$$

This F is interpreted by going into the F table with $(c - 1)$ degrees of freedom for the "between" mean square and $(N - c)$ degrees of freedom for the "within" mean square. For these data, these degrees of freedom are 11 and 188. For this number of degrees of freedom, the obtained F is shown to be significant beyond the 1 percent point, and hence the correlation ratio computed is highly significant.

Summary

If the data in a scatterplot are linear in their relationship, the value of eta and the Pearson r computed for these data would be identical. If the data are curvilinear, eta is larger than r; the discrepancy between the two is related to the size of the departure from linearity. *Eta has no sign.* An inspection of a scatterplot will show that in some parts of the range the relationship between the two variables is positive and at other parts negative. Eta then only measures the degree of the relationship. Eta is also affected by the number of columns and the frequencies within the columns. These should be large enough to give the means of the various columns stability.

TWO SPECIAL CORRELATION COEFFICIENTS

We shall conclude this section with brief discussions of correlation methods that involve more than two variables, the partial r and the multiple correlation coefficient (R).

The Partial r

It frequently happens that the relationship between two variables is influenced by a third variable. For example, suppose that we have the relationship between intelligence test scores and arithmetic grades for a set of students and also the correlation of these same intelligence scores with grades in English. In addition, we have the relationship between the arithmetic grades and the English grades.   Both of these school subjects are related to intelligence test scores, and they seem to be related to each other.   Is this last relationship a true one, or is it merely the effects of these two variables being related to the common one of intelligence?   With the partial correlation coefficient it is possible to control these effects of intelligence or to "partial them out."   We might also ask what is the relationship between English grades and arithmetic grades with the effect of intelligence partialed out.   A situation like this is referred to as a partial r of the first order based upon three zero-order r's.   The general formula for this partial-order r is:

$$r_{12.3} = \frac{r_{12} - (r_{13}r_{23})}{\sqrt{(1 - r_{13}{}^2)(1 - r_{23}{}^2)}} \qquad (16.13)$$

We would read $r_{12.3}$ as the correlation between variables one and two with the effects of variable three partialed out.   Similarly, it is possible to write a comparable equation for $r_{13.2}$ and $r_{23.1}$.

Second-order partials are those in which the relationship between two variables is computed with the effects of two other variables partialed out. Since these are rarely used, they will not be discussed here.

Suppose that we have the following three variables:

1 = chronological age

2 = weight

3 = scores on an arithmetic test

For several hundred students, we compute the correlations among three variables and obtain the following:

$$r_{12} = .80$$

$$r_{23} = .50$$

$$r_{13} = .60$$

From this we see that we have a correlation between weight and arithmetic which, with a sample of this size, is significant.   Suppose that we investigate the relationship between weight and scores on arithmetic test with the effects of chronological age partialed out.

$$
\begin{aligned}
r_{23.1} &= \frac{r_{23} - (r_{12})(r_{13})}{\sqrt{(1 - r_{12}^2)(1 - r_{13}^2)}} \\
&= \frac{.50 - (.80)(.60)}{\sqrt{(1 - .80^2)(1 - .60^2)}} \\
&= \frac{.50 - .48}{\sqrt{(.36)(.64)}} \\
&= \frac{.02}{.48} \\
&= .04
\end{aligned}
$$

Now we see that with the effects of chronological age removed, there is no significant relationship between weight and scores on an arithmetic test. Since the partial r is a Pearson r, it may be treated as such.   The tests for significance are similar.

Multiple Correlation

In an earlier chapter, we learned how to make predictions on one variable from another.   For example, we learned how to predict grade point averages on the basis of intelligence test scores.   It was suggested that prediction can usually be made more accurate if the predictors were increased in number.   For example, we may be able to do a better job of predicting freshman grade point averages if we use, in addition to the usual intelligence test, other predictors such as scores on a reading test, high-school rank, scores on a mathematics test, and so forth.   Prediction efficiency usually increases up to the addition of the fourth or fifth predictor, but after that the slight gains in predictive ability are not worth the amount of time required to include them.

In this book we are going to take up multiple correlation in its simplest form, the relationship between one variable and a combination of two other variables.   Suppose that we have the following three coefficients based upon three variables for a large group of university freshmen:

$$\text{Variable } 1 = \text{grade}$$
$$\text{Variable } 2 = \text{scores on the } \textit{Ohio State}$$
$$\textit{Psychological Examination}$$
$$\text{Variable } 3 = \text{scores on the } \textit{Cooperative}$$
$$\textit{Mathematics Test}$$
$$r_{12} = .50$$
$$r_{13} = .60$$
$$r_{23} = .40$$

We want to compute the multiple correlation coefficient between freshmen grades and the combined effects of the two tests.   The formula follows:

$$R_{1.23} = \sqrt{\frac{r_{12}^2 + r_{13}^2 - (2r_{12}r_{13}r_{23})}{1 - r_{23}^2}} \qquad (16.14)$$

$$= \sqrt{\frac{.50^2 + .60^2 - (2)(.50)(.60)(.40)}{1 - .40^2}}$$

$$= \sqrt{\frac{.25 + .36 - .24}{.84}}$$

$$= \sqrt{\frac{.37}{.84}}$$

$$= \sqrt{.4405}$$

$$= .66$$

The multiple R may be used in the same manner as the zero-order r. The standard error of estimate can be computed.

$$s_{R_{1.23}} = s_1\sqrt{1 - R^2} \qquad (16.15)$$

This standard error of estimate is interpreted in the same manner as before. It is also possible to set up an index of forecasting efficiency on the basis of the equation $R^2 + K^2 = 1$. Computing charts or abacs have been developed from which the multiple R can be easily read when only three variables are concerned; for an example, see Lord (1955).

NONPARAMETRIC CORRELATIONAL TECHNIQUES

Many times, data are collected in the form of ranks. Sometimes one variable may be in this form and the other comprised of measurement data. There are other times when measurement data are reduced to ranks, for example, when samples are small and when the assumptions for parametric statistics cannot be met. Various coefficients can be applied to such data, such as the Spearman rank-order correlation coefficient and Kendall's tau and his coefficient of concordance.

Spearman Rank-Order Correlation Coefficient (Rho)

This is the most widely used of the rank correlational methods. It is particularly well-suited to situations where the number of cases is 25 to 30 or less. It is also much easier and faster to compute than the Pearson r.

To illustrate the computation of the rank-order correlation coefficient, we shall use the data in Table 16.6. In this table the scores of 17 boys on the *Minnesota Paper Form Board* and on the *Otis Self-Administering Test of Mental Ability* are given. To obtain the coefficient, we go through the following steps:

1. Take the first column of scores (*Minnesota Paper Form Board*) and rank them, giving the high score a rank of 1. Since these scores have been arranged from high to low this is easy. However, notice that we have two individuals tied with scores of 49. These two 49's occupy ranks 4 and 5. These two ranks are averaged and both individuals are assigned this average rank which in this case is 4.5. Too many such ties will affect the size of the correlation coefficient; but usually there are not enough to justify the formulas that are available to correct these ties.

2. Rank the second set of scores, again assigning the rank of 1 to the highest score.

3. Obtain the difference between the two sets of ranks. The sign of this difference is of no importance as these differences are squared in the next operation.

4. Square each of these differences and sum this column of squares.

TABLE 16.6. Calculation of the Spearman Rank-Order
Correlation Coefficient

Individual	Minn. Paper Form Board	Otis Self-Administering Test	R_1	R_2	D	D^2
1	60	60	1	2	1	1
2	54	68	2	1	1	1
3	53	40	3	11.5	8.5	72.25
4	49	52	4.5	3	1.5	2.25
5	49	51	4.5	4.5	0	0
6	47	38	6	14	8	64
7	46	51	7	4.5	2.5	6.25
8	45	32	9	17	8	64
9	45	39	9	13	4	16
10	45	41	9	10	1	1
11	43	50	11	6	5	25
12	41	48	12	7.5	4.5	20.25
13	39	36	13	16	3	9
14	38	48	14	7.5	6.5	42.25
15	32	40	15.5	11.5	4	16
16	32	46	15.5	9	6.5	42.25
17	30	37	17	15	2	4

$$\Sigma = 386.50$$

5. Solve for the rank-order correlation coefficient by the use of the
following equation:

$$\rho = 1 - \frac{6\Sigma D^2}{N(N^2 - 1)} \tag{16.16}$$

where N = the number of pairs

ρ = rho, the rank-order correlation coefficient

For this problem,

$$\rho = 1 - \frac{6(386.5)}{17(289 - 1)}$$

$$= 1 - \frac{2319.0}{4896}$$

$$= 1 - .47$$

$$= .53$$

Interpretation of Rho. Rho is a product-moment correlation coefficient
for ranked data. For all practical purposes, it may be interpreted the same
as r. When N is small, special tables are available for testing the significance
of rho. If the size of the sample is over 10, the t test can be made, using the
following formula:

$$t = \frac{\rho}{\sqrt{1 - \rho^2}} \sqrt{N - 2} \tag{16.17}$$

This is the same formula used for testing the significance of an r. The
student may recall that a table can be used in lieu of this formula for r.

The same table may be used in testing the significance of rho when the number of pairs is 20–25 and above.

Summary.   In rho we have a coefficient that makes a good substitute for *r* when the number of cases is small.   Rho is almost useless when N is large, for by the time that all the data are ranked, a Pearson *r* could have been computed by the scattergram or some other method.   This statistic is interpreted in the same manner as *r* and has approximately the same size standard error.

Kendall's Tau-Correlation Between Ranks

Kendall's tau, T, can be applied wherever the Spearman rank-order coefficient is applicable.   As can be seen below, it is somewhat harder to compute than rho, but it has certain advantages over rho.   To illustrate, we shall use the data in Table 16.6.   We proceed as follows:

1.   Both columns of scores are ranked as previously.   For convenience, we copy these ranks below.

R_1 1, 2, 3,   4.5, 4.5, 6, 7,   9, 9, 9, 11, 12,   13, 14,   15.5, 15.5, 17
R_2 2, 1, 11.5, 3,   4.5, 14, 4.5, 17, 13, 10, 6, 7.5, 16, 7.5, 11.5, 9,   15

2.   We take the first rank in R_2, which is 2.   We count the number of ranks higher than this and the number of ranks lower than this that appear to the right of the 2.   We find this to be 15 and 1.   Then we take the second value in R_2, which is 1.   To the right this has 15 ranks higher than itself and none lower.   Then taking the third value, 11.5, we find 5 higher and 8 lower.   The fourth value 3, has 13 higher and no lower ranks to the right. However, this is paired with a tie in the natural order of R_1.   Such ties are handled by not counting the ranks to the right associated with these ties. So in this case, we count 12 ranks higher and none lower than 3.   We continue in this fashion across the series of ranks.   We can summarize this as follows:

$$S = (15 - 1) + (15 - 0) + (5 - 8) + (12 - 0) + (11 - 0)$$
$$+ (3 - 8) + (10 - 0) + (0 - 7) + (2 - 5) + (3 - 4) + (6 - 0)$$
$$+ (4 - 0) + (0 - 4) + (3 - 0) + (1 - 0) + (1 - 0) = 54$$

These are summed, giving S, which is substituted in the following formula for tau:

$$T = \frac{2S}{N(N - 1)} \tag{16.18}$$

$$= \frac{2(54)}{17(17 - 1)}$$

$$= \frac{108}{272}$$

$$= .397$$

The significance of tau may be computed by:

$$z = \frac{T}{s_T} = \frac{T}{\sqrt{2(2N + 5)/[9N(N - 1)]}} \tag{16.19}$$

where $N \geq 10$. When $N < 10$ tables for testing the significance of tau will be found in Siegel (1956). While rho and tau differ in size, they are of equal power, as a null hypothesis about rho or tau for the same data will be rejected at the same level of significance if there is a relationship between the two variables being correlated. Both rho and tau for the data of Table 16.7 are significant at the .05 level. Siegel (1956) notes that the effects of ties were slight. If the S above were obtained by not taking the ties into account, the result would be about the same.

Tau can be used to measure partial correlation by the formula:

$$T_{12.3} = \frac{T_{12} - (T_{13})(T_{23})}{\sqrt{(1 - T_{13}^2)(1 - T_{23}^2)}} \tag{16.20}$$

The above formula is similar to (16.13). This is interpreted like the partial r. The sampling distribution of this statistic is unknown.

Kendall's Coefficient of Concordance, W

If we wish to determine the relationship among three or more sets of ranks, one rank could be selected and a Spearman rho coefficient computed between it and all of the others, and this process could then be continued until a rho coefficient has been obtained between each set of two ranks. Then these rho's could be averaged for an overall measure of relationship.

Kendall, though, has developed a technique and a statistic which makes all of this unnecessary. Suppose that five judges (m) rank the projects of ten individuals (N) in a judging contest, and we wish to determine the overall relationship among the ratings of the five judges. The rankings of these judges have been set up in Table 16.7. First the rankings by the five judges of each of the projects are summed and the sums appear in column 3. Column 3 is summed to give the total sum of the ranks. This can be checked for the total sum of the ranks, as follows:

$$\text{Total sum of ranks} = \frac{mN(N + 1)}{2} \tag{16.21}$$

$$= \frac{(5)(10)(11)}{2} = 275$$

If there were no relationship among the ranks, we should expect the sum of the ranks for each row to be equal. For this case the sum of each would be the average sum of ranks or 275/10 which equals 27.5. We next obtain the difference of the sum of the ranks of each row from this mean and then square these differences. Then these squares are summed. This work appears in columns 4 and 5 of Table 16.7.

TABLE 16.7. Calculation of the Coefficient of Concordance, the Data Consisting of the Ranking of Ten Projects by Five Judges

(1)	(2)					(3)	(4)	(5)
	Judges' Ranks					Sum of		
Individual Project	1	2	3	4	5	Ranks	D	D^2
1	2	1	2	3	4	12	15.5	240.25
2	1	3	1	2	2	9	18.5	342.25
3	3	4	4	1	3	15	12.5	156.25
4	5	5	5	5	1	21	6.5	42.25
5	4	2	6	7	6	25	2.5	6.25
6	7	8	3	4	7	29	1.5	2.25
7	6	6	8	6	5	31	3.5	12.25
8	8	7	7	8	9	39	11.5	132.25
9	9	10	10	9	8	46	18.5	342.25
10	10	9	9	10	10	48	20.5	420.25
						$\Sigma = 275$		$\Sigma = 1696.50$

To compute W, we use the following formula:

$$W = \frac{12 \Sigma D^2}{m^2(N)(N^2 - 1)} \tag{16.22}$$

$$= \frac{12(1696.5)}{(25)(10)(100 - 1)}$$

$$= .82$$

Interpretation of W. The size of this coefficient of concordance indicates that there is high agreement among these five judges in the ranking of the ten projects. Perfect agreement is indicated by a $W = 1$ and lack of agreement by a $W = 0$. The significance of a coefficient of concordance may be tested by the use of tables developed by Kendall. For $m = 5$ and $N = 10$, we find that the W computed here is highly significant (see Table XIII, in the Appendix).

The Coefficient of Contingency

Like chi square, this statistic can be used with data from nominal or higher order scales. The contingency coefficient, C, does not have 1 as an upper limit, the upper limit being related to the number of categories. For a table made up of an equal number of columns and rows, k by k, the upper limit is $\sqrt{(k - 1)/k}$. Thus for a 3 × 3 table the upper limit is $\sqrt{2/3} = .82$, for a 4 × 4 table, $\sqrt{3/4} = .87$, etc. When the number of columns and rows differ as in 3 × 4, the upper limit follows that of the smaller number.

The contingency coefficient is obtained by the following formula:

$$C = \sqrt{\frac{\chi^2}{N + \chi^2}} \tag{16.23}$$

TABLE 16.8. The Use of the Contingency Coefficient

	Succeed	Condition	Fail	
Some college	20 ⑱	10 ⑧	10 ⑭	40
High school graduate	60 ㊺	10 ⑳	30 ㉟	100
Some or no high school	10 ㉗	20 ②	30 ㉑	60
	90	40	70	200

The data in Table 16.8 illustrate the use of this coefficient. Here a group of 200 young men are divided into three groups on the basis of the amount of education attained. Then their attainment in a course of study is tabled against educational achievement. The expected frequencies are obtained using the cell margins, and then chi square is computed. The expected frequencies are shown in circles in the lower left corner of each square.

O	E	$O - E$	$(O - E)^2$	$(O - E)^2/E$
20	18	2	4	.222
60	45	15	225	5.000
10	27	17	289	10.704
10	8	2	4	.500
10	20	10	100	5.000
20	12	8	64	5.333
10	14	4	16	1.143
30	35	5	25	.714
30	21	9	81	3.857
$\Sigma = 200$	200			$\chi^2 = 32.473$

This χ with $df = 4$ is significant beyond the .001 level.
Then

$$C = \sqrt{\frac{32.473}{200 + 32.466}}$$

$$= \sqrt{\frac{32.473}{232466}}$$

$$= .37$$

This value is not directly comparable to r, rho, tau, or any other correlation coefficient. Nor should C's computed from unlike tables be directly compared. Also, C has no sign; however, if direction is important in any relationship, its sign can be determined by an inspection of the data.

However, as a measure of the relationship between two sets of attributes, C is easy to compute, requires that no assumption be made about the population distribution, and can be applied to data that are normal, or skewed, continuous or discrete, and nominal or ordinal, for example.

The quickest way to test the significance of C is to test the significance of χ^2. If the latter is significant, so is C.

The major facts about the various correlation coefficients have been summarized in Table 16.9.

TABLE 16.9.   Summary of the Major Correlation Coefficients

		Variables	
Coefficient	Symbol	X	Y
Pearson product moment	r	Continuous	Continuous
Point biserial	r_{pb}	Continuous	True dichotomy
Biserial	r_b	Continuous	Continuous, but forced into a dichotomy
Tetrachoric	r_t	Continuous, but forced into a dichotomy	Continuous, but forced into a dichotomy
Phi or fourfold	Φ	True dichotomy	True dichotomy (see text)
Correlation ratio	η (eta)	Continuous	Continuous
Spearman rank order	ρ (rho)	Data in ranks or capable of being ranked	Same as for X
Kendall's coefficient of concordance	W	Used with three or more sets of ranks	
Kendall's tau	T	Data in ranks or capable of being ranked	
Contingency coefficient	C	Data may be normal, skewed, continuous, discrete, nominal, ordered, on in other forms	

Exercises

1. A scale to measure attitudes toward Russia is being constructed. One of the items is " Do you think that the Russian people like their government?" The scale is pretested on a sample of 200. The distribution of "Yes" and "No" responses with total score on the scale is as follows:

Total Scores	Yes	No
95–99	1	0
90–94	6	0
85–89	18	1
80–84	22	1
75–79	31	3
70–74	20	5
65–69	18	9
60–64	12	13

Total Scores (cont.)	Yes	No
55–59	6	10
50–54	4	8
45–49	1	5
40–44	0	3
35–39	1	0
30–34	0	1
25–29	0	1
	140	60

(a) Compute the point-biserial r between the item and the total score.

(b) Test the r_{pb} for significance.

2. With the data in Problem 1 above, compute the biserial r using formula (16.3).

3. Compute the phi coefficient for the following data:

	Right	Wrong
Upper	65	35
Lower	25	75

Is this a significant phi at the 5 percent level?

4. What is the tetrachoric r for the data in Problem 3?

5. Seven instructors are rated by freshmen and sophomore students on "clarity of presentation." The results are tabulated in this manner:

Instructor	Freshmen	Sophomores
1	44	58
2	39	42
3	36	18
4	35	22
5	33	31
6	29	38
7	22	38

What is the Spearman rho for these data?

6. Compute Kendall's tau for the above data.

7. Four judges (parole board members) rank eight convicts on "parole readiness."

	Judges			
Convict	(1)	(2)	(3)	(4)
1	1	1	1	1
2	2	4	3	2
3	3	3	2	4
4	4	2	4	3
5	5	6	5	5
6	6	5	6	7
7	7	7	8	6
8	8	8	7	8

(a) By using the coefficient of concordance, indicate the degree of consistency of the judges?

(b) Is the relationship statistically significant at the 1 percent level?

8. Compute η_{xy} for the data in Table 16.7. Is this coefficient significant at the 5 percent level?

9. In a research study on learning in arithmetic, a research worker studies the relation between spatial ability scores as well as between numerical ability scores. He produced the following correlations

	Spatial Ability	Numerical Ability	Concept Learning
Spatial ability	—	.522	.496
Numerical ability		—	.254
Concept learning			—

(a) What is the correlation between concept learning and spatial ability with the effects of numerical ability removed?

(b) What is the correlation between concept learning and numerical ability with the effects of spatial ability partialed out?

10. What is the multiple R between concept learning and the combined effects of spatial and numerical scores?

11. Use the data in Problem 8 at the end of Chapter 7 to calculate the Spearman rank-order correlations among the various sets of scores.

17

RELIABILITY, VALIDITY
AND ITEM ANALYSIS

One of the major uses of correlation coefficients is in the computation of reliability, validity, and item statistics. In this chapter, we shall first consider a bit of measurement theory, then the various types of reliability coefficients, the standard error of measurement, the statistical aspects of validity, and finally a brief survey of item analysis techniques.

MEASUREMENT THEORY

In modern educational and psychological measurement, each individual score or measurement is considered as being made up of two parts, a true score component and an error score component. This can be expressed as

$$X = X_t + X_e \qquad (17.1)$$

where X = any raw score or unit of measurement
X_t = true score component
X_e = error score component

The error component, or error score as it is sometimes called, is held to be random. Suppose that you were to weigh a number of objects. At times there would be slight errors in the way that you read the scale. These deviations would not always be in the same direction. Sometimes your readings would be too high and sometimes they would be too low. In the long run, they would tend to cancel out, and the mean of all of these errors of measurement would be zero. Such variations as these are described as *random* errors and their mean is always zero. But suppose that something was operating in our method or in our apparatus which caused us always to have an error which was on the high side. Errors such as these are described as *systematic*. Their mean would not be zero.

Whenever we give a test, there are many factors which enter into the error component of an individual's score.   Some of these are guessing, misreading of an item, daily fluctuations in an individual's health and emotional status, and many physical factors.   The size of this error component is related to the reliability of any measuring device.   The smaller the error component or error score, the more reliable the measuring instrument.   In its simplest form, reliability means consistency.   A reliable instrument leads to measurement units which are fairly similar from time to time.

Since any score can be broken into two parts, a true component and an error component, the variance of a test can also be so treated.   We can write this as follows:

$$s^2 = s_t^2 + s_e^2 \qquad (17.2)$$

which reads that the variance of a test is made up of the variance associated with true scores (true variance) and the variance associated with error scores (error variance).   It is assumed that the correlation between X_t and X_e is equal to zero.

Next we shall divide equation (17.2) through by a constant, s^2,

$$\frac{s^2}{s^2} = \frac{s_t^2}{s^2} + \frac{s_e^2}{s^2} = 1 \qquad (17.3)$$

and by transposing $\dfrac{s_t^2}{s^2} = 1 - \dfrac{s_e^2}{s^2}$

In modern test theory, reliability is defined as that part of the variance which is true variance, namely,

$$r_{tt} = \frac{s_t^2}{s^2} \qquad (17.4)$$

or by substituting an identity for the right-hand part of equation (17.4), we have

$$r_{tt} = 1 - \frac{s_e^2}{s^2} \qquad (17.5)$$

which reads that the reliability is 1 minus that part of the total variance which is error variance.

METHODS OF COMPUTING RELIABILITY COEFFICIENTS

There are a number of techniques used in the computation of reliability coefficients.   In this book we shall limit ourselves to a consideration of the more basic and simple techniques which are the methods of test-retest, parallel forms, split-halves, and Kuder-Richardson Formula No. 20.

Test-Retest Method

With this technique, a test is administered and then, at a later date, the same test is readministered to the same individuals. A Pearson product-moment correlation coefficient is computed between the two sets of scores. There are various conditions which affect this technique, limiting its effectiveness. The length of the time between the two administrations of the test is important in determining the size of the reliability coefficient. In general, the longer the time between the two administrations of the test, the lower the correlation. The research literature contains many studies involving intelligence tests, tests of special abilities, and interest inventories which bear this out. If the period between the administrations is very short, such as the second test immediately following the first, individuals may remember their answers and put the same responses down the second time without making a new effort to react to the test item. Such behavior tends to make reliability coefficients artificially high. When the period between testings is short, memory may be an important factor affecting the results. As the period increases in length, learning, maturation, senescence, and many other variables may enter the situation to lower the correlation coefficient. At the present time, this method is infrequently used when determining the reliability of paper-and-pencil tests. Coefficients computed by this method are frequently called *coefficients of stability*.

Parallel Forms Method

This technique is also referred to as the method of equivalent forms. With this technique, we administer form A to a group of individuals and follow this immediately or fairly soon with form B of the same test. These two forms of the same test are said to be parallel or equivalent, because they are made up of the same types of items covering the same materials; they have the same means and variances; and if one form correlates to a certain extent with some other measure, then the other form correlates to the same degree.

As in the previously discussed method, a Pearson product-moment correlation coefficient is computed between the two sets of scores. This coefficient is sometimes referred to as a *coefficient of equivalence*. This method is widely used at the present time. It may be called the technique with the most universal applicability. When other methods cannot be used, we can usually fall back upon this one. This is especially true when we wish to determine the reliability of speed tests. The memory factor which was important with the test-retest method is ruled out here. But such factors as learning, growth, and change are still present, and here again, the longer the period between the two test administrations, the lower the reliability coefficient tends to be.

The Split-Half Method

An advantage of this method is that only one test is needed for the computation of the reliability coefficient. The test papers are scored so that from every single paper we have two scores. This is usually done by counting the number of odd-numbered items answered correctly and the number of even-numbered items answered correctly. Sometimes other splits are made, such as items 1 and 2 go into the first score, 3 and 4 into the second score, and 5 and 6 into the first score. Almost any split will be acceptable, except one taking the first half of the items against the second half; because tests are usually made with the easier items first and because students tend to complete the first half of a test and not the second, a division of this sort will result in two tests of a different nature.

Each paper now has an even and an odd score on it, or two other types of scores depending on the type of split made. Again a Pearson product-moment correlation coefficient is computed between the two sets of scores. A reliability coefficient of this type is often called a *coefficient of internal consistency*.

It so happens that the reliability of a test is directly related to the length of the test. When we scored our test on an odd-even basis, we actually cut the length of our original test in half. The reliability coefficient which we have computed is then the equivalent of one for a test of half of the size of our original test. We make a correction for this effect by using what is known as the Spearman-Brown formula as follows:

$$r_{tt} = \frac{2r_{oe}}{1 + r_{oe}} \qquad (17.6)$$

where r_{tt} = the reliability of the original test

$\quad r_{oe}$ = the reliability coefficient obtained by correlating the scores on the odd items with the scores of the even items

Suppose that we have a 100-item test. As a result of computing the correlation coefficient between the odd scores and the even scores, we obtain a coefficient of .84 (r_{oe} = .84). By substitution, we find:

$$r_{tt} = \frac{2(.84)}{1 + .84}$$

$$= \frac{1.68}{1.84}$$

$$= .91$$

This Spearman-Brown formula is frequently referred to as the Spearman-Brown prophecy formula, as it is used to predict reliability coefficients. For example, suppose we have a 20-item test, and we know its reliability. By the use of this formula we can predict what the reliability of this test would be if 60 additional similar items were added. Or suppose that we have a 100-item test of known reliability, and because of time limitations, we wish to reduce it to a 50-item test. Again, by the use of this Spearman-Brown formula we can estimate the reliability of this shortened test. In its general form, the Spearman-Brown prophecy formula is written as follows:

$$r_{tt} = \frac{N'r}{1 + (N' - 1)r} \qquad (17.7)$$

where N' = the number of times the test is longer or shorter than the original test

r = the reliability of the test which is being lengthened or shortened

Here is how this formula is used. Suppose that we have a 20-item test with a reliability coefficient of .60. We wish to know what the reliability of this test would be if 80 similar items were added to make it a 100-item test. N' for this problem is 5 as the new test is five times the length of the original one. The solution is

$$r_{tt} = \frac{5(.60)}{1 + (4).60}$$

$$= \frac{3.00}{1 + 2.40}$$

$$= \frac{3.00}{3.40} = .88$$

To illustrate further, suppose that we have a 110-item test, the length of which is reduced to 55 items. The reliability of the original test is .88. What is the reliability of the shortened test? In this case N' is .5 as the new test is one-half the length of the original one. The solution follows:

$$r_{tt} = \frac{(.5)(.88)}{1 + (.5 - 1)(.88)}$$

$$= \frac{.44}{1 + (-.5)(.88)}$$

$$= \frac{.44}{1 + (-.44)}$$

$$= \frac{.44}{.56} = .786$$

Results obtained by the use of this formula agree very well with those obtained when tests are changed in length, and the coefficient is computed for the new test.

Internal consistency coefficients are very suitable for use in computing the reliability of academic tests. However, they must not be used with tests in which speed is an important factor. A speed test is defined as one in which the items are so easy that, given enough time, there is no reason why any individual cannot respond correctly to all of the items. On such a test, the scores on the odd-numbered items are likely to be very similar to those obtained from the even-numbered ones, and hence the resulting correlation coefficient will be exaggerated.

Kuder-Richardson Formula No. 20

This technique also yields a *coefficient of internal consistency* and as such has some of the limitations of the split-half method. If an item analysis has been made for a test (this will be discussed later in this chapter), the Kuder-Richardson formula is easily applied to the data to obtain the reliability coefficient. One of the outcomes of an item analysis is a difficulty measure for each item on the test. Difficulty is defined as the proportion or percentage of those responding to an item who answered it correctly. The symbol p is used to represent difficulty. An item with $p = .89$ was answered correctly by 89 percent of those who responded to it.

In working a Kuder-Richardson solution, we first set up a worksheet like that shown below. The first column consists of the number of the item.

(1) Item	(2) p	(3) q $(1 - p)$	(4) pq
1	.60	.40	.2400
2	.30	.70	.2100
3	.71	.29	.2059
etc.			
			$\Sigma pq =$

In the second column the difficulty value (p) of the item is recorded from the item analysis work. The third column is labeled q which always means $1 - p$. In all statistical work, $p + q = 1$. The last column is labeled pq, which is the product of columns 2 and 3. This column should be carried to four decimal places. Then this last column is summed.

The formula for Kuder-Richardson No. 20 is

$$r_{tt} = \frac{k}{k - 1} \left[1 - \frac{\Sigma pq}{s^2} \right] \tag{17.8}$$

where k = number of items on the test
       s^2 = the variance of the test
      pq = the quantity obtained from the worksheet

The Size of Reliability Coefficients

In general, reliability coefficients of well-made standardized tests tend to be high, .90 or above. There is no hard and fast rule that says that any reliability has to be of a certain size before any test or measuring instrument can be useful. Today we look upon reliability as a relative thing, and there are certain areas and certain techniques where reliability coefficients fall well below this .90, and the techniques are still used and found to be very useful. Rating scales are examples of this.

As noted above, the length of any test influences the size of the reliability coefficient for that instrument.   Since reliability coefficients are correlation coefficients, they too are greatly affected by the range of scores in the sample on which the reliability correlation is computed.   The more homogeneous the sample, the lower the reliability coefficient.   The size of the reliability coefficient will differ when computations are based upon different samples. Thus no test has a single, characteristic reliability coefficient.

STANDARD ERROR OF MEASUREMENT

Rather than use correlation coefficients to express the reliability of a test, some prefer to use a statistic called the standard error of measurement. This, unlike the reliability coefficient, is not affected by the range of scores of the sample tested.   It tends to be about the same for samples with different variances.   This standard error of measurement is the standard deviation of a sample of scores of an individual about his true score.   Suppose that it were possible to administer the same test repeatedly to the same individual, without any changes occurring in the individual.   These scores would be different.   If we took the mean of all of them, we could use this as an estimate of the individual's true score, and the standard deviation of these scores about this true score would be referred to as the standard error of measurement.

It is not reasonable to readminister the same test over and over again to the same individual; so the best that we can do is estimate the standard error of measurement.   This is done by the following formula:

$$s_e = s\sqrt{1 - r_{tt}} \tag{17.9}$$

where s_e = standard error of measurement
s = standard deviation of the test
r_{tt} = reliability of the test

This equation is very easily derived from equation (17.5) in the following manner:

$$r_{tt} = 1 - \frac{s_e^2}{s^2}$$

First, clear fractions and multiply all terms by s^2

$$r_{tt}s^2 = s^2 - s_e^2$$

Then transpose terms $\qquad s_e^2 = s^2 - r_{tt}s^2$

and factor the right-hand side of the equation.

$$s_e^2 = s^2(1 - r_{tt})$$

By taking the square root of both sides

$$s_e = s\sqrt{1 - r_{tt}}$$

Lord (1959) has shown that a good estimate of the standard error of measurement may be obtained directly by the use of the following formula:

$$s_e = .432\sqrt{k} \qquad (17.10)$$

where k is the number of items on the test.

Saupe (1961) applied this formula of Lord's to the Kuder-Richardson Formula No. 20, and reduced the latter to

$$r_{tt} = \frac{k}{k-1}\left[1 - \frac{.19k}{s^2}\right] \qquad (17.11)$$

Interpretation of the Standard Error of Measurement

Suppose that we administer a test with a reliability of .91 to a group. We find that the standard deviation is 11. A student obtains a score of 77 on this test. First, we calculate the standard error of measurement

$$s_e = s\sqrt{1 - r_{tt}}$$
$$= 11\sqrt{1 - .91}$$
$$= 11\sqrt{.09}$$
$$= 11(.3)$$
$$= 3.3$$

Since this standard error of measurement is a standard deviation, it is interpreted as such. We can now make the statement that the chances are two out of three that this individual's obtained score of 77 is not more than 3.3 units from his true score. Or we could make other statements, such as that the chances are 95 in 100 that this obtained score is not more than 6.6 units from his true score, and finally that the chances are 99 in 100 that this obtained score is not more than 9.9 units from his true score. Each of these probability statements is based upon the different areas cut off when various standard deviation units are measured from the mean. In this case the true score is taken as the mean.

The smaller this standard error of measurement, the more reliable the test and the more confidence that we can place in any score obtained by using the test. An inspection of equation (17.9) shows that if the test were perfectly reliable, that is, the reliability coefficient was equal to 1, the right-hand part of the equation would reduce to 0, and there would be no standard error of measurement. A perfectly reliable instrument would always yield true scores.

VALIDITY

At the present time, three general types of validity are used in gathering validity information about tests. These are content, construct, and criterion, the latter being of two kinds, predictive and concurrent.

Content Validity

Content validity is a nonstatistical type of validity that is usually associated with achievement tests. When a test is so constructed that it adequately covers both the content and the objectives of a course or part of a course of learning, it is said to have content validity. An adequate job of sampling items on the part of the test constructor is usually enough to assure that a test has content validity.

Construct Validity

Construct validity is determined by investigating the psychological qualities, traits, or factors measured by a test. Factorial validity is an example of this. Test constructors who build tests to measure abilities and adjustment have demonstrated that the traits studied can be reduced to statistical elements called factors. For example, mental ability has been reduced to factors that have been called verbal, numerical, spatial, and memory. A test that correlates significantly with such factors as these would be said to have factorial validity, a type of construct validity. Construct validity can be logical as well as statistical. For example, it might be hypothesized that differences in academic achievement are related to a construct called study-habit skills, other things being equal. If a study habits inventory is made and administered, construct validity is demonstrated if the inventory scores are correlated with other evidence of study habits.

Predictive Validity

This is a very common type of validity, and it is primarily statistical. It is the correlation between a set of test scores or some other predictor with an external measure. This external measure is referred to as a criterion. For example, we validate intelligence tests by obtaining a set of test scores on a group such as college freshmen, and then we later obtain the grade point averages that these freshmen made during their first semester of college. A correlation coefficient is then run between our two sets of measurements. In this illustration the grade point averages are the criterion. Some other variables used as criteria are ratings of performance, ratings of adjustment, units produced in a certain period of time, amount of sales, and number of errors made.

These validity coefficients tend to be much lower than reliability coefficients. An examination of the research over the years will show that they tend to fall within the band of .40–.60, with a median value of about .50. A little reflection will show why this is so. If we consider the relationship between intelligence test scores and grades, we know that there is more involved than intelligence in obtaining grades. We are overlooking such factors as motivation and interests of the student, grading practices of the teachers, emotional adjustment, health of the student, time available for study, and many other factors, all of which influence the grades that a student obtains. An examination of the intelligence test scores for any classroom will show that there are one or two individuals who have high measured ability and low achievement or lower ability and high achievement. Individuals like these reduce the size of the computed correlation coefficients.

When ratings are used as criteria, we find that the ratings tend to be unreliable because of the nature of the trait being rated, lack of knowledge of the ratees by the judges, and other errors associated with ratings. Again, the validity coefficients tend to be in the middle of the range. In industrial situations where tests of special ability are widely used, the situation is no better. Here the number of units produced in a given period of time is used as the criterion. Many factors affect the number of units turned out by each worker, and we again have to consider such factors as motivation of the workers, speed of the machines, availability of raw materials, and such physical aspects of the environment as noise, light, heat, and presence or absence of other workers.

As was pointed out in Chapter 8, the logical step after computing a validity coefficient is to set up the regression equation for the data, so that predictions can be made when future individuals take the same test. For example, in predicting freshmen grades in a particular school a regression equation was set up. When new students or applicants now take the admission tests, their scores can then be referred to the regression equation and a probability statement made for their success in that particular school. This would assume that both the type of freshmen and the grading practices of the school stay about the same. In actual practice, several, rather than one, predictors are used. Freshmen grade point indexes might be predicted using a test as above together with high school rank. Then a multiple R, (Chapter 16) would be computed between freshmen grades and the combined effects of the predictor test and high school rank. Additional predictors might also be added such as scores on a mathematics test or scores on interest and personality scales. The use of more than one variable raises the correlation coefficient and thus leads to better predictions.

As we have previously learned, when we make predictions, we attach a probability statement to our prediction. This was done using the standard error of estimate which is as follows (Chapters 8 and 16):

$$s_{yx} = s_y \sqrt{1 - r_{xy}^2}$$

or with R used instead of r if we have multiple regression. To review the use of this statistic, suppose that in a given situation we find the standard error of estimate to be .2 in predicting freshmen first-semester index from a test of academic ability. For a given student whose score on the predictor (X) is 120, we find that the predicted grade point average (Y) as read from the regression line is 5.0. We can then state that the chances are 2 out of 3 that the grade point average for this student, whose score on a test of mental ability is 120, will be between 4.8 and 5.2.   If we were to add and subtract two standard errors of estimate ($2 \times .2$), we can state that the chances are 95 in 100 that this individual's index will fall between 4.6 and 5.4; that is, his predicted index plus and minus .4.

An examination of the formula for the standard error of estimate shows that if r were perfect (equal to 1), the right-hand part of the equation reduces to 0, and there is no standard error of estimate.   From this it follows that the higher our validity, the better we can predict.   Let us look at the efficiency of these validity coefficients.   We can start out by noting the relationship between the coefficient of determination (a name given to r^2) and the coefficient of nondetermination (k^2).

$$r^2 + k^2 = 1 \qquad (17.12)$$

then
$$k^2 = 1 - r^2$$

and
$$k = \sqrt{1 - r^2} \qquad (17.13)$$

Instead of $r + k$ equaling 1, the sum of their squares equals 1.   When equation (17.13) is solved for various values of r, the corresponding values of k obtained are shown in Table 17.1.   From this it will be noted that as

TABLE 17.1.
Relationship
Between r and k

r	k
1.00	.00
.95	.31
.90	.44
.80	.60
.70	.71
.60	.80
.50	.87
.40	.92
.30	.95
.20	.98
.10	.995
.00	1.00

r increases, k decreases, but at a much slower rate.   When r has increased to .50, k is equal to .87.   When r is equal to .70, the value of k is very close to it.   Even when the value of r is in the .90's, the k values are considerable.

This k statistic is of little value in itself.   You may have noticed that it is one of the terms of the formula for the standard error of estimate.   The formula for the standard error of estimate could be written

$$s_{yx} = s(k)$$

We also use this statistic in making a statement about the predictive efficiency of our validity coefficient.   Suppose that we have a situation where the

validity coefficient between predictor and predicted variable is .45. First
we solve for k:

$$k = \sqrt{1 - r^2}$$
$$= \sqrt{1 - .45^2}$$
$$= \sqrt{1 - .2025}$$
$$= \sqrt{.7975}$$
$$= .89$$

Then we compute our index of forecasting efficiency by subtracting the
obtained k from 1 and multiplying the remainder by 100:

$$E = (1 - k)100 \tag{17.14}$$
$$= (1 - .89)100$$
$$= (.11)100$$
$$= 11\%$$

We can interpret this by saying that with a validity coefficient of .45 we can
predict 11 percent better than we would have been able to had there been
no relationship between the two variables. In other words, we have
decreased the size of the error of prediction by 11 percent.

This discussion may make it appear that tests are not much good in
predicting future behavior. But the point to remember is that we are
usually not interested in an individual's exact grade point average or score
on another test. We are more concerned about whether he will pass or
fail as a student, for instance, and be successful or eliminated as a trainee.
Rather than knowing his specific score, we are interested in his approximate
location on the other variable. Our tests usually do an efficient job in
placing individuals in this manner.

Attenuation

Since in any given situation both variables are unreliable to a certain
extent, any correlation coefficient computed between the two would tend to
be lower than the true, or theoretical, relationship between the two variables.
This lowered r is referred to as attenuated. Formulas have been developed
to correct for this attenuation. The most general one is

$$r_c = \frac{r_{xy}}{\sqrt{r_{xx}r_{yy}}} \tag{17.15}$$

where r_c = the correlation between X and Y corrected for attenuation
       r_{xx}, r_{yy} = the reliability coefficient of test X and criterion Y,
               respectively
          r_{xy} = the computed validity coefficient

In practice, it is best not to use this formula, for the reliability of our tests is at present quite high, and it is doubtful if it will ever be considerably improved. We have to use these tests in our daily work, and we must be aware that they are not perfect and that any prediction made with them is apt to be inaccurate to a certain extent. However, many of the criterion measures that we use are low in reliability because of inaccuracies inherent in our measurement techniques. Some research workers, therefore, feel justified in correcting for attenuation in the criterion scores only. Equation (17.15) then becomes

$$r_c = \frac{r_{xy}}{\sqrt{r_{yy}}} \tag{17.16}$$

It should be emphasized at this point that no test in itself contains validity or reliability. After all, a test is merely a piece of paper with symbols printed upon it. Whether or not any test has validity or reliability depends upon the manner in which the test is used. For a given situation, a particular test may have high validity and reliability; in another situation both may be low. It might be added that any test or scale has any number of validity or reliability coefficients, depending upon how, when, where, and by whom it was used.

Concurrent Validity

This type of validity is very similar to the preceding one, except that the criterion measures are collected at the time the test is administered. Tests or inventories used to separate individuals in different academic curricula, in different vocational groups, or at different levels of emotional adjustment would, if successful, be showing concurrent validity.

ITEM ANALYSIS

To determine the merit of any test item, test results must be subjected to an item analysis. As a result of this item analysis, three kinds of information are obtained concerning the item: (1) the difficulty of the item, (2) the discrimination index of the item, and (3) the effectiveness of the distractors. The first of these, the difficulty of the item, is the proportion of individuals who answer the item correctly. The second, the discrimination index, is a measure of how well the item separates two groups. The purpose of most tests is to "spread out" the individuals taking it. The item which separates good students from poor ones, adjusted individuals from maladjusted ones, or those with artistic ability from those without such ability is said to discriminate. The third result, the effectiveness of the distractors, applies only to multiple-choice items. But since most of our standardized tests and many of the teacher-made tests use this type of item almost exclusively, a thorough item analysis is made to see how the incorrect responses in the multiple-choice item are working. We shall now discuss each of these results of an item analysis in detail.

Item Difficulty

As previously defined in this chapter, the difficulty of an item (p) is the proportion of individuals who answer an item correctly. In a power test, that is, a test in which everyone has had a chance to read every item, the calculation of the item difficulty offers no problems. But when speed is a factor in a test—and many of our tests are of this nature—adjustments have to be made in the calculation of the item difficulty. Basically, item difficulty is the result of dividing the number who answered the item correctly by the number who took the test. On a speed test many people never get to the items near the end of the test. In that case the number of correct answers should be divided by the number of individuals who reached the item. The usual procedure in determining how far an individual went on a test is to assume that when the test period was over the individual was working on the item following the last one that he marked on his answer sheet. All items beyond this one are not assumed to have been reached. On the first half of any test such corrections make little difference; but unless something like this is done on the items near the end of the test, both the item difficulty values and the indexes of discrimination will be spuriously large. It also follows that as a result of corrections like this the size of the sample upon which the item statistics depend becomes much smaller, and correspondingly the reliability of the item statistics is reduced. Perhaps in constructing tests, even speed tests, it is a good idea to give the examinees enough time to answer all of the items. One way to do this is to attach a group of buffer items at the end of the test to keep those who finish first busy. These items are not scored.

The difficulty index is a very important item statistic, because it is very closely related to item discrimination. Suppose that we take an item with a difficulty of 99 percent which appeared on a test that was given to 100 students. This item makes $99 \times 1 = 99$ discriminations. That is, it separates the individual who missed it from the 99 who answered it correctly. An item with a difficulty of 98 percent makes 98×2 or 196 discriminations. In a similar fashion we could continue this reasoning downward until we came to items of 50 percent difficulty. With these we see that the number of discriminations on this item would be $50 \times 50 = 2500$ discriminations, the maximum number possible. It might appear then that the best test would be made up of items of 50 percent difficulty. If such a test were made, it would tend to cut the individuals taking it into two groups—those above the median and those below. With most tests, we wish to discriminate throughout the range. We wish to be able to grade students on the conventional letter system or on some other classification scheme using the results of the test. To have a test which discriminates over the entire range, items are selected which range from very easy to very difficult and which average, in the long run, to a difficulty value of 50 percent. From the viewpoint of item difficulty, a well-made test starts with a few very easy items, continues with the items of increasing difficulty, and ends with a few items which only a very few of the examinees answer correctly. There would be more difficulty values clustering about the center than at either extreme, but there would be a balance so that the average item difficulty is 50 percent.

There are times, however, when we do not wish to spread out individuals for grading purposes. On an examination for national science scholarships the test makers are interested in selecting the top 5 percent of the applicants. To do this requires the construction of a very difficult test with item difficulty values equal to .05. Since chance or guessing may influence scores on a test like this, the total scores on such a test can be corrected for guessing before the item analysis is made. The usual formula for correcting for guessing is

$$\text{Score} = R - \frac{W}{k-1} \qquad (17.17)$$

where R = the number of right answers on a student's paper
   W = the number of wrong answers on a student's paper
   k = the number of possible choices in the test item

For the ordinary true-false item, $k = 2$. For five-responses multiple-choice items, $k = 5$. There are other cases in which one may be interested in accepting, for example, 70 percent or 30 percent of the applicants. In these cases items for the test should all be of either .70 or .30 difficulty, respectively.

Item Discrimination

There are two general ways of demonstrating item discrimination: (1) a test of the significance of the difference between two proportions, and (2) correlational techniques. In the first method, the percent or proportion of individuals who answer the item correctly in the high group is tested against the proportion in the low group. If the difference is a significant one, the item is accepted as being one which discriminates. A disadvantage of this technique is that while it selects those items which discriminate, it does not reveal how well each one discriminates (see Chapter 12).

In much item-analysis work, the student will find that it is customary to compare the responses in the top 27 percent of the papers with those in the lowest 27 percent of the papers. This goes back to the early item-analysis work of T. L. Kelley who demonstrated that when the high and low groups were made up of the top and bottom 50 percent, those papers clustering about the median had little influence on the discrimination index. A comparison of the upper 40 percent with the lower 40 percent produced more clear-cut results. This difference becomes increasingly sharp as the papers in the high and low groups become more extreme. Also as the number of papers in the two groups decreases, the standard errors increase and the item statistics become more unreliable. Kelley demonstrated that when the responses of the individuals in the upper 27 percent were compared with those in the lower 27 percent, the ratio of the difference between the means of the two groups over the probable error[1] of the difference between the means was at a maximum. Since that time, many workers have accepted his findings and used this value of 27 percent in selecting the high and low groups. A major reason for this is that a number of useful computing devices have been made which are based upon high and low groups consisting of the upper and lower 27 percent. That other percentages will work just as well has been suggested by research which compared results based upon groups using 27 percent with those using a series of other percentages.

In the correlational approach to item analysis, a correlation coefficient is computed that shows the relationship of the responses to the total test score. In other words, we are investigating how well the item is doing what the

TABLE 17.2. Responses of Two Hundred Students to One Item of a Fifty-Six-Item Test

Test Score	Right	Wrong
51–53	6	1
48–50	18	2
45–47	22	4
42–44	18	7
39–41	28	6
36–38	15	8
33–35	12	12
30–32	8	10
27–29	5	4
24–26		4
21–23	1	4
18–20		3
15–17		1
12–14		1
	133	67

test itself is doing. Suppose that we have the responses of 200 individuals to a 56-item test. To begin with, we are going to use a method which uses all of the papers. We set up a distribution of scores on the Y axis of our scatterplot, and since the test item is usually scored on a right or wrong basis, we have only two categories on the X axis (see Table 17.2).

We take the first paper, note the total score and whether or not the item was answered correctly, and tally the item at the appropriate place on the

[1] Probable error = .6745 standard error. This is an outmoded statistic.

frequency distributions.   Then the next paper is taken, the response tallied, and this process is continued for all of the papers.   When the tallying is finished, either a point-biserial or biserial r may be computed.   If the distribution of test scores is dichotomized as the response to the item is, either the tetrachoric r or the phi coefficient can be used.   This same process would have to be repeated for the other 55 items on this test.

Admittedly, this is a tremendous amount of clerical work and if it were not for a large number of computing and data processing devices that have been set up, many would think twice before getting involved in item analysis work.   Flanagan was one of the first to produce one of these short cuts. From his chart correlation coefficients are read directly when one enters the chart with the percent answering the item correctly in the upper or lower 27 percent of the papers.   Flanagan's chart is reproduced in Fig. 16.2 of Chapter 16.   Guilford (1954) has produced a chart for obtaining phi coefficients when one enters it with the percentages in the high and low groups answering the item correctly (see Chapter 16, Fig. 16.3).   For this chart, the high and low groups need not be based upon the upper and lower 27 percent of the cases.   The only requirement is that there be an equal number of individuals in each group.   A short method for estimating the tetrachoric r has already been demonstrated (Chapter 16).   Computing devices are also available which shorten the work in obtaining both the biserial and point biserial, but none of these is as simple as the methods mentioned above.

Each of these different correlation coefficients may be tested for significance by the use of the different techniques mentioned in Chapter 16.   Flanagan's r may be taken as an estimate of a Pearson r, and the tables used for estimating the significance of a Pearson r may be used in testing significance.   In selecting items for a standardized test or future editions of a teacher's own test, items with the highest discrimination indices should be selected, since the items are being put into the new test on the basis of their item difficulty values.   It should be mentioned here that when the upper and lower 27 percent of the papers are used, item difficulty values are based upon the number of individuals in these two extreme groups who answer the item correctly rather than upon all of the papers.

The Effectiveness of Distractors

In estimating the effectiveness of the different distractors of the multiple-choice item, two procedures may be used.   The responses to the different distractors of each test item can be counted for the high and low groups. Good distractors are those which are selected more frequently by members of the low-scoring group.   When a reversal is found, that is, a particular distractor more popular in the high group than in the low group, the test maker may revise the distractor, trying to make it less appealing to the better students, or rewrite the entire item.   Analysis of distractors may also reveal options used by no one in either the high or the low group.   Such distractors contribute nothing to the test. When such nonfunctioning distractors appear, they should be revised in an attempt to make them useful.

The other method of studying the distractors is to obtain the mean score of the individuals who respond to each of the distractors as well as to the correct answer. When this technique is used, it is not unusual to find that the mean score for individuals who selected a certain distractor is higher than the mean score for those who selected the correct answer. Here again we have evidence of a distractor lowering the discriminatory power of an item. Good distractors will yield lower mean scores than the papers associated with the correct answer. With this technique, also, certain distractors may appear that are selected by no one.

Item Analysis When the Number of Papers is Small

The item-analysis techniques described above are all associated with large or fairly large samples. In many situations, all that one has is about 30 papers. With such samples a crude sort of item analysis can be made by using the upper ten papers versus the lower ten. The percent who answer the item correctly in each group can then be determined, and from these an estimate of the item difficulty can be made. Estimates as to whether or not an item is discriminating can be made by an inspection of the number of individuals in the high and low groups for each item. Those items with no, or a negative, discrimination can be spotted at once. For the category of actually discriminating items, we might adopt such a standard as that there has to be a difference of at least two between the frequency of the high and low group before the item is considered as discriminating. While this technique is crude, it is better than nothing and will be helpful in making better classroom tests.[2]

Exercises

1. Below are tabulated the responses of 25 individuals to each of the items on a 15-item test.
   (a) Obtain an odd and even score for each individual and then compute the reliability of the test.
   (b) Use Kuder-Richardson Formula No. 20 to compute the reliability of the test.
   (c) Calculate the standard deviation of the test scores.
   (d) What is the standard error of measurement for this test?
   (e) Select an individual with a score of 10 on this test and interpret the standard error of measurement.

[2] Item-analysis techniques are discussed in detail in any educational or psychological measurement book (Downie, 1958, Remmers and Gage, 1955).

Item No.	1	2	3	4	5	6	7	8	9	10	11	12	13	14	15	Score
Individual A	+	+	+	0	+	+	0	0	0	0	+	0	0	0	0	6
B	+	+	+	+	+	+	0	+	+	+	0	+	+	+	+	13
C	0	+	+	+	+	+	0	0	0	+	0	+	+	+	0	9
D	+	0	+	0	0	+	+	+	0	0	+	0	0	+	0	7
E	+	+	+	+	+	+	+	+	+	0	+	+	+	+	+	14
F	+	0	0	+	+	+	+	+	+	+	+	+	+	0	+	12
G	+	+	+	0	0	+	+	+	0	0	+	+	+	+	+	11
H	0	0	+	+	0	+	+	0	0	0	0	0	0	0	0	4
I	+	+	0	+	+	0	+	+	+	+	+	0	+	+	+	12
J	+	+	+	+	0	+	+	+	+	0	+	+	+	+	+	13
K	+	0	0	+	+	0	0	+	0	0	+	0	+	0	0	6
L	0	+	+	+	+	+	0	0	0	0	+	0	+	0	+	8
M	+	+	+	0	0	+	0	0	0	0	+	0	+	+	+	8
N	+	+	+	+	+	+	+	+	0	+	+	0	+	+	+	13
O	+	+	+	+	0	+	0	0	0	+	0	+	+	+	0	9
P	+	+	+	+	+	0	+	+	+	0	0	0	0	0	0	8
Q	+	+	+	+	+	+	0	0	0	+	0	0	+	0	0	8
R	+	+	+	+	+	+	0	+	+	+	0	+	0	0	0	10
S	0	+	0	0	0	+	0	0	0	0	0	0	0	0	0	3
T	+	+	+	+	+	+	+	+	+	+	+	+	+	+	+	15
U	+	+	0	+	+	0	0	+	0	+	0	0	0	+	+	9
V	0	+	+	+	0	+	0	+	0	0	+	0	0	0	0	6
W	+	+	0	+	+	+	+	+	+	+	+	+	0	+	+	13
X	+	+	+	+	+	+	0	+	+	+	+	0	+	+	0	12
Y	+	+	+	+	0	+	+	+	+	+	+	+	+	+	+	14
No. Correct	20	21	19	20	16	22	12	18	11	13	16	10	17	15	13	243

2. (a) A certain 25-item test has a reliability coefficient of .72. To this are added 75 similar and well-made items. What is the reliability of the new test?

(b) Suppose that a test made of 150 items takes 80 minutes to administer. The author of the test decides to shorten it to 50 items so that it will be a 25–30 minute test. The reliability of the original test is .93. What might you expect the reliability of the shortened test to be?

(c) Another test has a reliability coefficient of .60. This test is made up of 20 items. How many well-made and similar items will have to be added to increase the reliability to .90?

3. (a) A certain test has a reliability coefficient of .92 and a validity coefficient of .48 with criterion Y. The standard deviation of this criterion is 10.2 and that of the test is 9.6. Calculate the standard error of estimate when predicting Y from X.

(b) Suppose that from a regression equation for the above data you calculate a criterion score of 77 for an individual. How would you associate the standard error of estimate with this predicted score?

(c) Calculate the index of forecasting efficiency for this validity coefficient. What does this mean?

4. Sometimes we square the validity coefficient and call it a coefficient of determination. We then interpret this as being the amount of variance in Y that is accounted for or determined by the variance in X. With this same line of reasoning, how might one best describe k^2?

5. Take the data in Problem 3(a) and apply the attenuation formula for correcting test scores. Exactly what have you done? Can you defend the use of this statistic?

6. Investigate the pros and cons of the use of correction formulas in scoring test papers. Any educational and psychological measurement book may be consulted.
7. If test papers are available, apply an item analysis, calculating for each item the difficulty value and the discrimination index. Use any of the computing charts or devices discussed in this chapter. Summarize your results. Examine the items that are not good. Have you any ideas why they did not hold up in the item analysis?

18

DISTRIBUTION-FREE
STATISTICAL TESTS

While a few distribution-free or nonparametric statistics have been known and used for many decades, it was not until recently that statisticians have devoted much attention to them. The modern period, so to speak, began in the mid-thirties, and growth has continued at an accelerated rate up to the present. In distribution-free or nonparametric tests, no assumptions are made about the precise form of the sampled population. Sometimes certain assumptions are made, such as that a distribution is continuous, or that the sampled populations have identical shapes or distributions symmetrical about the same point. However, never are the assumptions so elaborate as to imply a completely specified population distribution, as is the case with the normal curve. Most of the statistics studied so far— with the exception of centiles, chi square, and several of the correlation coefficients —have implied a normal distribution of the parameter, and z, t, and F are parametric tests.

Bradley (1960) makes a detailed listing of the advantages and disadvantages of distribution-free statistical tests. Some of the major points he made are:

1. Simplicity of derivation. The derivation of classical tests requires a level of competence in mathematics far above that attained by the typical research worker; whereas most distribution-free statistics can be derived using simple combinational formulas.

2. Ease of application. Frequently, all that is needed as mathematical operations for distribution-free statistical tests is ranking, counting, adding, and subtracting.

3. Speed of application. When sample size is small or moderate, distribution-free models are generally faster than parametric techniques.

4. Scope of application. Because they are based on fewer and less elaborate assumptions than the classical tests, distribution-free statistical tests can be correctly applied to a much larger class of populations.

5. Susceptibility to violation of assumptions. Since the assumptions are fewer and less elaborate with nonparametric statistical tests, they are less

susceptibile to violation.   These violations are easier to detect with non-parametric tests.   The effect of the violation of assumptions is important with both types of statistics, but Bradley feels that the effects of violation of assumptions can be more readily and economically taken care of with distribution-free statistical tests.

6.   Type of measurement required.   Distribution-free statistical tests usually require at least ordinal data, though sometimes nominal data may be used.   Parametric tests generally require measurements on an interval or ratio scale.

7.   Influence of sample size.   When sample sizes are ≤ 10, distribution-free statistical tests are easier, quicker, and only slightly less efficient, even if all the assumptions of the parametric test have been met.   At such sample size, violations of parametric assumptions are most devastating; hence in these cases nonparametric tests are most appropriate.   As sample size increases, the nonparametric tests become more laborious and time-consuming and frequently become a much less efficient statistical test.

8.   Statistical efficiency.   In terms of practicality—the amount of human effort required to conduct and analyze an experiment—nonparametric statistics are frequently more convenient than their parametric counterparts In terms of a mathematical criterion of statistical efficiency, distribution-free tests are often superior or equal to their parametric counterparts when the assumptions of the nonparametric test are met, but the assumptions of the parametric test are not.   If both tests are applied when all assumptions of the parametric test can be met, distribution-free statistics are very slightly less efficient at extremely small size but become increasingly less efficient as sample size increases.

Moses (1952) also noted that nonparametric tests were (1) easier to apply, (2) applicable to rank data, (3) usable when two sets of observations come from different populations, (4) the only alternative when sample size is small, and (5) useful at a specified significance level as stated, whatever happened to be the shape of the distribution from which the sample distribution was drawn.   He also noted that among their disadvantages was their lower statistical efficiency.

At present, much information on these statistical tests is available in Bradley (1960), Siegel (1956), and Tate and Clelland (1957).   In this chapter, a few of the more frequently encountered nonparametric tests will be considered.

TESTS FOR CORRELATED SAMPLES

The Sign Test

Among the simplest of these tests is the *sign* test.   In discussing this test, we shall refer to the material in Table 18.1.   In that table data are found in pairs.   Individuals are matched and assigned to one of the two groups at random at the beginning of the experiment.   A treatment is applied and

TABLE 18.1. The Sign Test

X	Y	X − Y
16	4	+
12	18	−
22	10	+
16	14	+
14	12	+
10	14	−
20	10	+
18	12	+
10	4	+
22	12	+

the resulting scores for the pairs of individuals are shown in the table. In the use of a test like this, it is assumed that the variable under consideration is distributed continuously and that both members of each pair are treated similarly except for the experimental variable.

In analyzing data using this test, we consider each pair of scores separately, noting whether the second score is smaller or larger than the first, and then we assign the appropriate sign as shown. Ties may be handled by dropping them from the computations or by giving one tie a plus sign and the next a minus sign, and so on.

The null hypothesis tested here is that the median change is 0. This hypothesis is rejected if there are too few of any one sign. Where there are 10 or less pairs we apply a test of significance by the use of the binomial expansion with $p = .5$ and $N =$ the number of pairs. For our data, $N = 10$. From Table 18.1, we note that we have 8 pluses and 2 minuses. By chance we would expect 5 of each. The question is, does this frequency of 8 pluses differ significantly from what we would expect by chance? With the use of the binomial expansion, we find the probability of obtaining 8 or more + signs is equal to .0009766 + .0097656 + .0439452 which adds up to .0547. The process of doubling this probability for a two-tailed test gives a p of .1094 of .11 which forces us to let the null hypothesis stand.

When the number of pairs is greater than 10, the results may be evaluated using a z score and the formula for the mean and standard deviation of the binomial (formulas 9.2 and 9.3). A correction for discontinuity must also be made (see description in Chapter 9).

Since this test uses only information on the direction of the differences between pairs, it is not the most efficient test. The next test combines with the sign of the difference the relative size of the difference. It is a more powerful test.

Wilcoxon's Matched-Pairs Signed-Ranks Test

To illustrate this test of significance, we shall again use the data presented in Table 18.1 which have been recopied into Table 18.2. First we obtain

TABLE 18.2.   Data of Table 18.1 Used to Illustrate the
Wilcoxon Matched-Pairs Signed-Ranks Test

X	Y	Difference	Absolute Rank of Difference	R(+)	R(−)
16	4	12	9.5	9.5	
12	18	−6	5		5
22	10	12	9.5	9.5	
16	14	2	1.5	1.5	
14	12	2	1.5	1.5	
10	14	−4	3		3
20	10	10	7.5	7.5	
18	12	6	5	5	
10	4	6	5	5	
22	12	10	7.5	7.5	
				$\Sigma R(+) = 47.0$	$\Sigma R(-) = 8$

the difference between each pair of scores.   Then we rank the absolute values of these differences, "absolute" meaning to disregard signs in our ranking.   For these data the two differences of 2 are the smallest.   Since these occupy positions one and two of the ranking, they are given the average of the two ranks, this being 1.5.   The next smallest difference is −4.   This is given a rank of 3.   And in this manner, we continue until all the differences are ranked.   Whenever, a difference of 0 appears, it is disregarded in the computations.

In the last two columns of Table 18.2, the ranks have been summed according to the sign of the differences.   The smaller of these is taken as Wilcoxon's T statistic.

If there were no difference between the two groups, T would equal $\overline{T}$, the mean sum of the ranks.   This latter statistic can be obtained by the following formula:

$$\overline{T} = \frac{N(N+1)}{4} \tag{18.1}$$

For these data, $\overline{T} = \dfrac{10(10+1)}{4}$

$$= \frac{10(11)}{4} = \frac{110}{4}$$

$$= 27.5$$

If the obtained T differs significantly from $\overline{T}$, we can reject the null hypothesis. For smaller sums of ranks, for N's between 7 and 25, Wilcoxon has developed a table (reproduced as Table IX in the Appendix) which may be entered directly to test the significance of T.   For our problem, let us assume a two-tailed test with our alpha = .05.   From Table IX, for $N = 10$, we see that a T of 8 or less is significant at the .05 level for the two-tailed test. Our T is exactly 8; hence we reject the null hypothesis at the 5 percent level.

A comparison of our findings obtained on the sign test with that for the Wilcoxon test shows contradictory results.   With the sign test, we were unable to reject the null hypothesis which was rejected at the 5 percent level for Wilcoxon's test. This points out the fact that the Wilcoxon test is a more powerful test than the sign test, because it takes into account more information than the sign test. In this case the magnitudes of differences are used and lead to the different results.

When N is greater than 25, the sum of the ranks may be taken as normally distributed with

$$\bar{T} = \frac{(N)(N + 1)}{4}$$

$$s = \sqrt{\frac{(2N + 1)\bar{T}}{6}} \quad \text{or} \quad \sqrt{\frac{(N)(N + 1)(2N + 1)}{24}} \tag{18.2}$$

and the sum of the T's may be treated with the familiar z test with $T - \bar{T}$ as the deviation.

TESTS FOR UNCORRELATED DATA

The Median Test

This test is applied to see if two groups come from populations which have the same median. In using this test, the size of the two samples need not be the same. In Table 18.3 are shown arithmetic addition scores for

TABLE 18.3. Scores on an Addition Test

X	Y
12	7
16	12
18	14
7	18
6	5
4	16
11	9
12	10
8	14
20	3
18	18
16	9
10	7
	4

27 individuals. We shall test the hypothesis of no difference between these two sets of scores by using the median test. Group X contains 13 scores and Group Y, 14. We first compute the median of the entire set of 27 scores. For these data, we find this to be 11.

If both of these distributions came from the same populations, half of the X values and half of the Y values would lie above this median of 11, and half of each of the two distributions would lie below it. A contingency table is set up as follows:

	X	Y	
Above median	7	6	13
	a	b	k
Not above median	6	8	14
	c	d	l
	13	14	27
	m	n	N

We next make a test of significance using chi square as follows:

$$\chi^2 = \frac{N[\,|ad - bc| - (N/2)]^2}{(k)(l)(m)(n)}$$

$$= \frac{27[(56 - 36) - (27/2)]^2}{(13)(14)(13)(14)}$$

$$= \frac{27(42.25)}{33124}$$

$$= .034$$

which with 1 *df* is not significant.

When the cell frequencies in the contingency become very small, 1 or 2, this chi-square solution, even when corrected by Yates' correction for continuity, should not be used. A more complicated method, known as Fisher's exact method, must be used. This may be found in McNemar (1962, pp. 236–239) or Walker and Lev (1953, pp. 103–106).

The median test is also applicable when there are more than two groups. The technique is the same. First the median of all of the scores taken together is obtained. Then a contingency table similar to the one above is set up containing the number of scores above the median and the number not above the median for each of the groups. Chi square is then applied to the data in the contingency table, and the appropriate conclusion drawn. In this type of problem, the expected frequency for a cell is half of the number of cases in the group. It should be noted that when a score falls exactly at the median, this score is included in the group referred to as "not above the median."

Mann-Whitney U Test

A more powerful test than the median test for uncorrelated data is the Mann-Whitney *U* Test. The test is used with independently drawn random samples, the sizes of which need not be the same. When the sample sizes are very small, that is, when both N_1 and N_2 are made up of 8 or less measures, the reader is referred to Siegel (1956) for a method and tables that apply to such sample sizes. When the larger of the two samples is 9 or more, the procedure is as follows.

TABLE 18.4. Two Small Independent Samples Illustrating the Use of the Mann-Whitney U Test

X	Y	R_X	R_Y
14	18	11.5	15
12	16	9	14
13	15	10	13
10	14	8	11.5
7	19	5.5	16
6	7	3.5	5.5
4	8	2	7
	6		3.5
	3		1
$N_X = 7$	$N_Y = 9$	$\Sigma R_X = 49.5$	$\Sigma R_Y = 86.5$

In Table 18.4, we have two samples, N_X with 7 cases and N_Y with 9 cases. In this case we are testing the hypothesis that both samples come from the same population. First, all the scores are ranked in one composite distribution in an increasing order of size, algebraic signs being considered when negative measures are present. In Table 18.4, the score of 3 in column Y is the lowest one; hence it receives a rank of 1. The score of 4 in column X is the second lowest and is correspondingly given a rank of 2. We have a score of 6 in both the X and Y distribution. Such ties are handled by giving them the average of the next two ranks, which for this distribution is 3.5. The ranking continues until all scores receive a rank. Then the columns of ranks are summed.

At this point an arithmetic check can be made on the work. The sum of the two columns of ranks must be equal to $N(N + 1)/2$. For this problem,

$$\Sigma R_X + \Sigma R_Y = \frac{N(N + 1)}{2}$$

$$49.5 + 86.5 = \frac{16(17)}{2}$$

$$136 = 136$$

U is obtained as follows:

$$U_1 = N_1 N_2 + \frac{N_1(N_1 + 1)}{2} - \Sigma R_X \qquad (18.3\ a)$$

$$U_2 = N_1 N_2 + \frac{N_2(N_2 + 1)}{2} - \Sigma R_y \qquad (18.3\ b)$$

For our problem,

$$U_1 = (7)(9) + \frac{7(8)}{2} - 49.5$$

$$= 63 + 28 - 49.5$$

$$= 41.5$$

Equations (18.3 a) and (18.3 b) give different results, and to complete our problem we need the smaller of the two. By solving equation (18.3 b) we have

$$U_2 = (7)(9) + \frac{(9)(10)}{2} - 86.5$$

$$= 63 + 45 - 86.5$$

$$= 21.5$$

The student can check to see if he has the smaller value of U by the following:

$$U_2 = N_1N_2 - U_1$$

$$= (7)(9) - 41.5$$

$$= 63 - 41.5$$

$$= 21.5$$

U is evaluated by the use of Table X in the Appendix. Notice that Table X is made up of four parts for p values of .001, .01, .025, and .05 or, if we were making a directional test, p's of .002, .02, .05, and .10. For example, suppose that $N_1 = 10$, and $N_2 = 15$, from the (b) part of Table X we see that a U of 33 or less makes it possible to reject the null hypothesis at the 1 percent level for a two-tailed test or at the 2 percent level for a one-tailed test. Suppose that we set alpha equal to .01 for our problem. Examination of part (b) of Table X shows that, when $N_1 = 7$ and $N_2 = 9$, U must be 9 or less to be significant. Our obtained U of 21.5 is therefore not significant, and the null hypothesis stands.

When either N_1 or N_2 is larger than 20, we solve for the U statistic which is considered to be normally distributed for samples of this size. To illustrate this technique, some fictitious data have been assembled in Table 18.5. In Group X (N_1) there are 21 cases and in Group Y (N_2) there are 10. The data are treated exactly as they were previously. First the two sets of scores are ranked together, with the smallest score being given the smallest rank. Then these two columns of ranks are summed. Again these can be checked. $(N)(N + 1)/2 =$ sum of the two sets of ranks. Next U_1 is found by formula (18.3 a),

$$U_1 = N_1N_2 + \frac{N_1(N_1 + 1)}{2} - \Sigma R_X$$

$$= (21)(10) + \frac{21(21 + 1)}{2} - 272.5$$

$$U_1 = 210 + 231 - 272.5$$
$$= 168.5$$

TABLE 18.5. Illustration of Mann-Whitney U-Test for Larger Sets of Data

X	Y	R_X	R_Y
7	18	12.5	31
10	14	18	27
12	15	21.5	29
6	16	10	30
8	12	14.5	21.5
4	10	6.5	18
6	8	10	14.5
14	13	27	24
2	13	2.5	24
4	3	6.5	4.5
6		10	
7		12.5	
3		4.5	
5		8	
2		2.5	
1		1	
13		24	
14		27	
11		20	
10		18	
9		16	
$N_1 = 21$	$N_2 = 10$	$\Sigma R_X = 272.5$	$\Sigma R_Y = 223.5$

The z ratio is then computed by the use of the following equation:

$$z = \frac{U_1 - (N_1 N_2/2)}{\sqrt{[N_1 N_2 (N_1 + N_2 + 1)]/12}} \qquad (18.4)$$

where the numerator is U_1 minus the second term which is the mean of U, and the denominator is the standard deviation of the U.

$$z = \frac{168.5 - (21)(10)/2}{\sqrt{[(21)(10)(21 + 10 + 1)]/12}}$$

$$= \frac{168.5 - 105}{\sqrt{6720/12}}$$

$$= \frac{63.5}{\sqrt{560}}$$

$$= \frac{63.5}{23.7}$$

$$= 2.68$$

A z value of this size leads to the rejection of the null hypothesis at the 1 percent level.

This problem could have also been solved for U_2.

$$U_2 = N_1N_2 + \frac{N_2(N_2 + 1)}{2} - \Sigma R_Y$$

$$= (21)(10) + \frac{10(10 + 1)}{2} - 223.5$$

$$= 210 + 55 - 223.5$$

$$= 41.5$$

If this value of 41.5 is placed in the numerator of formula (18.4) in place of U_1, it will be found that the value of the numerator of z this time is -63.5. It does not matter, then, for which U value we solve. The size of the z is unaffected, but the sign is affected. In a two-tailed test this makes no difference in the interpretation of z.

The Mann-Whitney test is said by Siegel (1956) to be a powerful test and an excellent substitute for the t test.

Wald-Wolfowitz Runs Test

Another test applicable to unrelated samples is the Wald-Wolfowitz Runs Test. With this technique, we test the hypothesis of no difference in respect to average value, variability, and skewness, for example. In Table 18.6 are two sets of data taken on two independent samples. The

TABLE 18.6. Two Sets of Independent Data for the Wald-Wolfowitz Runs Test

X	Y
12	7
8	9
6	16
18	17
14	20
15	19
3	2
5	10
4	22
1	21
$N_1 = 10$	$N_2 = 10$

scores are arranged in a continuous series from high to low, and the identity of the distribution from which the score came is recorded below it. The data in Table 18.6 are set up as follows:

22	21	20	19	18	17	16	15	14	12	10	9	8	7	6	5	4	3	2	1
Y	Y	Y	Y	X	Y	Y	X	X	X	Y	Y	X	Y	X	X	X	X	Y	X
		1		2	3			4		5		6	7		8			9	10

After this is done, the number of runs is determined. Starting with the score of 22, we have four scores in a row that came from the Y distribution. These four scores constitute the first run. The score of 18 alone is from the X distribution. This is run 2. All the runs are then marked as shown and the number of runs counted.

If the two sets of data are from the same population, we would expect the number of runs to be large. That is, there would be a good mixture of high, medium, and low scores in each distribution, and this would lead to a large number of short runs. When N_1 and N_2 (the numbers in each distribution) are 20 or less, the significance of the number of runs observed can be tested directly from Tables (Table XI in the Appendix). From these tables we see that for the values of N in our sample, the number of runs is not significant, and hence there is no difference between the two samples.

When the size of the two samples is over 20, the significance of the difference is tested as follows:

$$z = \frac{[r - (2N_1N_2/N_1 + N_2) + 1] - .5}{2N_1N_2(2N_1N_2 - N_1 - N_2)/[(N_1 + N_2)^2(N_1 + N_2 - 1)]} \quad (18.5)$$

where
$\qquad\qquad r =$ number of runs
$(2N_1N_2)/(N_1 + N_2) =$ mean of the runs
$\qquad$ denominator $=$ the standard deviation
$\qquad\qquad -.5 =$ corrects the term for continuity

With this technique the problem of ties is an important one. If the ties are all in one sample or the other, no problem arises. If the ties are in both samples, they should be mixed in all possible ways. If the results agree by all three ways, there is no problem. But if the results differ, the probability of each z is determined and the average of these taken in the evaluation of the null hypothesis. As an example, suppose that in two series of scores, a score of 14 appears three times, twice in the X distribution and once in the Y distribution. It could be arranged in the series of scores three ways:

14 14 14		14 14 14		14 14 14
	or		or	
X X Y		X Y X		Y X X

Then for this series of ties, the problem would have to be solved three times, determining the different number of runs which the various combinations cause.

This test is not as good as some of the others because of the general nature of the hypothesis that may be tested with it. Moses (1952) states that tests which test hypotheses against many alternatives simultaneously are not very good in the prevention of the acceptance of the null hypothesis erroneously with respect to one alternative. Since this test is designed to disclose differences of many types, it is not as efficient as the Mann-Whitney test or others which are set up to test specific differences.

Kruskal-Wallis H Test

The Kruskal-Wallis H Test is used to test whether or not a group of independent samples is from the same or different populations. Data to illustrate this test are presented in Table 18.7.

TABLE 18.7.   The Kruskal-Wallis H Test

X	R_x	Y	R_y	Z	R_z
12	13.5	13	16	13	16
16	21	18	22	14	19
14	19	14	19	7	8.5
2	1.5	13	16	8	10.5
12	13.5	8	10.5	4	4.5
		7	8.5	3	3
		6	7	2	1.5
		4	4.5	5	6
				9	12
$\Sigma R_x = 68.5$		$\Sigma R_y = 103.5$		$\Sigma R_z = 81.0$	

Table 18.7 shows three sets of data.   The scores of the three sets are combined and ranked with the lowest score receiving a rank value of 1. Ties are treated in the usual fashion for ranking data.   Then the ranks of the three columns are summed.   If the sample proportions are similar, the total sum of the ranks would be divided proportionately among the various samples on the basis of sample size.   The sums of the ranks of the various samples are then tested against these proportions of the total sum of ranks, by use of the following formula:

$$H = \frac{12}{N(N + 1)} \left[\sum \frac{R_i^2}{N_i} \right] - 3(N + 1) \qquad (18.6)$$

where N = the number in all samples combined
   R_i = sum of ranks and N_i the numbers in i samples
For the data in Table 18.7,

$$H = \frac{12}{(22)(23)} \left[\frac{(68.5)^2}{5} + \frac{(103.5)^2}{8} + \frac{(81)^2}{9} \right] - 3(23)$$

$$= \frac{12}{506} [938.45 + 1339.03 + 729] - 69$$

$$= .0237(3006.48) - 69$$

$$= 71.3 - 69$$

$$= 2.3$$

If the number of cases in the samples is from one to five, special tables are used in the interpretation of H (Table XII in the Appendix). When the samples contain five or more cases, H is interpreted as chi square with the number of samples minus one degree of freedom. For this problem $df = 2$, and this H is not significant.

This is a powerful nonparametric test.

Exercises

1. In the data below, column X represents 12 scores of members of a control group in an experiment. Column Y represents the scores of 12 matched individuals who were given the same test after a period of stress. Use the *sign test* to test the hypothesis of no difference.

X	Y
46	36
68	50
60	58
58	40
42	44
43	43
40	29
56	36
38	46
58	48
42	38
48	42

2. With the data in Problem 1, test the hypothesis of no difference using Wilcoxon's matched-pairs signed-ranks test.

3. Below are the scores of a group of normals and a group of psychotics on the *Picture Completion Scale of the Wechsler-Bellevue*. Test the hypothesis of no difference using the Median Test.

N	P
6	7
6	2
14	12
13	13
15	8
6	6
8	4
7	2
10	2
14	12
10	
14	

4. In the data below are three samples of scores obtained on the *Arithmetic Scale of the Wechsler-Bellevue*. Apply the median test to all three samples.

A	B	C
8	2	12
7	4	3
14	6	10
10	14	4
8	10	14
6	8	11
	6	10
	2	8

5. Apply the Mann-Whitney *U* Test to the data in Problem 3.
6. Assume the data in Problem 1 to be uncorrelated. Apply the Mann-Whitney *U* test.
7. Two groups of children made the following scores on the vocabulary test of the *Stanford-Binet*. By use of the Mann-Whitney *U* Test, test for differences in the two groups.

Group I		Group II
10	33	14
18	36	18
36	26	22
22	24	16
28	31	38
29	13	26
32	19	28
15	23	12
18	25	
36	27	11
21	32	19
27		16

8. Apply the Wald-Wolfowitz Runs Test to the data in Problem 7 above.
9. By using the data in Problem 4, test the hypothesis of no difference using the Kruskal-Wallis *H* test.
10. The following data from Borislow[1] show the changed response scores of three groups on the *Edwards Personal Preference Schedule*.

Control Group	Social Desirability Group	Personal Desirability Group
47	76	87
38	76	76
34	75	52
32	73	51
32	62	50
30	47	42
		38

Test the differences among these three groups, using any and all appropriate nonparametric tests.

[1] *Journal of Applied Psychology*, 1958, 42, 25.

APPENDIX

APPENDIX

FORMULAS

ANSWERS TO EXERCISES

Chapter 2

1. (a) 18.33
   (b) 109.67
   (c) 1.0974
   (d) −17.86

   (e) −1.0859
   (f) −48.13
   (g) −10.5022
   (h) 75

2. (a) 365.36
   (b) .074
   (c) .000056
   (d) −.666

   (e) −913.78
   (f) .03072
   (g) −.777
   (h) 5.9202

3. (a) 40
   (b) 9000
   (c) .025
   (d) −50.5

   (e) −360
   (f) 70
   (g) −10.058
   (h) 4.04

4. (a) 3.75
   (b) 3.875
   (c) 4.42
   (d) 2.67
   (e) 1.83
   (f) .686
   (g) −1.25
   (h) .562
   (i) 1.63
   (j) −24.25
   (k) 720

   (l) 40.608
   (m) 0
   (n) 64
   (o) −44
   (p) a^2b
   (q) .44
   (r) $x^2 + 2xy + y^2$
   (s) 3
   (t) fx^2
   (u) x^4y^3z

5. (a) 57
   (b) 175
   (c) 554
   (d) 27.9
   (e) 94.2
   (f) .00949

   (g) .0158
   (h) 3.00
   (i) .333
   (j) $.7\sqrt{-1}$ or $.7i$
   (k) 276.5

6. (a) 14.4
   (b) 24.3
   (c) 17.8
   (d) .1
   (e) 1.0

   (f) 90.2
   (g) 88.0
   (h) 56.4
   (i) 48.6
   (j) .1

7. (a) 5
   (b) 4
   (c) 2
   (d) 2

   (e) 7
   (f) 1
   (g) 2
   (h) 1

261

Chapter 3

		Exact Limits	Midpoints	Interval Size
1.	(a)	1.5–5.5	3.5	4
	(b)	14.5–20.5	17.5	6
	(c)	−.5–3.5	1.5	4
	(d)	4.5–9.5	7	5
	(e)	−1.5−−6.5	−4	5
	(f)	−3.5–3.5	0	7
	(g)	1.45–2.55	2	1.1
	(h)	.495–.755	.625	.26

2. (a) 1
   (b) 2 or 3
   (c) 7, 8, 9, or 10
   (d) 2
   (e) .3, .4, or .5

6. $C_{10} = 29.8$ $C_{20} = 36.4$ Mdn $= 45.4$ $Q_3 = 50.2$
   $C_{90} = 54.7$ $C_{80} = 51.2$ $Q_1 = 38.3$ $D_7 = 49.2$

7. (a) 30.5   (d) 20.3
   (b) 24.2   (e) 34.5
   (c) 31

Chapter 4

1. $\bar{X} = 41.9$ Mdn $= 41.7$ Mo. $= 40$
2. $\bar{X} = 8.6$ Mdn $= 8.5$ Mo. $= 8$ or 11
3. When using an interval of 3 and the bottom interval 30–32:
   $\bar{X} = 55.4$ Mdn $= 55.5$ Mo. $= 55$
4. (a) Mdn $= \$13512$
   (b) $Q_3 = \$14502.62$ $Q_1 = \$11524.50$
5. (a) Mdn $= 1.83$
   (b) $Q_3 = 2.96$ $Q_1 = .88$
6. $\bar{X} = 77.5$ Mdn $= 80.9$ Mo. $= 82$
7. $\bar{X} = 55.4$ Mdn $= 56.2$ Mo. $= 64.5$
8. (a) 48.2
   (b) 83.3

		(a)	(b)	(c)	(d)
9.	$\bar{X}$	19.9	15.6	20.4	10.8
	Mdn	20.5	14.2	21.0	10.3
	Mo.	—	14.0	—	10.0

10. (a) $\bar{X} = 104$
    (b) Mdn $= 102.2$ using an interval of 3 and the bottom interval 87–89.

Chapter 5

1. $s = 3.9$
2. (a) $Q = 11.9$
   (b) $s = 14.9$

3. (a) $Q = 2.1$
4. $\bar{X} = 85.2; s = 13.1$
5. $\bar{X} = 517.6; s = 62.3$

6. (1) $s = 7.3$
   (2) $s = 3.1$
   (3) $s = 9.9$
   (6) $s = 13.6$
   (7) $s = 21.0$

   (9) (a) $s = 3.5$
       (b) $s = 2.7$
       (c) $s = 3.9$
       (d) $s = 1.8$
   (10) $s = 8.2$

Chapter 6

1. (a) $-1.97; -.76; .36; 1.21; 1.86; 2.33$
   (b) $30.3; 42.4; 53.6; 62.1; 68.6; 73.3$
2. .1064   .2422
   .4932   .0199
   .4987   .2881
   .3413   .4993
3. (a) 196.8   371.1
        496.6   260
         .65   106
       79.4   .35
   (b) 61   26
       <1   48
       99+   79
       84   99+
5. (a) 48%, 22%, 46%
   (b) 43.5%, 57 cases; 12.1%, 16 cases; 3.58%, 5 cases
   (c) 25; 22

Chapter 7

3. .81
4. .78
5. $r = .93$
   Mental Ability: $\bar{X} = 43.8, s = 6.1$
   English: $\bar{X} = 175.6, s = 19.4$
6. .84
7.

	WAIS*	J	C	ML	P & H
WAIS	—	−.55	.54	−.74	−.50
J		—	−.86	.82	.68
C			—	−.87	−.90
ML				—	.73
P & H					—

* All r's computed by raw-score formula.

8.

	Minn.Cl.* Nos.	Minn.Cl. Names	MPFB	Otis
Minn.Cl. Nos.	—	.88	.42	.16
Minn.Cl. Names		—	.33	.20
MPFB			—	.70
Otis				—

* All r's computed by raw-score formula.

Chapter 8

1. (a) 7
   (b) 24
   (c) -7
   (d) 50.88
2. 113.4
3. 3.0
4. $Y' = 2.9 + 1.968X$
   $s_{yx} = 5$
5. (b) $b_{yx} = .70$; $a_{yx} = 7.0$
       $b_{xy} = 1.2$; $a_{xy} = 3.1$
   (d) $s_{yx} = 12.8$; $s_{xy} = 9.7$
   (e) 81

Chapter 9

1. (a) .077
   (b) .25
   (c) .000125
   (d) .5; .5
   (e) .204
2. (a) .0156
   (b) .0278
   (c) .5
   (d) .00038
3. (a) .21
   (b) .09
4. (a) .34
   (b) .23
5. .00087
6. $p = .19$; No
7. (a) 8
   (b) .084
   (c) .046
8. Coca-Cola, $p = .08$; Pepsi-Cola, $p = .22$; No
9. (a) .028
   (b) .05
   (c) $(\frac{1}{2})^{30}$

Chapter 10

4. (a) 2.03
   (b) $p = .0244$
5. (a) 3.2
   (b) 17.9

Chapter 11

1. $z = 4.12$
2. $z = 4.56$
3. $t = 1.35$
4. $t = .760$
5. $t = 3.66$
6. $11.9–23.1$

Chapter 12

1. (a) 1.59 using formula 12.6
   (b) 1.94
2. $t = 4.17$
3. $t = 2.15$
4. $t = 1.91$
5. $t = 3.37$

Chapter 13

1. $t = 1.51$
2. $.1$
3. $z = .83$
4. $z = -8.57$
5. $.79$

Chapter 14

1. $\chi^2 = 5.71$
2. (a) $\chi^2 = 5.76$
   (b) $\chi^2 = 2.77$
3. Item 1, $\chi^2 = 1.13$
   Item 2, $\chi^2 = 13.20$
4. $\chi^2 = 3.48$
5. $\chi^2 = 5.90$
6. $\chi^2 = 11.16$
7. (1) $\chi^2 = 2.54$ (4) $\chi^2 = 3.61$
   (2) $\chi^2 = 17.50$ (5) $\chi^2 = 11.36$
   (3) $\chi^2 = 3.46$
8. $\chi^2 = 6.31$
9. $\chi^2 = 3.89$
10. (b) 6
    (c) $\chi^2 = 5.882$
    (d) $\chi^2 = 59.26$

Chapter 15

1. (a) $F = .302$
2. $F = .54$
3. $F = .167$

Chapter 16

1. (a) .54
   (b) $t = 9.03$
2. .71
3. .40; yes; $\chi^2 = 32$
4. .59
5. .31
6. .10
7. (a) .92
   (b) yes
8. .82
9. (a) .44
   (b) .02
10. $R = .496$
11.

	Minn. Cl. Nos.	Minn. Cl. Names	MPFB	Otis
Minn. Cl. Nos.	x	.76	.60	.35
Minn. Cl. Names		x	.34	.41
MPFB			x	.72
Otis				x

Chapter 17

1. (a) .70
   (b) .76
   (c) .33
   (d) 1.6 using the K-R 20 coefficient
2. (a) .91
   (b) .82
   (c) 100
3. (a) 9
   (c) 12.3
5. .50

Chapter 18

1. 1.81
2. Reject H_0 at 1% point
3. $X^2 = .81$
4. $X^2 = 3.17$
5. $U = 86$
6. $U = 120.5$
7. $Z = 1.86$
8. Difference not significant
9. $H = 3.28$
10. Median Test, $X^2 = 9.94$
    Kruskal-Wallis Test, $H = 71.84$

REFERENCES

Bartlett, M. S.   Some examples of statistical research in agriculture and applied biology. *Journal of the Royal Statistical Society*, 1937, *4*, 137–170.

Bradley, J.   *Distribution-Free Statistical Tests*, WADO Technical Report 60–661, 1960, Wright-Patterson Air Force Base, Ohio.

Cochran, W. G.   Some consequences when the assumptions underlying the analysis of variance have not been met. *Biometrics*, 1947, *3*, 22–28.

Cochran, W. G. and G. M. Cox.   *Experimental Design*. New York: Wiley, 2nd ed., 1957.

Downie, N. M.   *Fundamentals of Measurement*. New York: Oxford University Press, 1958.

Edward, A. L.   *Statistical Methods for the Behavioral Sciences*. New York: Rinehart, 1954.

Edwards, A. L.   *Experimental Design in Psychological Research*. New York: Rinehart, rev. ed., 1960.

Guilford, J. P.   *Psychometric Methods*. New York: McGraw-Hill, rev. ed., 1954.

Guilford, J. P.   *Fundamental Statistics in Psychology and Education*. New York: McGraw-Hill, 3rd ed., 1956.

Gulliken, H.   *Theory of Mental Tests*. New York: Wiley, 1950.

Huff, D.   *How to Lie with Statistics*. New York: Norton, 1954.

Jaspen, N.   Serial correlation. *Psychometrika*, 1946, *11*, 23–30.

Jenkins, W. L.   Triserial *r*—a neglected statistic. *Journal of Applied Psychology*, 1956, *40*, 63–64.

Lindquist, E. C.   *Educational Measurement*. Washington, D.C.: The American Council on Education, 1951.

Lord, F. M.   Nomograph for computing multiple correlation coefficients. *Journal of the American Statistical Association*, 1955, *50*, 1073–1077.

Lord, F. M.   Tests of the same length do have the same standard error. *Educational and Psychological Measurement*, 1959, *19*, 233–239.

McNemar, Q.   *Psychological Statistics*. New York: Wiley, 3rd ed., 1962.

Moses, E. L.   Non-parametric statistics for psychological research. *Psychological Bulletin*, 1952, *49*, 122–143.

Peatman, J. B.   *Introduction to Applied Statistics*. New York: Harper and Row, 1963.

Remmers, H. H. and N. L. Gage.   *Educational Measurement and Evaluation*. New York: Harper, 1955.

Saupe, J. L.   Some useful estimates of KR formula #20 reliability coefficient. *Educational and Psychological Measurement*, 1961, *21*, 63–71.

Sellitz, C. et al.   *Research Methods in Social Relations*. New York: Henry Holt, 1959.

Siegel, S.   *Nonparametric Statistics for the Behavioral Sciences*. New York: McGraw-Hill, 1956.

Snedecor, G. W.   *Statistical Methods Applied to Experiments in Agriculture and Biology*. Ames, Iowa: Iowa State College Press, 5th ed., 1956.

Stevens, S. S. On the theory of scales of measurement. *Science*, 1946, *103*, 670–680.

Stevens, S. S. Measurement and Man. *Science*, 1958, *127*, 383–389.

Tate, M. W. and R. C. Clelland. *Non-Parametric and Short-Cut Statistics*. Danville, Ill.: Interstate Printers and Publishers, 1957.

Tukey, J. W. Comparing individual means in the analysis of variance. *Biometrics*, 1949, *5*, 99–114.

Walker, Helen M. *Studies in the History of Statistical Method*. Baltimore: Williams and Wilkins Co., 1929.

Walker, H. M. and J. Lev. *Statistical Inference*. New York: Henry Holt, 1953.

TABLES

TABLE I.   Squares, Square Roots and Reciprocals of Integers from 1 to 1000

n	n^2	$\sqrt{n}$	$\dfrac{1}{n}$	$\dfrac{1}{\sqrt{n}}$
1	1	1.0000	1.000000	1.0000
2	4	1.4142	.500000	.7071
3	9	1.7321	.333333	.5774
4	16	2.0000	.250000	.5000
5	25	2.2361	.200000	.4472
6	36	2.4495	.166667	.4082
7	49	2.6458	.142857	.3780
8	64	2.8284	.125000	.3536
9	81	3.0000	.111111	.3333
10	100	3.1623	.100000	.3162
11	121	3.3166	.090909	.3015
12	144	3.4641	.083333	.2887
13	169	3.6056	.076923	.2774
14	196	3.7417	.071429	.2673
15	225	3.8730	.066667	.2582
16	256	4.0000	.062500	.2500
17	289	4.1231	.058824	.2425
18	324	4.2426	.055556	.2357
19	361	4.3589	.052632	.2294
20	400	4.4721	.050000	.2236
21	441	4.5826	.047619	.2182
22	484	4.6904	.045455	.2132
23	529	4.7958	.043478	.2085
24	576	4.8990	.041667	.2041
25	625	5.0000	.040000	.2000
26	676	5.0990	.038462	.1961
27	729	5.1962	.037037	.1925
28	784	5.2915	.035714	.1890
29	841	5.3852	.034483	.1857
30	900	5.4772	.033333	.1826
31	961	5.5678	.032258	.1796
32	1024	5.6569	.031250	.1768
33	1089	5.7446	.030303	.1741
34	1156	5.8310	.029412	.1715
35	1225	5.9161	.028571	.1690

SOURCE: J. G. Peatman: *Descriptive and Sampling Statistics.* New York: Harper, 1947. Reprinted by permission of the publisher.

TABLE I (*Continued*)

n	n^2	$\sqrt{n}$	$\dfrac{1}{n}$	$\dfrac{1}{\sqrt{n}}$
36	1296	6.0000	.027778	.1667
37	1369	6.0828	.027027	.1644
38	1444	6.1644	.026316	.1622
39	1521	6.2450	.025641	.1601
40	1600	6.3246	.025000	.1581
41	1681	6.4031	.024390	.1562
42	1764	6.4807	.023810	.1543
43	1849	6.5574	.023256	.1525
44	1936	6.6332	.022727	.1508
45	2025	6.7082	.022222	.1491
46	2116	6.7823	.021739	.1474
47	2209	6.8557	.021277	.1459
48	2304	6.9282	.020833	.1443
49	2401	7.0000	.020408	.1429
50	2500	7.0711	.020000	.1414
51	2601	7.1414	.019608	.1400
52	2704	7.2111	.019231	.1387
53	2809	7.2801	.018868	.1374
54	2916	7.3485	.018519	.1361
55	3025	7.4162	.018182	.1348
56	3136	7.4833	.017857	.1336
57	3249	7.5498	.017544	.1325
58	3364	7.6158	.017241	.1313
59	3481	7.6811	.016949	.1302
60	3600	7.7460	.016667	.1291
61	3721	7.8102	.016393	.1280
62	3844	7.8740	.016129	.1270
63	3969	7.9373	.015873	.1260
64	4096	8.0000	.015625	.1250
65	4225	8.0623	.015385	.1240
66	4356	8.1240	.015152	.1231
67	4489	8.1854	.014925	.1222
68	4624	8.2462	.014706	.1213
69	4761	8.3066	.014493	.1204
70	4900	8.3666	.014286	.1195
71	5041	8.4261	.014085	.1187
72	5184	8.4853	.013889	.1179
73	5329	8.5440	.013699	.1170
74	5476	8.6023	.013514	.1162
75	5625	8.6603	.013333	.1155
76	5776	8.7178	.013158	.1147
77	5929	8.7750	.012987	.1140
78	6084	8.8318	.012821	.1132
79	6241	8.8882	.012658	.1125
80	6400	8.9443	.012500	.1118
81	6561	9.0000	.012346	.1111
82	6724	9.0554	.012195	.1104
83	6889	9.1104	.012048	.1098
84	7056	9.1652	.011905	.1091
85	7225	9.2195	.011765	.1085

TABLE I (*Continued*)

n	n^2	$\sqrt{n}$	$\dfrac{1}{n}$	$\dfrac{1}{\sqrt{n}}$
86	7396	9.2736	.011628	.1078
87	7569	9.3274	.011494	.1072
88	7744	9.3808	.011364	.1066
89	7921	9.4340	.011236	.1060
90	8100	9.4868	.011111	.1054
91	8281	9.5394	.010989	.1048
92	8464	9.5917	.010870	.1043
93	8649	9.6437	.010753	.1037
94	8836	9.6954	.010638	.1031
95	9025	9.7468	.010526	.1026
96	9216	9.7980	.010417	.1021
97	9409	9.8489	.010309	.1015
98	9604	9.8995	.010204	.1010
99	9801	9.9499	.010101	.1005
100	10000	10.0000	.010000	.1000
101	10201	10.0499	.009901	.0995
102	10404	10.0995	.009804	.0990
103	10609	10.1489	.009709	.0985
104	10816	10.1980	.009615	.0981
105	11025	10.2470	.009524	.0976
106	11236	10.2956	.009434	.0971
107	11449	10.3441	.009346	.0967
108	11664	10.3923	.009259	.0962
109	11881	10.4403	.009174	.0958
110	12100	10.4881	.009091	.0953
111	12321	10.5357	.009009	.0949
112	12544	10.5830	.008929	.0945
113	12769	10.6301	.008850	.0941
114	12996	10.6771	.008772	.0937
115	13225	10.7238	.008696	.0933
116	13456	10.7703	.008621	.0928
117	13689	10.8167	.008547	.0925
118	13924	10.8628	.008475	.0921
119	14161	10.9087	.008403	.0917
120	14400	10.9545	.008333	.0913
121	14641	11.0000	.008264	.0909
122	14884	11.0454	.008197	.0905
123	15129	11.0905	.008130	.0902
124	15376	11.1355	.008065	.0898
125	15625	11.1803	.008000	.0894
126	15876	11.2250	.007937	.0891
127	16129	11.2694	.007874	.0887
128	16384	11.3137	.007813	.0884
129	16641	11.3578	.007752	.0880
130	16900	11.4018	.007692	.0877
131	17161	11.4455	.007634	.0874
132	17424	11.4891	.007576	.0870
133	17689	11.5326	.007519	.0867
134	17956	11.5758	.007463	.0864
135	18225	11.6190	.007407	.0861

TABLE I (*Continued*)

n	n^2	$\sqrt{n}$	$\dfrac{1}{n}$	$\dfrac{1}{\sqrt{n}}$
136	18496	11.6619	.007353	.0857
137	18769	11.7047	.007299	.0854
138	19044	11.7473	.007246	.0851
139	19321	11.7898	.007194	.0848
140	19600	11.8322	.007143	.0845
141	19881	11.8743	.007092	.0842
142	20164	11.9164	.007042	.0839
143	20449	11.9583	.006993	.0836
144	20736	12.0000	.006944	.0833
145	21025	12.0416	.006897	.0830
146	21316	12.0830	.006849	.0828
147	21609	12.1244	.006803	.0825
148	21904	12.1655	.006757	.0822
149	22201	12.2066	.006711	.0819
150	22500	12.2474	.006667	.0816
151	22801	12.2882	.006623	.0814
152	23104	12.3288	.006579	.0811
153	23409	12.3693	.006536	.0808
154	23716	12.4097	.006494	.0806
155	24025	12.4499	.006452	.0803
156	24336	12.4900	.006410	.0801
157	24649	12.5300	.006369	.0798
158	24964	12.5698	.006329	.0796
159	25281	12.6095	.006289	.0793
160	25600	12.6491	.006250	.0791
161	25921	12.6886	.006211	.0788
162	26244	12.7279	.006173	.0786
163	26569	12.7671	.006135	.0783
164	26896	12.8062	.006098	.0781
165	27225	12.8452	.006061	.0778
166	27556	12.8841	.006024	.0776
167	27889	12.9228	.005988	.0774
168	28224	12.9615	.005952	.0772
169	28561	13.0000	.005917	.0769
170	28900	13.0384	.005882	.0767
171	29241	13.0767	.005848	.0765
172	29584	13.1149	.005814	.0762
173	29929	13.1529	.005780	.0760
174	30276	13.1909	.005747	.0758
175	30625	13.2288	.005714	.0756
176	30976	13.2665	.005682	.0754
177	31329	13.3041	.005650	.0752
178	31684	13.3417	.005618	.0750
179	32041	13.3791	.005587	.0747
180	32400	13.4164	.005556	.0745
181	32761	13.4536	.005525	.0743
182	33124	13.4907	.005495	.0741
183	33489	13.5277	.005464	.0739
184	33856	13.5647	.005435	.0737
185	34225	13.6015	.005405	.0735

TABLE I (*Continued*)

n	n^2	$\sqrt{n}$	$\dfrac{1}{n}$	$\dfrac{1}{\sqrt{n}}$
186	34596	13.6382	.005376	.0733
187	34969	13.6748	.005348	.0731
188	35344	13.7113	.005319	.0729
189	35721	13.7477	.005291	.0727
190	36100	13.7840	.005263	.0725
191	36481	13.8203	.005236	.0724
192	36864	13.8564	.005208	.0722
193	37249	13.8924	.005181	.0720
194	37636	13.9284	.005155	.0718
195	38025	13.9642	.005128	.0716
196	38416	14.0000	.005102	.0714
197	38809	14.0357	.005076	.0712
198	39204	14.0712	.005051	.0711
199	39601	14.1067	.005025	.0709
200	40000	14.1421	.005000	.0707
201	40401	14.1774	.004975	.0705
202	40804	14.2127	.004950	.0704
203	41209	14.2478	.004926	.0702
204	41616	14.2829	.004902	.0700
205	42025	14.3178	.004878	.0698
206	42436	14.3527	.004854	.0697
207	42849	14.3875	.004831	.0695
208	43264	14.4222	.004808	.0693
209	43681	14.4568	.004785	.0692
210	44100	14.4914	.004762	.0690
211	44521	14.5258	.004739	.0688
212	44944	14.5602	.004717	.0687
213	45369	14.5945	.004695	.0685
214	45796	14.6287	.004673	.0684
215	46225	14.6629	.004651	.0682
216	46656	14.6969	.004630	.0680
217	47089	14.7309	.004608	.0679
218	47524	14.7648	.004587	.0677
219	47961	14.7986	.004566	.0676
220	48400	14.8324	.004545	.0674
221	48841	14.8661	.004525	.0673
222	49284	14.8997	.004505	.0671
223	49729	14.9332	.004484	.0670
224	50176	14.9666	.004464	.0668
225	50625	15.0000	.004444	.0667
226	51076	15.0333	.004425	.0665
227	51529	15.0665	.004405	.0664
228	51984	15.0997	.004386	.0662
229	52441	15.1327	.004367	.0661
230	52900	15.1658	.004348	.0659
231	53361	15.1987	.004329	.0658
232	53824	15.2315	.004310	.0657
233	54289	15.2643	.004292	.0655
234	54756	15.2971	.004274	.0654
235	55225	15.3297	.004255	.0652

TABLE I (*Continued*)

n	n^2	$\sqrt{n}$	$\dfrac{1}{n}$	$\dfrac{1}{\sqrt{n}}$
236	55696	15.3623	.004237	.0651
237	56169	15.3948	.004219	.0650
238	56644	15.4272	.004202	.0648
239	57121	15.4596	.004184	.0647
240	57600	15.4919	.004167	.0645
241	58081	15.5242	.004149	.0644
242	58564	15.5563	.004132	.0643
243	59049	15.5885	.004115	.0642
244	59536	15.6205	.004098	.0640
245	60025	15.6525	.004082	.0639
246	60516	15.6844	.004065	.0638
247	61009	15.7162	.004049	.0636
248	61504	15.7480	.004032	.0635
249	62001	15.7797	.004016	.0634
250	62500	15.8114	.004000	.0632
251	63001	15.8430	.003984	.0631
252	63504	15.8745	.003968	.0630
253	64009	15.9060	.003953	.0629
254	64516	15.9374	.003937	.0627
255	65025	15.9687	.003922	.0626
256	65536	16.0000	.003906	.0625
257	66049	16.0312	.003891	.0624
258	66564	16.0624	.003876	.0623
259	67081	16.0935	.003861	.0621
260	67600	16.1245	.003846	.0620
261	68121	16.1555	.003831	.0619
262	68644	16.1864	.003817	.0618
263	69169	16.2173	.003802	.0617
264	69696	16.2481	.003788	.0615
265	70225	16.2788	.003774	.0614
266	70756	16.3095	.003759	.0613
267	71289	16.3401	.003745	.0612
268	71824	16.3707	.003731	.0611
269	72361	16.4012	.003717	.0610
270	72900	16.4317	.003704	.0609
271	73441	16.4621	.003690	.0607
272	73984	16.4924	.003676	.0606
273	74529	16.5227	.003663	.0605
274	75076	16.5529	.003650	.0604
275	75625	16.5831	.003636	.0603
276	76176	16.6132	.003623	.0602
277	76729	16.6433	.003610	.0601
278	77284	16.6733	.003597	.0600
279	77841	16.7033	.003584	.0599
280	78400	16.7332	.003571	.0598
281	78961	16.7631	.003559	.0597
282	79524	16.7929	.003546	.0595
283	80089	16.8226	.003534	.0594
284	80656	16.8523	.003521	.0593
285	81225	16.8819	.003509	.0592

TABLE I (*Continued*)

n	n^2	$\sqrt{n}$	$\dfrac{1}{n}$	$\dfrac{1}{\sqrt{n}}$
286	81796	16.9115	.003497	.0591
287	82369	16.9411	.003484	.0590
288	82944	16.9706	.003472	.0589
289	83521	17.0000	.003460	.0588
290	84100	17.0294	.003448	.0587
291	84681	17.0587	.003436	.0586
292	85264	17.0880	.003425	.0585
293	85849	17.1172	.003413	.0584
294	86436	17.1464	.003401	.0583
295	87025	17.1756	.003390	.0582
296	87616	17.2047	.003378	.0581
297	88209	17.2337	.003367	.0580
298	88804	17.2627	.003356	.0579
299	89401	17.2916	.003344	.0578
300	90000	17.3205	.003333	.0577
301	90601	17.3494	.003322	.0576
302	91204	17.3781	.003311	.0575
303	91809	17.4069	.003300	.0574
304	92416	17.4356	.003289	.0574
305	93025	17.4642	.003279	.0573
306	93636	17.4929	.003268	.0572
307	94249	17.5214	.003257	.0571
308	94864	17.5499	.003247	.0570
309	95481	17.5784	.003236	.0569
310	96100	17.6068	.003226	.0568
311	96721	17.6352	.003215	.0567
312	97344	17.6635	.003205	.0566
313	97969	17.6918	.003195	.0565
314	98596	17.7200	.003185	.0564
315	99225	17.7482	.003175	.0563
316	99856	17.7764	.003165	.0563
317	100489	17.8045	.003155	.0562
318	101124	17.8326	.003145	.0561
319	101761	17.8606	.003135	.0560
320	102400	17.8885	.003125	.0559
321	103041	17.9165	.003115	.0558
322	103684	17.9444	.003106	.0557
323	104329	17.9722	.003096	.0556
324	104976	18.0000	.003086	.0556
325	105625	18.0278	.003077	.0555
326	106276	18.0555	.003067	.0554
327	106929	18.0831	.003058	.0553
328	107584	18.1108	.003049	.0552
329	108241	18.1384	.003040	.0551
330	108900	18.1659	.003030	.0550
331	109561	18.1934	.003021	.0550
332	110224	18.2209	.003012	.0549
333	110889	18.2483	.003003	.0548
334	111556	18.2757	.002994	.0547
335	112225	18.3030	.002985	.0546

TABLE I (*Continued*)

n	n^2	$\sqrt{n}$	$\dfrac{1}{n}$	$\dfrac{1}{\sqrt{n}}$
336	112896	18.3303	.002976	.0546
337	113569	18.3576	.002967	.0545
338	114244	18.3848	.002959	.0544
339	114921	18.4120	.002950	.0543
340	115600	18.4391	.002941	.0542
341	116281	18.4662	.002933	.0542
342	116964	18.4932	.002924	.0541
343	117649	18.5203	.002915	.0540
344	118336	18.5472	.002907	.0539
345	119025	18.5742	.002899	.0538
346	119716	18.6011	.002890	.0538
347	120409	18.6279	.002882	.0537
348	121104	18.6548	.002874	.0536
349	121801	18.6815	.002865	.0535
350	122500	18.7083	.002857	.0535
351	123201	18.7350	.002849	.0534
352	123904	18.7617	.002841	.0533
353	124609	18.7883	.002833	.0532
354	125316	18.8149	.002825	.0531
355	126025	18.8414	.002817	.0531
356	126736	18.8680	.002809	.0530
357	127449	18.8944	.002801	.0529
358	128164	18.9209	.002793	.0529
359	128881	18.9473	.002786	.0528
360	129600	18.9737	.002778	.0527
361	130321	19.0000	.002770	.0526
362	131044	19.0263	.002762	.0526
363	131769	19.0526	.002755	.0525
364	132496	19.0788	.002747	.0524
365	133225	19.1050	.002740	.0523
366	133956	19.1311	.002732	.0523
367	134689	19.1572	.002725	.0522
368	135424	19.1833	.002717	.0521
369	136161	19.2094	.002710	.0521
370	136900	19.2354	.002703	.0520
371	137641	19.2614	.002695	.0519
372	138384	19.2873	.002688	.0518
373	139129	19.3132	.002681	.0518
374	139876	19.3391	.002674	.0517
375	140625	19.3649	.002667	.0516
376	141376	19.3907	.002660	.0516
377	142129	19.4165	.002653	.0515
378	142884	19.4422	.002646	.0514
379	143641	19.4679	.002639	.0514
380	144400	19.4936	.002632	.0513
381	145161	19.5192	.002625	.0512
382	145924	19.5448	.002618	.0512
383	146689	19.5704	.002611	.0511
384	147456	19.5959	.002604	.0510
385	148225	19.6214	.002597	.0510

Table I (*Continued*)

n	n²	√n̄	$\frac{1}{n}$	$\frac{1}{\sqrt{n}}$
386	148996	19.6469	.002591	.0509
387	149769	19.6723	.002584	.0508
388	150544	19.6977	.002577	.0508
389	151321	19.7231	.002571	.0507
390	152100	19.7484	.002564	.0506
391	152881	19.7737	.002558	.0506
392	153664	19.7990	.002551	.0505
393	154449	19.8242	.002545	.0504
394	155236	19.8494	.002538	.0504
395	156025	19.8746	.002532	.0503
396	156816	19.8997	.002525	.0503
397	157609	19.9249	.002519	.0502
398	158404	19.9499	.002513	.0501
399	159201	19.9750	.002506	.0501
400	160000	20.0000	.002500	.0500
401	160801	20.0250	.002494	.0499
402	161604	20.0499	.002488	.0499
403	162409	20.0749	.002481	.0498
404	163216	20.0998	.002475	.0498
405	164025	20.1246	.002469	.0497
406	164836	20.1494	.002463	.0496
407	165649	20.1742	.002457	.0496
408	166464	20.1990	.002451	.0495
409	167281	20.2237	.002445	.0494
410	168100	20.2485	.002439	.0494
411	168921	20.2731	.002433	.0493
412	169744	20.2978	.002427	.0493
413	170569	20.3224	.002421	.0492
414	171396	20.3470	.002415	.0491
415	172225	20.3715	.002410	.0491
416	173056	20.3961	.002404	.0490
417	173889	20.4206	.002398	.0490
418	174724	20.4450	.002392	.0489
419	175561	20.4695	.002387	.0489
420	176400	20.4939	.002381	.0488
421	177241	20.5183	.002375	.0487
422	178084	20.5426	.002370	.0487
423	178929	20.5670	.002364	.0486
424	179776	20.5913	.002358	.0486
425	180625	20.6155	.002353	.0485
426	181476	20.6398	.002347	.0485
427	182329	20.6640	.002342	.0484
428	183184	20.6882	.002336	.0483
429	184041	20.7123	.002331	.0483
430	184900	20.7364	.002326	.0482
431	185761	20.7605	.002320	.0482
432	186624	20.7846	.002315	.0481
433	187489	20.8087	.002309	.0481
434	188356	20.8327	.002304	.0480
435	189225	20.8567	.002299	.0479

TABLE I (*Continued*)

n	n^2	$\sqrt{n}$	$\dfrac{1}{n}$	$\dfrac{1}{\sqrt{n}}$
436	190096	20.8806	.002294	.0479
437	190969	20.9045	.002288	.0478
438	191844	20.9284	.002283	.0478
439	192721	20.9523	.002278	.0477
440	193600	20.9762	.002273	.0477
441	194481	21.0000	.002268	.0476
442	195364	21.0238	.002262	.0476
443	196249	21.0476	.002257	.0475
444	197136	21.0713	.002252	.0475
445	198025	21.0950	.002247	.0474
446	198916	21.1187	.002242	.0474
447	199809	21.1424	.002237	.0473
448	200704	21.1660	.002232	.0472
449	201601	21.1896	.002227	.0472
450	202500	21.2132	.002222	.0471
451	203401	21.2368	.002217	.0471
452	204304	21.2603	.002212	.0470
453	205209	21.2838	.002208	.0470
454	206116	21.3073	.002203	.0469
455	207025	21.3307	.002198	.0469
456	207936	21.3542	.002193	.0468
457	208849	21.3776	.022188	.0468
458	209764	21.4009	.002183	.0467
459	210681	21.4243	.002179	.0467
460	211600	21.4476	.002174	.0466
461	212521	21.4709	.002169	.0466
462	213444	21.4942	.002165	.0465
463	214369	21.5174	.002160	.0465
464	215296	21.5407	.002155	.0464
465	216225	21.5639	.002151	.0464
466	217156	21.5870	.002146	.0463
467	218089	21.6102	.002141	.0463
468	219024	21.6333	.002137	.0462
469	219961	21.6564	.002132	.0462
470	220900	21.6795	.002128	.0461
471	221841	21.7025	.002123	.0461
472	222784	21.7256	.002119	.0460
473	223729	21.7486	.002114	.0460
474	224676	21.7715	.002110	.0459
475	225625	21.7945	.002105	.0459
476	226576	21.8174	.002101	.0458
477	227529	21.8403	.002096	.0458
478	228484	21.8632	.002092	.0457
479	229441	21.8861	.002088	.0457
480	230400	21.9089	.002083	.0456
481	231361	21.9317	.002079	.0456
482	232324	21.9545	.002075	.0455
483	233289	21.9773	.002070	.0455
484	234256	22.0000	.002066	.0455
485	235225	22.0227	.002062	.0454

TABLE I (*Continued*)

n	n^2	$\sqrt{n}$	$\dfrac{1}{n}$	$\dfrac{1}{\sqrt{n}}$
486	236196	22.0454	.002058	.0454
487	237169	22.0681	.002053	.0453
488	238144	22.0907	.002049	.0453
489	239121	22.1133	.002045	.0452
490	240100	22.1359	.002041	.0452
491	241081	22.1585	.002037	.0451
492	242064	22.1811	.002033	.0451
493	243049	22.2036	.002028	.0450
494	244036	22.2261	.002024	.0450
495	245025	22.2486	.002020	.0449
496	246016	22.2711	.002016	.0448
497	247009	22.2935	.002012	.0449
498	248004	22.3159	.002008	.0449
499	249001	22.3383	.002004	.0448
500	250000	22.3607	.002000	.0447
501	251001	22.3830	.001996	.0447
502	252004	22.4054	.001992	.0446
503	253009	22.4277	.001988	.0446
504	254016	22.4499	.001984	.0445
505	255025	22.4722	.001980	.0445
506	256036	22.4944	.001976	.0445
507	257049	22.5167	.001972	.0444
508	258064	22.5389	.001969	.0444
509	259081	22.5610	.001965	.0443
510	260100	22.5832	.001961	.0443
511	261121	22.6053	.001957	.0442
512	262144	22.6274	.001953	.0442
513	263169	22.6495	.001949	.0442
514	264196	22.6716	.001946	.0441
515	265225	22.6936	.001942	.0441
516	266256	22.7156	.001938	.0440
517	267289	22.7376	.001934	.0440
518	268324	22.7596	.001931	.0439
519	269361	22.7816	.001927	.0439
520	270400	22.8035	.001923	.0439
521	271441	22.8254	.001919	.0438
522	272484	22.8473	.001916	.0438
523	273529	22.8692	.001912	.0437
524	274576	22.8910	.001908	.0437
525	275625	22.9129	.001905	.0436
526	276676	22.9347	.001901	.0436
527	277729	22.9565	.001898	.0436
528	278784	22.9783	.001894	.0435
529	279841	23.0000	.001890	.0435
530	280900	23.0217	.001887	.0434
531	281961	23.0434	.001883	.0434
532	283024	23.0651	.001880	.0434
533	284089	23.0868	.001876	.0433
534	285156	23.1084	.001873	.0433
535	286225	23.1301	.001869	.0432

279

TABLE I (*Continued*)

n	n²	√n	$\frac{1}{n}$	$\frac{1}{\sqrt{n}}$
536	287296	23.1517	.001866	.0432
537	288369	23.1733	.001862	.0432
538	289444	23.1948	.001859	.0431
539	290521	23.2164	.001855	.0431
540	291600	23.2379	.001852	.0430
541	292681	23.2594	.001848	.0430
542	293764	23.2809	.001845	.0430
543	294849	23.3024	.001842	.0429
544	295936	23.3238	.001838	.0429
545	297025	23.3452	.001835	.0428
546	298116	23.3666	.001832	.0428
547	299209	23.3880	.001828	.0428
548	300304	23.4094	.001825	.0427
549	301401	23.4307	.001821	.0427
550	302500	23.4521	.001818	.0426
551	303601	23.4734	.001815	.0426
552	304704	23.4947	.001812	.0426
553	305809	23.5160	.001808	.0425
554	306916	23.5372	.001805	.0425
555	308025	23.5584	.001802	.0424
556	309136	23.5797	.001799	.0424
557	310249	23.6008	.001795	.0424
558	311364	23.6220	.001792	.0423
559	312481	23.6432	.001789	.0423
560	313600	23.6643	.001786	.0423
561	314721	23.6854	.001783	.0422
562	315844	23.7065	.001779	.0422
563	316969	23.7276	.001776	.0421
564	318096	23.7487	.001773	.0421
565	319225	23.7697	.001770	.0421
566	320356	23.7908	.001767	.0420
567	321489	23.8118	.001764	.0420
568	322624	23.8328	.001761	.0420
569	323761	23.8537	.001757	.0419
570	324900	23.8747	.001754	.0419
571	326041	23.8956	.001751	.0418
572	327184	23.9165	.001748	.0418
573	328329	23.9374	.001745	.0418
574	329476	23.9583	.001742	.0417
575	330625	23.9792	.001739	.0417
576	331776	24.0000	.001736	.0417
577	332929	24.0208	.001733	.0416
578	334084	24.0416	.001730	.0416
579	335241	24.0624	.001727	.0416
580	336400	24.0832	.001724	.0415
581	337561	24.1039	.001721	.0415
582	338724	24.1247	.001718	.0415
583	339889	24.1454	.001715	.0414
584	341056	24.1661	.001712	.0414
585	342225	24.1868	.001709	.0413

Table I (*Continued*)

n	n^2	$\sqrt{n}$	$\dfrac{1}{n}$	$\dfrac{1}{\sqrt{n}}$
586	343396	24.2074	.001706	.0413
587	344569	24.2281	.001704	.0413
588	345744	24.2487	.001701	.0412
589	346921	24.2693	.001698	.0412
590	348100	24.2899	.001695	.0412
591	349281	24.3105	.001692	.0411
592	350464	24.3311	.001689	.0411
593	351649	24.3516	.001686	.0411
594	352836	24.3721	.001684	.0410
595	354025	24.3926	.001681	.0410
596	355216	24.4131	.001678	.0410
597	356409	24.4336	.001675	.0409
598	357604	24.4540	.001672	.0409
599	358801	24.4745	.001669	.0409
600	360000	24.4949	.001667	.0408
601	361201	24.5153	.001664	.0408
602	362404	24.5357	.001661	.0408
603	363609	24.5561	.001658	.0407
604	364816	24.5764	.001656	.0407
605	366025	24.5967	.001653	.0407
606	367236	24.6171	.001650	.0406
607	368449	24.6374	.001647	.0406
608	369664	24.6577	.001645	.0406
609	370881	24.6779	.001642	.0405
610	372100	24.6982	.001639	.0405
611	373321	24.7184	.001637	.0405
612	374544	24.7386	.001634	.0404
613	375769	24.7588	.001631	.0404
614	376996	24.7790	.001629	.0404
615	378225	24.7992	.001626	.0403
616	379456	24.8193	.001623	.0403
617	380689	24.8395	.001621	.0403
618	381924	24.8596	.001618	.0402
619	383161	24.8797	.001616	.0402
620	384400	24.8998	.001613	.0402
621	385641	24.9199	.001610	.0401
622	386884	24.9399	.001608	.0401
623	388129	24.9600	.001605	.0401
624	389376	24.9800	.001603	.0400
625	390625	25.0000	.001600	.0400
626	391876	25.0200	.001597	.0400
627	393129	25.0400	.001595	.0399
628	394384	25.0599	.001592	.0399
629	395641	25.0799	.001590	.0399
630	396900	25.0998	.001587	.0398
631	398161	25.1197	.001585	.0398
632	399424	25.1396	.001582	.0398
633	400689	25.1595	.001580	.0397
634	401956	25.1794	.001577	.0397
635	403225	25.1992	.001575	.0397

TABLE I (*Continued*)

n	n^2	$\sqrt{n}$	$\dfrac{1}{n}$	$\dfrac{1}{\sqrt{n}}$
636	404496	25.2190	.001572	.0397
637	405769	25.2389	.001570	.0396
638	407044	25.2587	.001567	.0396
639	408321	25.2784	.001565	.0396
640	409600	25.2982	.001563	.0395
641	410881	25.3180	.001560	.0395
642	412164	25.3377	.001558	.0395
643	413449	25.3574	.001555	.0394
644	414736	25.3772	.001553	.0394
645	416025	25.3969	.001550	.0394
646	417316	25.4165	.001548	.0393
647	418609	25.4362	.001546	.0393
648	419904	25.4558	.001543	.0393
649	421201	25.4755	.001541	.0393
650	422500	25.4951	.001538	.0392
651	423801	25.5147	.001536	.0392
652	425104	25.5343	.001534	.0392
653	426409	25.5539	.001531	.0391
654	427716	25.5734	.001529	.0391
655	429025	25.5930	.001527	.0391
656	430336	25.6125	.001524	.0390
657	431649	25.6320	.001522	.0390
658	432964	25.6515	.001520	.0390
659	434281	25.6710	.001517	.0390
660	435600	25.6905	.001515	.0389
661	436921	25.7099	.001513	.0389
662	438244	25.7294	.001511	.0389
663	439569	25.7488	.001508	.0388
664	440896	25.7682	.001506	.0388
665	442225	25.7876	.001504	.0388
666	443556	25.8070	.001502	.0387
667	444889	25.8263	.001499	.0387
668	446224	25.8457	.001497	.0387
669	447561	25.8650	.001495	.0387
670	448900	25.8844	.001493	.0386
671	450241	25.9037	.001490	.0386
672	451584	25.9230	.001488	.0386
673	452929	25.9422	.001486	.0385
674	454276	25.9615	.001484	.0385
675	455625	25.9808	.001481	.0385
676	456976	26.0000	.001479	.0385
677	458329	26.0192	.001477	.0384
678	459684	26.0384	.001475	.0384
679	461041	26.0576	.001473	.0384
680	462400	26.0768	.001471	.0383
681	463761	26.0960	.001468	.0383
682	465124	26.1151	.001466	.0383
683	466489	26.1343	.001464	.0383
684	467856	26.1534	.001462	.0382
685	469225	26.1725	.001460	.0382

TABLE I (*Continued*)

n	n^2	$\sqrt{n}$	$\dfrac{1}{n}$	$\dfrac{1}{\sqrt{n}}$
686	470596	26.1916	.001458	.0382
687	471969	26.2107	.001456	.0382
688	473344	26.2298	.001453	.0381
689	474721	26.2488	.001451	.0381
690	476100	26.2679	.001449	.0381
691	477481	26.2869	.001447	.0380
692	478864	26.3059	.001445	.0380
693	480249	26.3249	.001443	.0380
694	481636	26.3439	.001441	.0380
695	483025	26.3629	.001439	.0379
696	484416	26.3818	.001437	.0379
697	485809	26.4008	.001435	.0379
698	487204	26.4197	.001433	.0379
699	488601	26.4386	.001431	.0378
700	490000	26.4575	.001429	.0378
701	491401	26.4764	.001427	.0378
702	492804	26.4953	.001425	.0377
703	494209	26.5141	.001422	.0377
704	495616	26.5330	.001420	.0377
705	497025	26.5518	.001418	.0377
706	498436	26.5707	.001416	.0376
707	499849	26.5895	.001414	.0376
708	501264	26.6083	.001412	.0376
709	502681	26.6271	.001410	.0376
710	504100	26.6458	.001408	.0375
711	505521	26.6646	.001406	.0375
712	506944	26.6833	.001404	.0375
713	508369	26.7021	.001403	.0375
714	509796	26.7208	.001401	.0374
715	511225	26.7395	.001399	.0374
716	512656	26.7582	.001397	.0374
717	514089	26.7769	.001395	.0373
718	515524	26.7955	.001393	.0373
719	516961	26.8142	.001391	.0373
720	518400	26.8328	.001389	.0373
721	519841	26.8514	.001387	.0372
722	521284	26.8701	.001385	.0372
723	522729	26.8887	.001383	.0372
724	524176	26.9072	.001381	.0372
725	525625	26.9258	.001379	.0371
726	527076	26.9444	.001377	.0371
727	528529	26.9629	.001376	.0371
728	529984	26.9815	.001374	.0371
729	531441	27.0000	.001372	.0370
730	532900	27.0185	.001370	.0370
731	534361	27.0370	.001368	.0370
732	535824	27.0555	.001366	.0370
733	537289	27.0740	.001364	.0369
734	538756	27.0924	.001362	.0369
735	540225	27.1109	.001361	.0369

TABLE I (*Continued*)

n	n^2	$\sqrt{n}$	$\dfrac{1}{n}$	$\dfrac{1}{\sqrt{n}}$
736	541696	27.1293	.001359	.0369
737	543169	27.1477	.001357	.0368
738	544644	27.1662	.001355	.0368
739	546121	27.1846	.001353	.0368
740	547600	27.2029	.001351	.0368
741	549081	27.2213	.001350	.0367
742	550564	27.2397	.001348	.0367
743	552049	27.2580	.001346	.0367
744	553536	27.2764	.001344	.0367
745	555025	27.2947	.001342	.0366
746	556516	27.3130	.001340	.0366
747	558009	27.3313	.001339	.0366
748	559504	27.3496	.001337	.0366
749	561001	27.3679	.001335	.0365
750	562500	27.3861	.001333	.0365
751	564001	27.4044	.001332	.0365
752	565504	27.4226	.001330	.0365
753	567009	27.4408	.001328	.0364
754	568516	27.4591	.001326	.0364
755	570025	27.4773	.001325	.0364
756	571536	27.4955	.001323	.0364
757	573049	27.5136	.001321	.0363
758	574564	27.5318	.001319	.0363
759	576081	27.5500	.001318	.0363
760	577600	27.5681	.001316	.0363
761	579121	27.5862	.001314	.0363
762	580644	27.6043	.001312	.0362
763	582169	27.6225	.001311	.0362
764	583696	27.6405	.001309	.0362
765	585225	27.6586	.001307	.0362
766	586756	27.6767	.001305	.0361
767	588289	27.6948	.001304	.0361
768	589824	27.7128	.001302	.0361
769	591361	27.7308	.001300	.0361
770	592900	27.7489	.001299	.0360
771	594441	27.7669	.001297	.0360
772	595984	27.7849	.001295	.0360
773	597529	27.8029	.001294	.0360
774	599076	27.8209	.001292	.0359
775	600625	27.8388	.001290	.0359
776	602176	27.8568	.001289	.0359
777	603729	27.8747	.001287	.0359
778	605284	27.8927	.001285	.0359
779	606841	27.9106	.001284	.0358
780	608400	27.9285	.001282	.0358
781	609961	27.9464	.001280	.0358
782	611524	27.9643	.001279	.0358
783	613089	27.9821	.001277	.0357
784	614656	28.0000	.001276	.0357
785	616225	28.0179	.001274	.0357

TABLE I (*Continued*)

n	n^2	$\sqrt{n}$	$\dfrac{1}{n}$	$\dfrac{1}{\sqrt{n}}$
786	617796	28.0357	.001272	.0357
787	619369	28.0535	.001271	.0356
788	620944	28.0713	.001269	.0356
789	622521	28.0891	.001267	.0356
790	624100	28.1069	.001266	.0356
791	625681	28.1247	.001264	.0356
792	627264	28.1425	.001263	.0355
793	628849	28.1603	.001261	.0355
794	630436	28.1780	.001259	.0355
795	632025	28.1957	.001258	.0355
796	633616	28.2135	.001256	.0354
797	635209	28.2312	.001255	.0354
798	636804	28.2489	.001253	.0354
799	638401	28.2666	.001252	.0354
800	640000	28.2843	.001250	.0354
801	641601	28.3019	.001248	.0353
802	643204	28.3196	.001247	.0353
803	644809	28.3373	.001245	.0353
804	646416	28.3549	.001244	.0353
805	648025	28.3725	.001242	.0352
806	649636	28.3901	.001241	.0352
807	651249	28.4077	.001239	.0352
808	652864	28.4253	.001238	.0352
809	654481	28.4429	.001236	.0352
810	656100	28.4605	.001235	.0351
811	657721	28.4781	.001233	.0351
812	659344	28.4956	.001232	.0351
813	660969	28.5132	.001230	.0351
814	662596	28.5307	.001229	.0351
815	664225	28.5482	.001227	.0350
816	665856	28.5657	.001225	.0350
817	667489	28.5832	.001224	.0350
818	669124	28.6007	.001222	.0350
819	670761	28.6182	.001221	.0349
820	672400	28.6356	.001220	.0349
821	674041	28.6531	.001218	.0349
822	675684	28.6705	.001217	.0349
823	677329	28.6880	.001215	.0349
824	678976	28.7054	.001214	.0348
825	680625	28.7228	.001212	.0348
826	682276	28.7402	.001211	.0348
827	683929	28.7576	.001209	.0348
828	685584	28.7750	.001208	.0348
829	687241	28.7924	.001206	.0347
830	688900	28.8097	.001205	.0347
831	690561	28.8271	.001203	.0347
832	692224	28.8444	.001202	.0347
833	693889	28.8617	.001200	.0346
834	695556	28.8791	.001199	.0346
835	697225	28.8964	.001198	.0346

Table I (*Continued*)

n	n^2	$\sqrt{n}$	$\dfrac{1}{n}$	$\dfrac{1}{\sqrt{n}}$
836	698896	28.9137	.001196	.0346
837	700569	28.9310	.001195	.0346
838	702244	28.9482	.001193	.0345
839	703921	28.9655	.001192	.0345
840	705600	28.9828	.001190	.0345
841	707281	29.0000	.001189	.0345
842	708964	29.0172	.001188	.0345
843	710649	29.0345	.001186	.0344
844	712336	29.0517	.001185	.0344
845	714025	29.0689	.001183	.0344
846	715716	29.0861	.001182	.0344
847	717409	29.1033	.001181	.0344
848	719104	29.1204	.001179	.0343
849	720801	29.1376	.001178	.0343
850	722500	29.1548	.001176	.0343
851	724201	29.1719	.001175	.0343
852	725904	29.1890	.001174	.0343
853	727609	29.2062	.001172	.0342
854	729316	29.2233	.001171	.0342
855	731025	29.2404	.001170	.0342
856	732736	29.2575	.001168	.0342
857	734449	29.2746	.001167	.0342
858	736164	29.2916	.001166	.0341
859	737881	29.3087	.001164	.0341
860	739600	29.3258	.001163	.0341
861	741321	29.3428	.001161	.0341
862	743044	29.3598	.001160	.0341
863	744769	29.3769	.001159	.0340
864	746496	29.3939	.001157	.0340
865	748225	29.4109	.001156	.0340
866	749956	29.4279	.001155	.0340
867	751689	29.4449	.001153	.0340
868	753424	29.4618	.001152	.0339
869	755161	29.4788	.001151	.0339
870	756900	29.4958	.001149	.0339
871	758641	29.5127	.001148	.0339
872	760384	29.5296	.001147	.0339
873	762129	29.5466	.001145	.0338
874	763876	29.5635	.001144	.0338
875	765625	29.5804	.001143	.0338
876	767376	29.5973	.001142	.0338
877	769129	29.6142	.001140	.0338
878	770884	29.6311	.001139	.0337
879	772641	29.6479	.001138	.0337
880	774400	29.6648	.001136	.0337
881	776161	29.6816	.001135	.0337
882	777924	29.6985	.001134	.0337
883	779689	29.7153	.001133	.0337
884	781456	29.7321	.001131	.0336
885	783225	29.7489	.001130	.0336

TABLE I (*Continued*)

n	n^2	$\sqrt{n}$	$\dfrac{1}{n}$	$\dfrac{1}{\sqrt{n}}$
886	784996	29.7658	.001129	.0336
887	786769	29.7825	.001127	.0336
888	788544	29.7993	.001126	.0336
889	790321	29.8161	.001125	.0335
890	792100	29.8329	.001124	.0335
891	793881	29.8496	.001122	.0335
892	795664	29.8664	.001121	.0335
893	797449	29.8831	.001120	.0335
894	799236	29.8998	.001119	.0334
895	801025	29.9166	.001117	.0334
896	802816	29.9333	.001116	.0334
897	804609	29.9500	.001115	.0334
898	806404	29.9666	.001114	.0334
899	808201	29.9833	.001112	.0334
900	810000	30.0000	.001111	.0333
901	811801	30.0167	.001110	.0333
902	813604	30.0333	.001109	.0333
903	815409	30.0500	.001107	.0333
904	817216	30.0666	.001106	.0333
905	819025	30.0832	.001105	.0332
906	820836	30.0998	.001104	.0332
907	822649	30.1164	.001103	.0332
908	824464	30.1330	.001101	.0332
909	826281	30.1496	.001100	.0332
910	828100	30.1662	.001099	.0331
911	829921	30.1828	.001098	.0331
912	831744	30.1993	.001096	.0331
913	833569	30.2159	.001095	.0331
914	835396	30.2324	.001094	.0331
915	837225	30.2490	.001093	.0331
916	839056	30.2655	.001092	.0330
917	840889	30.2820	.001091	.0330
918	842724	30.2985	.001089	.0330
919	844561	30.3150	.001088	.0330
920	846400	30.3315	.001087	.0330
921	848241	30.3480	.001086	.0330
922	850084	30.3645	.001085	.0329
923	851929	30.3809	.001083	.0329
924	853776	30.3974	.001082	.0329
925	855625	30.4138	.001081	.0329
926	857476	30.4302	.001080	.0329
927	859329	30.4467	.001079	.0328
928	861184	30.4631	.001078	.0328
929	863041	30.4795	.001076	.0328
930	864900	30.4959	.001075	.0328
931	866761	30.5123	.001074	.0328
932	868624	30.5287	.001073	.0328
933	870489	30.5450	.001072	.0327
934	872356	30.5614	.001071	.0327
935	874225	30.5778	.001070	.0327

TABLE I (*Continued*)

n	n^2	$\sqrt{n}$	$\dfrac{1}{n}$	$\dfrac{1}{\sqrt{n}}$
936	876096	30.5941	.001068	.0327
937	877969	30.6105	.001067	.0327
938	879844	30.6268	.001066	.0327
939	881721	30.6431	.001065	.0326
940	883600	30.6594	.001064	.0326
941	885481	30.6757	.001063	.0326
942	887364	30.6920	.001062	.0326
943	889249	30.7083	.001060	.0326
944	891136	30.7246	.001059	.0325
945	893025	30.7409	.001058	.0325
946	894916	30.7571	.001057	.0325
947	896809	30.7734	.001056	.0325
948	898704	30.7896	.001055	.0325
949	900601	30.8058	.001054	.0325
950	902500	30.8221	.001053	.0324
951	904401	30.8383	.001052	.0324
952	906304	30.8545	.001050	.0324
953	908209	30.8707	.001049	.0324
954	910116	30.8869	.001048	.0324
955	912025	30.9031	.001047	.0324
956	913936	30.9192	.001046	.0323
957	915849	30.9354	.001045	.0323
958	917764	30.9516	.001044	.0323
959	919681	30.9677	.001043	.0323
960	921600	30.9839	.001042	.0323
961	923521	31.0000	.001041	.0323
962	925444	31.0161	.001040	.0322
963	927369	31.0322	.001038	.0322
964	929296	31.0483	.001037	.0322
965	931225	31.0644	.001036	.0322
966	933156	31.0805	.001035	.0322
967	935089	31.0966	.001034	.0322
968	937024	31.1127	.001033	.0321
969	938961	31.1288	.001032	.0321
970	940900	31.1448	.001031	.0321
971	942841	31.1609	.001030	.0321
972	944784	31.1769	.001029	.0321
973	946729	31.1929	.001028	.0321
974	948676	31.2090	.001027	.0320
975	950625	31.2250	.001026	.0320
976	952576	31.2410	.001025	.0320
977	954529	31.2570	.001024	.0320
978	956484	31.2730	.001022	.0320
979	958441	31.2890	.001021	.0320
980	960400	31.3050	.001020	.0319
981	962361	31.3209	.001019	.0319
982	964324	31.3369	.001018	.0319
983	966289	31.3528	.001017	.0319
984	968256	31.3688	.001016	.0319
985	970225	31.3847	.001015	.0319

TABLE I (*Continued*)

n	n^2	$\sqrt{n}$	$\dfrac{1}{n}$	$\dfrac{1}{\sqrt{n}}$
986	972196	31.4006	.001014	.0318
987	974169	31.4166	.001013	.0318
988	976144	31.4325	.001012	.0318
989	978121	31.4484	.001011	.0318
990	980100	31.4643	.001010	.0318
991	982081	31.4802	.001009	.0318
992	984064	31.4960	.001008	.0318
993	986049	31.5119	.001007	.0317
994	988036	31.5278	.001006	.0317
995	990025	31.5436	.001005	.0317
996	992016	31.5595	.001004	.0317
997	994009	31.5753	.001003	.0317
998	996004	31.5911	.001002	.0317
999	998001	31.6070	.001001	.0316
1000	1000000	31.6228	.001000	.0316

289

TABLE II. Areas and Ordinates of the Normal Curve in Terms of x/σ

(1)	(2)	(3)	(4)	(5)
z	A	B	C	y
Standard Score $\left(\dfrac{x}{\sigma}\right)$	Area from Mean to $\dfrac{x}{\sigma}$	Area in Larger Portion	Area in Smaller Portion	Ordinate at $\dfrac{x}{\sigma}$
0.00	.0000	.5000	.5000	.3989
0.01	.0040	.5040	.4960	.3989
0.02	.0080	.5080	.4920	.3989
0.03	.0120	.5120	.4880	.3988
0.04	.0160	.5160	.4840	.3986
0.05	.0199	.5199	.4801	.3984
0.06	.0239	.5239	.4761	.3982
0.07	.0279	.5279	.4721	.3980
0.08	.0319	.5319	.4681	.3977
0.09	.0359	.5359	.4641	.3973
0.10	.0398	.5398	.4602	.3970
0.11	.0438	.5438	.4562	.3965
0.12	.0478	.5478	.4522	.3961
0.13	.0517	.5517	.4483	.3956
0.14	.0557	.5557	.4443	.3951
0.15	.0596	.5596	.4404	.3945
0.16	.0636	.5636	.4364	.3939
0.17	.0675	.5675	.4325	.3932
0.18	.0714	.5714	.4286	.3925
0.19	.0753	.5753	.4247	.3918
0.20	.0793	.5793	.4207	.3910
0.21	.0832	.5832	.4168	.3902
0.22	.0871	.5871	.4129	.3894
0.23	.0910	.5910	.4090	.3885
0.24	.0948	.5948	.4052	.3876
0.25	.0987	.5987	.4013	.3867
0.26	.1026	.6026	.3974	.3857
0.27	.1064	.6064	.3936	.3847
0.28	.1103	.6103	.3897	.3836
0.29	.1141	.6141	.3859	.3825
0.30	.1179	.6179	.3821	.3814
0.31	.1217	.6217	.3783	.3802
0.32	.1255	.6255	.3745	.3790
0.33	.1293	.6293	.3707	.3778
0.34	.1331	.6331	.3669	.3765
0.35	.1368	.6368	.3632	.3752
0.36	.1406	.6406	.3594	.3739
0.37	.1443	.6443	.3557	.3725
0.38	.1480	.6480	.3520	.3712
0.39	.1517	.6517	.3483	.3697
0.40	.1554	.6554	.3446	.3683
0.41	.1591	.6591	.3409	.3668
0.42	.1628	.6628	.3372	.3653
0.43	.1664	.6664	.3336	.3637
0.44	.1700	.6700	.3300	.3621

SOURCE: A. L. Edwards. *Statistical Methods for the Behavioral Sciences.* New York: Rinehart, 1954. Reprinted by permission of the publisher.

TABLE II (*Continued*)

(1) z Standard Score $\left(\frac{x}{\sigma}\right)$	(2) A Area from Mean to $\frac{x}{\sigma}$	(3) B Area in Larger Portion	(4) C Area in Smaller Portion	(5) y Ordinate at $\frac{x}{\sigma}$
0.45	.1736	.6736	.3264	.3605
0.46	.1772	.6772	.3228	.3589
0.47	.1808	.6808	.3192	.3572
0.48	.1844	.6844	.3156	.3555
0.49	.1879	.6879	.3121	.3538
0.50	.1915	.6915	.3085	.3521
0.51	.1950	.6950	.3050	.3503
0.52	.1985	.6985	.3015	.3485
0.53	.2019	.7019	.2981	.3467
0.54	.2054	.7054	.2946	.3448
0.55	.2088	.7088	.2912	.3429
0.56	.2123	.7123	.2877	.3410
0.57	.2157	.7157	.2843	.3391
0.58	.2190	.7190	.2810	.3372
0.59	.2224	.7224	.2776	.3352
0.60	.2257	.7257	.2743	.3332
0.61	.2291	.7291	.2709	.3312
0.62	.2324	.7324	.2676	.3292
0.63	.2357	.7357	.2643	.3271
0.64	.2389	.7389	.2611	.3251
0.65	.2422	.7422	.2578	.3230
0.66	.2454	.7454	.2546	.3209
0.67	.2486	.7486	.2514	.3187
0.68	.2517	.7517	.2483	.3166
0.69	.2549	.7549	.2451	.3144
0.70	.2580	.7580	.2420	.3123
0.71	.2611	.7611	.2389	.3101
0.72	.2642	.7642	.2358	.3079
0.73	.2673	.7673	.2327	.3056
0.74	.2704	.7704	.2296	.3034
0.75	.2734	.7734	.2266	.3011
0.76	.2764	.7764	.2236	.2989
0.77	.2794	.7794	.2206	.2966
0.78	.2823	.7823	.2177	.2943
0.79	.2852	.7852	.2148	.2920
0.80	.2881	.7881	.2119	.2897
0.81	.2910	.7910	.2090	.2874
0.82	.2939	.7939	.2061	.2850
0.83	.2967	.7967	.2033	.2827
0.84	.2995	.7995	.2005	.2803
0.85	.3023	.8023	.1977	.2780
0.86	.3051	.8051	.1949	.2756
0.87	.3078	.8078	.1922	.2732
0.88	.3106	.8106	.1894	.2709
0.89	.3133	.8133	.1867	.2685

TABLE II (*Continued*)

(1)	(2)	(3)	(4)	(5)
z	A	B	C	y
Standard Score $\left(\dfrac{x}{\sigma}\right)$	Area from Mean to $\dfrac{x}{\sigma}$	Area in Larger Portion	Area in Smaller Portion	Ordinate at $\dfrac{x}{\sigma}$
0.90	.3159	.8159	.1841	.2661
0.91	.3186	.8186	.1814	.2637
0.92	.3212	.8212	.1788	.2613
0.93	.3238	.8238	.1762	.2589
0.94	.3264	.8264	.1736	.2565
0.95	.3289	.8289	.1711	.2541
0.96	.3315	.8315	.1685	.2516
0.97	.3340	.8340	.1660	.2492
0.98	.3365	.8365	.1635	.2468
0.99	.3389	.8389	.1611	.2444
1.00	.3413	.8413	.1587	.2420
1.01	.3438	.8438	.1562	.2396
1.02	.3461	.8461	.1539	.2371
1.03	.3485	.8485	.1515	.2347
1.04	.3508	.8508	.1492	.2323
1.05	.3531	.8531	.1469	.2299
1.06	.3554	.8554	.1446	.2275
1.07	.3577	.8577	.1423	.2251
1.08	.3599	.8599	.1401	.2227
1.09	.3621	.8621	.1379	.2203
1.10	.3643	.8643	.1357	.2179
1.11	.3665	.8665	.1335	.2155
1.12	.3686	.8686	.1314	.2131
1.13	.3708	.8708	.1292	.2107
1.14	.3729	.8729	.1271	.2083
1.15	.3749	.8749	.1251	.2059
1.16	.3770	.8770	.1230	.2036
1.17	.3790	.8790	.1210	.2012
1.18	.3810	.8810	.1190	.1989
1.19	.3830	.8830	.1170	.1965
1.20	.3849	.8849	.1151	.1942
1.21	.3869	.8869	.1131	.1919
1.22	.3888	.8888	.1112	.1895
1.23	.3907	.8907	.1093	.1872
1.24	.3925	.8925	.1075	.1849
1.25	.3944	.8944	.1056	.1826
1.26	.3962	.8962	.1038	.1804
1.27	.3980	.8980	.1020	.1781
1.28	.3997	.8997	.1003	.1758
1.29	.4015	.9015	.0985	.1736
1.30	.4032	.9032	.0968	.1714
1.31	.4049	.9049	.0951	.1691
1.32	.4066	.9066	.0934	.1669
1.33	.4082	.9082	.0918	.1647
1.34	.4099	.9099	.0901	.1626

TABLE II (*Continued*)

(1) z Standard Score $\left(\frac{x}{\sigma}\right)$	(2) A Area from Mean to $\frac{x}{\sigma}$	(3) B Area in Larger Portion	(4) C Area in Smaller Portion	(5) y Ordinate at $\frac{x}{\sigma}$
1.35	.4115	.9115	.0885	.1604
1.36	.4131	.9131	.0869	.1582
1.37	.4147	.9147	.0853	.1561
1.38	.4162	.9162	.0838	.1539
1.39	.4177	.9177	.0823	.1518
1.40	.4192	.9192	.0808	.1497
1.41	.4207	.9207	.0793	.1476
1.42	.4222	.9222	.0778	.1456
1.43	.4236	.9236	.0764	.1435
1.44	.4251	.9251	.0749	.1415
1.45	.4265	.9265	.0735	.1394
1.46	.4279	.9279	.0721	.1374
1.47	.4292	.9292	.0708	.1354
1.48	.4306	.9306	.0694	.1334
1.49	.4319	.9319	.0681	.1315
1.50	.4332	.9332	.0668	.1295
1.51	.4345	.9345	.0655	.1276
1.52	.4357	.9357	.0643	.1257
1.53	.4370	9370	.0630	.1238
1.54	.4382	.9382	.0618	.1219
1.55	.4394	.9394	.0606	.1200
1.56	.4406	.9406	.0594	.1182
1.57	.4418	.9418	.0582	.1163
1.58	.4429	.9429	.0571	.1145
1.59	.4441	.9441	.0559	.1127
1.60	.4452	.9452	.0548	.1109
1.61	.4463	.9463	.0537	.1092
1.62	.4474	.9474	.0526	.1074
1.63	.4484	.9484	.0516	.1057
1.64	.4495	.9495	.0505	.1040
1.65	.4505	.9505	.0495	.1023
1.66	.4515	.9515	.0485	.1006
1.67	.4525	.9525	.0475	.0989
1.68	.4535	.9535	.0465	.0973
1.69	.4545	.9545	.0455	.0957
1.70	.4554	.9554	.0446	.0940
1.71	.4564	.9564	.0436	.0925
1.72	.4573	.9573	.0427	.0909
1.73	.4582	.9582	.0418	.0893
1.74	.4591	.9591	.0409	.0878
1.75	.4599	.9599	.0401	.0863
1.76	.4608	.9608	.0392	.0848
1.77	.4616	.9616	.0384	.0833
1.78	.4625	.9625	.0375	.0818
1.79	.4633	.9633	.0367	.0804

TABLE II (*Continued*)

(1) z Standard Score $\left(\frac{x}{\sigma}\right)$	(2) A Area from Mean to $\frac{x}{\sigma}$	(3) B Area in Larger Portion	(4) C Area in Smaller Portion	(5) y Ordinate at $\frac{x}{\sigma}$
1.80	.4641	.9641	.0359	.0790
1.81	.4649	.9649	.0351	.0775
1.82	.4656	.9656	.0344	.0761
1.83	.4664	.9664	.0336	.0748
1.84	.4671	.9671	.0329	.0734
1.85	.4648	.9678	.0322	.0721
1.86	.4686	.9686	.0314	.0707
1.87	.4693	.9693	.0307	.0694
1.88	.4699	.9699	.0301	.0681
1.89	.4706	.9706	.0294	.0669
1.90	.4713	.9713	.0287	.0656
1.91	.4719	.9719	.0281	.0644
1.92	.4726	.9726	.0274	.0632
1.93	.4732	.9732	.0268	.0620
1.94	.4738	.9738	.0262	.0608
1.95	.4744	.9744	.0256	.0596
1.96	.4750	.9750	.0250	.0584
1.97	.4756	.9756	.0244	.0573
1.98	.4761	.9761	.0239	.0562
1.99	.4767	.9767	.0233	.0551
2.00	.4772	.9772	.0228	.0540
2.01	.4778	.9778	.0222	.0529
2.02	.4783	.9783	.0217	.0519
2.03	.4788	.9788	.0212	.0508
2.04	.4793	.9793	.0207	.0498
2.05	.4798	.9798	.0202	.0488
2.06	.4803	.9803	.0197	.0478
2.07	.4808	.9808	.0192	.0468
2.08	.4812	.9812	.0188	.0459
2.09	.4817	.9817	.0183	.0449
2.10	.4821	.9821	.0179	.0440
2.11	.4826	.9826	.0174	.0431
2.12	.4830	.9830	.0170	.0422
2.13	.4834	.9834	.0166	.0413
2.14	.4838	.9838	.0162	.0404
2.15	.4842	.9842	.0158	.0396
2.16	.4846	.9846	.0154	.0387
2.17	.4850	.9850	.0150	.0379
2.18	.4854	.9854	.0146	.0371
2.19	.4857	.9857	.0143	.0363
2.20	.4861	.9861	.0139	.0355
2.21	.4864	.9864	.0136	.0347
2.22	.4868	.9868	.0132	.0339
2.23	.4871	.9871	.0129	.0332
2.24	.4875	.9875	.0125	.0325

TABLE II (*Continued*)

(1)	(2)	(3)	(4)	(5)
z	A	B	C	y
Standard Score $\left(\frac{x}{\sigma}\right)$	Area from Mean to $\frac{x}{\sigma}$	Area in Larger Portion	Area in Smaller Portion	Ordinate at $\frac{x}{\sigma}$
2.25	.4878	.9878	.0122	.0317
2.26	.4881	.9881	.0119	.0310
2.27	.4884	.9884	.0116	.0303
2.28	.4887	.9887	.0113	.0297
2.29	.4890	.9890	.0110	.0290
2.30	.4893	.9893	.0107	.0283
2.31	.4896	.9896	.0104	.0277
2.32	.4898	.9898	.0102	.0270
2.33	.4901	.9901	.0099	.0264
2.34	.4904	.9904	.0096	.0258
2.35	.4906	.9906	.0094	.0252
2.36	.4909	.9909	.0091	.0246
2.37	.4911	.9911	.0089	.0241
2.38	.4913	.9913	.0087	.0235
2.39	.4916	.9916	.0084	.0229
2.40	.4918	.9918	.0082	.0224
2.41	.4920	.9920	.0080	.0219
2.42	.4922	.9922	.0078	.0213
2.43	.4925	.9925	.0075	.0208
2.44	.4927	.9927	.0073	.0203
2.45	.4929	.9929	.0071	.0198
2.46	.4931	.9931	.0069	.0194
2.47	.4932	.9932	.0068	.0189
2.48	.4934	.9934	.0066	.0184
2.49	.4936	.9936	.0064	.0180
2.50	.4938	.9938	.0062	.0175
2.51	.4940	.9940	.0060	.0171
2.52	.4941	.9941	.0059	.0167
2.53	.4943	.9943	.0057	.0163
2.54	.4945	.9945	.0055	.0158
2.55	.4946	.9946	.0054	.0154
2.56	.4948	.9948	.0052	.0151
2.57	.4949	.9949	.0051	.0147
2.58	.4951	.9951	.0049	.0143
2.59	.4952	.9952	.0048	.0139
2.60	.4953	.9953	.0047	.0136
2.61	.4955	.9955	.0045	.0132
2.62	.4956	.9956	.0044	.0129
2.63	.4957	.9957	.0043	.0126
2.64	.4959	.9959	.0041	.0122
2.65	.4960	.9960	.0040	.0119
2.66	.4961	.9961	.0039	.0116
2.67	.4962	.9962	.0038	.0113
2.68	.4963	.9963	.0037	.0110
2.69	.4964	.9964	.0036	.0107

TABLE II (*Continued*)

(1) z Standard Score $\left(\dfrac{x}{\sigma}\right)$	(2) A Area from Mean to $\dfrac{x}{\sigma}$	(3) B Area in Larger Portion	(4) C Area in Smaller Portion	(5) y Ordinate at $\dfrac{x}{\sigma}$
2.70	.4965	.9965	.0035	.0104
2.71	.4966	.9966	.0034	.0101
2.72	.4967	.9967	.0033	.0099
2.73	.4968	.9968	.0032	.0096
2.74	.4969	.9969	.0031	.0093
2.75	.4970	.9970	.0030	.0091
2.76	.4971	.9971	.0029	.0088
2.77	.4972	.9972	.0028	.0086
2.78	.4973	.9973	.0027	.0084
2.79	.4974	.9974	.0026	.0081
2.80	.4974	.9974	.0026	.0079
2.81	.4975	.9975	.0025	.0077
2.82	.4976	.9976	.0024	.0075
2.83	.4977	.9977	.0023	.0073
2.84	.4977	.9977	.0023	.0071
2.85	.4978	.9978	.0022	.0069
2.86	.4979	.9979	.0021	.0067
2.87	.4979	.9979	.0021	.0065
2.88	.4980	.9980	.0020	.0063
2.89	.4981	.9981	.0019	.0061
2.90	.4981	.9981	.0019	.0060
2.91	.4982	.9982	.0018	.0058
2.92	.4982	.9982	.0018	.0056
2.93	.4983	.9983	.0017	.0055
2.94	.4984	.9984	.0016	.0053
2.95	.4984	.9984	.0016	.0051
2.96	.4985	.9985	.0015	.0050
2.97	.4985	.9985	.0015	.0048
2.98	.4986	.9986	.0014	.0047
2.99	.4986	.9986	.0014	.0046
3.00	.4987	.9987	.0013	.0044
3.01	.4987	.9987	.0013	.0043
3.02	.4987	.9987	.0013	.0042
3.03	.4988	.9988	.0012	.0040
3.04	.4988	.9988	.0012	.0039
3.05	.4989	.9989	.0011	.0038
3.06	.4989	.9989	.0011	.0037
3.07	.4989	.9989	.0011	.0036
3.08	.4990	.9990	.0010	.0035
3.09	.4990	.9990	.0010	.0034
3.10	.4990	.9990	.0010	.0033
3.11	.4991	.9991	.0009	.0032
3.12	.4991	.9991	.0009	.0031
3.13	.4991	.9991	.0009	.0030
3.14	.4992	.9992	.0008	.0029

TABLE II (*Continued*)

(1) z Standard Score $\left(\frac{x}{\sigma}\right)$	(2) A Area from Mean to $\frac{x}{\sigma}$	(3) B Area in Larger Portion	(4) C Area in Smaller Portion	(5) y Ordinate at $\frac{x}{\sigma}$
3.15	.4992	.9992	.0008	.0028
3.16	.4992	.9992	.0008	.0027
3.17	.4992	.9992	.0008	.0026
3.18	.4993	.9993	.0007	.0025
3.19	.4993	.9993	.0007	.0025
3.20	.4993	.9993	.0007	.0024
3.21	.4993	.9993	.0007	.0023
3.22	.4994	.9994	.0006	.0022
3.23	.4994	.9994	.0006	.0022
3.24	.4994	.9994	.0006	.0021
3.30	.4995	.9995	.0005	.0017
3.40	.4997	.9997	.0003	.0012
3.50	.4998	.9998	.0002	.0009
3.60	.4998	.9998	.0002	.0006
3.70	.4999	.9999	.0001	.0004

TABLE III. Distribution of *t* Probability

df	.1	.05	.01	.001
1	6.314	12.706	63.657	636.619
2	2.920	4.303	9.925	31.598
3	2.353	3.182	5.841	12.941
4	2.132	2.776	4.604	8.610
5	2.015	2.571	4.032	6.859
6	1.943	2.447	3.707	5.959
7	1.895	2.365	3.499	5.405
8	1.860	2.306	3.355	5.041
9	1.833	2.262	3.250	4.781
10	1.812	2.228	3.169	4.587
11	1.796	2.201	3.106	4.437
12	1.782	2.179	3.055	4.318
13	1.771	2.160	3.012	4.221
14	1.761	2.145	2.977	4.140
15	1.753	2.131	2.947	4.073
16	1.746	2.120	2.921	4.015
17	1.740	2.110	2.898	3.965
18	1.734	2.101	2.878	3.922
19	1.729	2.093	2.861	3.883
20	1.725	2.086	2.845	3.850
21	1.721	2.080	2.831	3.819
22	1.717	2.074	2.819	3.792
23	1.714	2.069	2.807	3.767
24	1.711	2.064	2.797	3.745
25	1.708	2.060	2.787	3.725
26	1.706	2.056	2.779	3.707
27	1.703	2.052	2.771	3.690
28	1.701	2.048	2.763	3.674
29	1.699	2.045	2.756	3.659
30	1.697	2.042	2.750	3.646
40	1.684	2.021	2.704	3.551
60	1.671	2.000	2.660	3.460
120	1.658	1.980	2.617	3.373
∞	1.645	1.960	2.576	3.291

SOURCE: Table III is abridged from Table III of R. A. Fisher and F. Yates: *Statistical Tables for Biological, Agricultural, and Medical Research*, published by Oliver and Boyd Ltd., Edinburgh, by permission of the authors and publisher.

TABLE IV. Distribution of χ^2

df	.99	.98	.95	.90	.80	.70	.50	.30	.20	.10	.05	.02	.01	.001
							Probability							
1	$.0^3157$	$.0^3628$	.00393	.0158	.0642	.148	.455	1.074	1.642	2.706	3.841	5.412	6.635	10.827
2	.0201	.0404	.103	.211	.446	.713	1.386	2.408	3.219	4.605	5.991	7.824	9.210	13.815
3	.115	.185	.352	.584	1.005	1.424	2.366	3.665	4.642	6.251	7.815	9.837	11.345	16.268
4	.297	.429	.711	1.064	1.649	2.195	3.357	4.878	5.989	7.779	9.488	11.668	13.277	18.465
5	.554	.752	1.145	1.610	2.343	3.000	4.351	6.064	7.289	9.236	11.070	13.388	15.086	20.517
6	.872	1.134	1.635	2.204	3.070	3.828	5.348	7.231	8.558	10.645	12.592	15.033	16.812	22.457
7	1.239	1.564	2.167	2.833	3.822	4.671	6.346	8.383	9.803	12.017	14.067	16.622	18.475	24.322
8	1.646	2.032	2.733	3.490	4.594	5.527	7.344	9.524	11.030	13.362	15.507	18.168	20.090	26.125
9	2.088	2.532	3.325	4.168	5.380	6.393	8.343	10.656	12.242	14.684	16.919	19.679	21.666	27.877
10	2.558	3.059	3.940	4.865	6.179	7.267	9.342	11.781	13.442	15.987	18.307	21.161	23.209	29.588
11	3.053	3.609	4.575	5.578	6.989	8.148	10.341	12.899	14.631	17.275	19.675	22.618	24.725	31.264
12	3.571	4.178	5.226	6.304	7.807	9.034	11.340	14.011	15.812	18.549	21.026	24.054	26.217	32.909
13	4.107	4.765	5.892	7.042	8.634	9.926	12.340	15.119	16.985	19.812	22.362	25.472	27.688	34.528
14	4.660	5.368	6.571	7.790	9.467	10.821	13.339	16.222	18.151	21.064	23.685	26.873	29.141	36.123
15	5.229	5.985	7.261	8.547	10.307	11.721	14.339	17.322	19.311	22.307	24.996	28.259	30.578	37.697
16	5.812	6.614	7.962	9.312	11.152	12.624	15.338	18.418	20.465	23.542	26.296	29.633	32.000	39.252
17	6.408	7.255	8.672	10.085	12.002	13.531	16.338	19.511	21.615	24.769	27.587	30.995	33.409	40.790
18	7.015	7.906	9.390	10.865	12.857	14.440	17.338	20.601	22.760	25.989	28.869	32.346	34.805	42.312
19	7.633	8.567	10.117	11.651	13.716	15.352	18.338	21.689	23.900	27.204	30.144	33.687	36.191	43.820
20	8.260	9.237	10.851	12.443	14.578	16.266	19.337	22.775	25.038	28.412	31.410	35.020	37.566	45.315
21	8.897	9.915	11.591	13.240	15.445	17.182	20.337	23.858	26.171	29.615	32.671	36.343	38.932	46.797
22	9.542	10.600	12.338	14.041	16.314	18.101	21.337	24.939	27.301	30.813	33.924	37.659	40.289	48.268
23	10.196	11.293	13.091	14.848	17.187	19.021	22.337	26.018	28.429	32.007	35.172	38.968	41.638	49.728
24	10.856	11.992	13.848	15.659	18.062	19.943	23.337	27.096	29.553	33.196	36.415	40.270	42.980	51.179
25	11.524	12.697	14.611	16.473	18.940	20.867	24.337	28.172	30.675	34.382	37.652	41.566	44.314	52.620
26	12.198	13.409	15.379	17.292	19.820	21.792	25.336	29.246	31.795	35.563	38.885	42.856	45.642	54.052
27	12.879	14.125	16.151	18.114	20.703	22.719	26.336	30.319	32.912	36.741	40.113	44.140	46.963	55.476
28	13.565	14.847	16.928	18.939	21.588	23.647	27.336	31.391	34.027	37.916	41.337	45.419	48.278	56.893
29	14.256	15.574	17.708	19.768	22.475	24.577	28.336	32.461	35.139	39.087	42.557	46.693	49.588	58.302
30	14.953	16.306	18.493	20.599	23.364	25.508	29.336	33.530	36.250	40.256	43.773	47.962	50.892	59.703

SOURCE: Table IV is reprinted from Table IV of R. A. Fisher and F. Yates: *Statistical Tables for Biological, Agricultural, and Medical Research*, published by Oliver and Boyd Ltd., Edinburgh, by permission of the authors and publishers.

TABLE V.   5 Percent (Lightface Type) and 1 Percent

f_1 Degrees of Freedom (for

f_2	1	2	3	4	5	6	7	8	9	10	11	12
1	161	200	216	225	230	234	237	239	241	242	243	244
	4,052	4,999	5,403	5,625	5,764	5,859	5,928	5,981	6,022	6,056	6,082	6,106
2	18.51	19.00	19.16	19.25	19.30	19.33	19.36	19.37	19.38	19.39	19.40	19.41
	98.49	99.00	99.17	99.25	99.30	99.33	99.34	99.36	99.38	99.40	99.41	99.42
3	10.13	9.55	9.28	9.12	9.01	8.94	8.88	8.84	8.81	8.78	8.76	8.74
	34.12	30.82	29.46	28.71	28.24	27.91	29.67	27.49	27.34	27.23	27.13	27.05
4	7.71	6.94	6.59	6.39	6.26	6.16	6.09	6.04	6.00	5.96	5.93	5.91
	21.20	18.00	16.69	15.98	15.52	15.21	14.98	14.80	14.66	14.54	14.45	14.37
5	6.61	5.79	5.41	5.19	5.05	4.95	4.88	4.82	4.78	4.74	4.70	4.68
	16.26	13.27	12.06	11.39	10.97	10.67	10.45	10.27	10.15	10.05	9.96	9.89
6	5.99	5.14	4.76	4.53	4.39	4.28	4.21	4.15	4.10	4.06	4.03	4.00
	13.74	10.92	9.78	9.15	8.75	8.47	8.26	8.10	7.98	7.87	7.79	7.72
7	5.59	4.74	4.35	4.12	3.97	3.87	3.79	3.73	3.68	3.63	3.60	3.57
	12.25	9.55	8.45	7.85	7.46	7.19	7.00	6.84	6.71	6.62	6.54	6.47
8	5.32	4.46	4.07	3.84	3.69	3.58	3.50	3.44	3.39	3.34	3.31	3.28
	11.26	8.65	7.59	7.01	6.63	6.37	6.19	6.03	5.91	5.82	5.74	5.67
9	5.12	4.26	3.86	3.63	3.48	3.37	3.29	3.23	3.18	3.13	3.10	3.07
	10.56	8.02	6.99	6.42	6.06	5.80	5.62	5.47	5.35	5.26	5.18	5.11
10	4.96	4.10	3.71	3.48	3.33	3.22	3.14	3.07	3.02	2.97	2.94	2.91
	10.04	7.56	6.55	5.99	5.64	5.39	5.21	5.06	4.95	4.85	4.78	4.71
11	4.84	3.98	3.59	3.36	3.20	3.09	3.01	2.95	2.90	2.86	2.82	2.79
	9.65	7.20	6.22	5.67	5.32	5.07	4.88	4.74	4.63	4.54	4.46	4.40
12	4.75	3.88	3.49	3.26	3.11	3.00	2.92	2.85	2.80	2.76	2.72	2.69
	9.33	6.93	5.95	5.41	5.06	4.82	4.65	4.50	4.39	4.30	4.22	4.16
13	4.67	3.80	3.41	3.18	3.02	2.92	2.84	2.72	2.77	2.63	2.63	2.60
	9.07	6.70	5.74	5.20	4.86	4.62	4.44	4.30	4.19	4.10	4.02	3.96
14	4.60	3.74	3.34	3.11	2.96	2.85	2.77	2.70	2.65	2.60	2.56	2.53
	8.86	6.51	5.56	5.03	4.69	4.46	4.28	4.14	4.03	3.94	3.86	3.80
15	4.54	3.68	3.29	3.06	2.90	2.79	2.70	2.64	2.59	2.55	2.51	2.48
	8.68	6.36	5.42	4.89	4.56	4.32	4.14	4.00	3.89	3.80	3.73	3.67
16	4.49	3.63	3.24	3.01	2.85	2.74	2.66	2.59	2.54	2.49	2.45	2.42
	8.53	6.23	5.29	4.77	4.44	4.20	4.03	3.89	3.78	3.69	3.61	3.55
17	4.45	3.59	3.20	2.96	2.81	2.70	2.62	2.55	2.50	2.45	2.41	2.38
	8.40	6.11	5.18	4.67	4.34	4.10	3.93	3.79	3.68	3.59	3.52	3.45
18	4.41	3.55	3.16	2.93	2.77	2.66	2.58	2.51	2.46	2.41	2.37	2.34
	8.28	6.01	5.09	4.58	4.25	4.01	3.85	3.71	3.60	3.51	3.44	3.37

SOURCE: G. W. Snedecor. *Statistical Methods.* Ames, Iowa: Iowa State

Greater Mean Square)

14	16	20	24	30	40	50	75	100	200	500	∞	f_2
245	246	248	249	250	251	252	253	253	254	254	254	1
6,142	**6,169**	**6,208**	**6,234**	**6,258**	**6,286**	**6,302**	**6,323**	**6,334**	**6,352**	**6,361**	**6,366**	
19.42	19.43	19.44	19.45	19.46	19.47	19.47	19.48	19.49	19.49	19.50	19.50	2
99.43	**99.44**	**99.45**	**99.46**	**99.47**	**99.48**	**99.48**	**99.49**	**99.49**	**99.49**	**99.50**	**99.50**	
8.71	8.69	8.66	8.64	8.62	8.60	8.58	8.57	8.56	8.54	8.54	8.53	3
26.92	**26.83**	**26.69**	**26.60**	**26.50**	**26.41**	**26.35**	**26.27**	**26.23**	**26.18**	**26.14**	**26.12**	
5.87	5.84	5.80	5.77	5.74	5.71	5.70	5.68	5.66	5.65	5.64	5.63	4
14.24	**14.15**	**14.02**	**13.93**	**13.83**	**13.74**	**13.69**	**13.61**	**13.57**	**13.52**	**13.48**	**13.46**	
4.64	4.60	4.56	4.53	4.50	4.46	4.44	4.42	4.40	4.38	4.37	4.36	5
9.77	**9.68**	**9.55**	**9.47**	**9.38**	**9.29**	**9.24**	**9.17**	**9.13**	**9.07**	**9.04**	**9.02**	
3.96	3.92	3.87	3.84	3.81	3.77	3.75	3.72	3.71	3.69	3.68	3.67	6
7.60	**7.52**	**7.39**	**7.31**	**7.23**	**7.14**	**7.09**	**7.02**	**6.99**	**6.94**	**6.90**	**6.88**	
3.52	3.49	3.44	3.41	3.38	3.34	3.32	3.29	3.28	3.25	3.24	3.23	7
6.35	**6.27**	**6.15**	**6.07**	**5.98**	**5.90**	**5.85**	**5.78**	**5.75**	**5.70**	**5.67**	**5.65**	
3.23	3.20	3.15	3.12	3.08	3.05	3.03	3.00	2.98	2.96	2.94	2.93	8
5.56	**5.48**	**5.36**	**5.28**	**5.20**	**5.11**	**5.06**	**5.00**	**4.96**	**4.91**	**4.88**	**4.86**	
3.02	2.98	2.93	2.90	2.86	2.82	2.80	2.77	2.76	2.73	2.72	2.71	9
5.00	**4.92**	**4.80**	**4.73**	**4.64**	**4.56**	**4.51**	**4.45**	**4.41**	**4.36**	**4.33**	**4.31**	
2.86	2.82	2.77	2.74	2.70	2.67	2.64	2.61	2.59	2.56	2.55	2.54	10
4.60	**4.52**	**4.41**	**4.33**	**4.25**	**4.17**	**4.12**	**4.05**	**4.01**	**3.96**	**3.93**	**3.91**	
2.74	2.70	2.65	2.61	2.57	2.53	2.50	2.47	2.45	2.42	2.41	2.40	11
4.29	**4.21**	**4.10**	**4.02**	**3.94**	**3.86**	**3.80**	**3.74**	**3.70**	**3.66**	**3.62**	**3.60**	
2.64	2.60	2.54	2.50	2.46	2.42	2.40	2.36	2.35	2.32	2.31	2.30	12
4.05	**3.98**	**3.86**	**3.78**	**3.70**	**3.61**	**3.56**	**3.49**	**3.46**	**3.41**	**3.38**	**3.36**	
2.55	2.51	2.46	2.42	2.38	2.34	2.32	2.28	2.26	2.24	2.22	2.21	13
3.85	**3.78**	**3.67**	**3.59**	**3.51**	**3.42**	**3.37**	**3.30**	**3.27**	**3.21**	**3.18**	**3.16**	
2.48	2.44	2.39	2.35	2.31	2.27	2.24	2.21	2.19	2.16	2.14	2.13	14
3.70	**3.62**	**3.51**	**3.43**	**3.34**	**3.26**	**3.21**	**3.14**	**3.11**	**3.06**	**3.02**	**3.00**	
2.43	2.39	2.33	2.29	2.25	2.21	2.18	2.15	2.12	2.10	2.08	2.07	15
3.56	**3.48**	**3.36**	**3.29**	**3.20**	**3.12**	**3.07**	**3.00**	**2.97**	**2.92**	**2.89**	**2.87**	
2.37	2.33	2.28	2.24	2.20	2.16	2.13	2.09	2.07	2.04	2.02	2.01	16
3.45	**3.37**	**3.25**	**3.18**	**3.10**	**3.01**	**2.96**	**2.89**	**2.86**	**2.80**	**2.77**	**2.75**	
2.33	2.29	2.23	2.19	2.15	2.11	2.08	2.04	2.02	1.99	1.97	1.96	17
3.35	**3.27**	**3.16**	**3.08**	**3.00**	**2.92**	**2.86**	**2.79**	**2.76**	**2.70**	**2.67**	**2.65**	
2.29	2.25	2.19	2.15	2.11	2.07	2.04	2.00	1.98	1.95	1.93	1.92	18
3.27	**3.19**	**3.07**	**3.00**	**2.91**	**2.83**	**2.78**	**2.71**	**2.68**	**2.62**	**2.59**	**2.57**	

College Press, 1956. Reprinted by permission of the author and publisher.

TABLE V

f_2	1	2	3	4	5	6	7	8	9	10	11	12
									f_1 Degrees of Freedom (for			
19	4.38	3.52	3.13	2.90	2.74	2.63	2.55	2.48	2.43	2.38	2.34	2.31
	8.18	**5.93**	**5.01**	**4.50**	**4.17**	**3.94**	**3.77**	**3.63**	**3.52**	**3.43**	**3.36**	**3.30**
20	4.35	3.49	3.10	2.87	2.71	2.60	2.52	2.45	2.40	2.35	2.31	2.28
	8.10	**5.85**	**4.94**	**4.43**	**4.10**	**3.87**	**3.71**	**3.56**	**3.45**	**3.37**	**3.30**	**3.23**
21	4.32	3.47	3.07	2.84	2.68	2.57	2.49	2.42	2.37	2.32	2.28	2.25
	8.02	**5.78**	**4.87**	**4.37**	**4.04**	**3.81**	**3.65**	**3.51**	**3.40**	**3.31**	**3.24**	**3.17**
22	4.30	3.44	3.05	2.82	2.66	2.55	2.47	2.40	2.35	2.30	2.26	2.23
	7.94	**5.72**	**4.82**	**4.31**	**3.99**	**3.76**	**3.59**	**3.45**	**3.35**	**3.26**	**3.18**	**3.12**
23	4.28	3.42	3.03	2.80	2.64	2.53	2.45	2.38	2.32	2.28	2.24	2.20
	7.88	**5.66**	**4.76**	**4.26**	**3.94**	**3.71**	**3.54**	**3.41**	**3.30**	**3.21**	**3.14**	**3.07**
24	4.26	3.40	3.01	2.78	2.62	2.51	2.43	2.36	2.30	2.26	2.22	2.18
	7.82	**5.61**	**4.72**	**4.22**	**3.90**	**3.67**	**3.50**	**3.36**	**3.25**	**3.17**	**3.09**	**3.03**
25	4.24	3.38	2.99	2.76	2.60	2.49	2.41	2.34	2.28	2.24	2.20	2.16
	7.77	**5.57**	**4.68**	**4.18**	**3.86**	**3.63**	**3.46**	**3.32**	**3.21**	**3.13**	**3.05**	**2.99**
26	4.22	3.37	2.98	2.74	2.59	2.47	2.39	2.32	2.27	2.22	2.18	2.15
	7.72	**5.53**	**4.64**	**4.14**	**3.82**	**3.59**	**3.42**	**3.29**	**3.17**	**3.09**	**3.02**	**2.96**
27	4.21	3.35	2.96	2.73	2.57	2.46	2.37	2.30	2.25	2.20	2.16	2.13
	7.68	**5.49**	**4.60**	**4.11**	**3.79**	**3.56**	**3.39**	**3.26**	**3.14**	**3.06**	**2.98**	**2.93**
28	4.20	3.34	2.95	2.71	2.56	2.44	2.36	2.29	2.24	2.19	2.15	2.12
	7.64	**5.45**	**4.57**	**4.07**	**3.76**	**3.53**	**3.36**	**3.23**	**3.11**	**3.03**	**2.95**	**2.90**
29	4.18	3.33	2.93	2.70	2.54	2.43	2.35	2.28	2.22	2.18	2.14	2.10
	7.60	**5.42**	**4.54**	**4.04**	**3.73**	**3.50**	**3.33**	**3.20**	**3.08**	**3.00**	**2.92**	**2.87**
30	4.17	3.32	2.92	2.69	2.53	2.42	2.34	2.27	2.21	2.16	2.12	2.09
	7.56	**5.39**	**4.51**	**4.02**	**3.70**	**3.47**	**3.30**	**3.17**	**3.06**	**2.98**	**2.90**	**2.84**
32	4.15	3.30	2.90	2.67	2.51	2.40	2.32	2.25	2.19	2.14	2.10	2.07
	7.50	**5.34**	**4.46**	**3.97**	**3.66**	**3.42**	**3.25**	**3.12**	**3.01**	**2.94**	**2.86**	**2.80**
34	4.13	3.28	2.88	2.65	2.49	2.38	2.30	2.23	2.17	2.12	2.08	2.05
	7.44	**5.29**	**4.42**	**3.93**	**3.61**	**3.38**	**3.21**	**3.08**	**2.97**	**2.89**	**2.82**	**2.76**
36	4.11	3.26	2.86	2.63	2.48	2.36	2.28	2.21	2.15	2.10	2.06	2.03
	7.39	**5.25**	**4.38**	**3.89**	**3.58**	**3.35**	**3.18**	**3.04**	**2.94**	**2.86**	**2.78**	**2.72**
38	4.10	3.25	2.85	2.62	2.46	2.35	2.26	2.19	2.14	2.09	2.05	2.02
	7.35	**5.21**	**4.34**	**3.86**	**3.54**	**3.32**	**3.15**	**3.02**	**2.91**	**2.82**	**2.75**	**2.69**
40	4.08	3.23	2.84	2.61	2.45	2.34	2.25	2.18	2.12	2.07	2.04	2.00
	7.31	**5.18**	**4.31**	**3.83**	**3.51**	**3.29**	**3.12**	**2.99**	**2.88**	**2.80**	**2.73**	**2.66**
42	4.07	3.22	2.83	2.59	2.44	2.32	2.24	2.17	2.11	2.06	2.02	1.99
	7.27	**5.15**	**4.29**	**3.80**	**3.49**	**3.26**	**3.10**	**2.96**	**2.86**	**2.77**	**2.70**	**2.64**
44	4.06	3.21	2.82	2.58	2.43	2.31	2.23	2.16	2.10	2.05	2.01	1.98
	7.24	**5.12**	**4.26**	**3.78**	**3.46**	**3.24**	**3.07**	**2.94**	**2.84**	**2.75**	**2.68**	**2.62**

Greater Mean Square)

14	16	20	24	30	40	50	75	100	200	500	∞	f_2
2.26	2.21	2.15	2.11	2.07	2.02	2.00	1.96	1.94	1.91	1.90	1.88	19
3.19	3.12	3.00	2.92	2.84	2.76	2.76	2.63	2.60	2.54	2.51	2.49	
2.23	2.18	2.12	2.08	2.04	1.99	1.96	1.92	1.90	1.87	1.85	1.84	20
3.13	3.05	2.94	2.86	2.77	2.69	2.63	2.56	2.53	2.47	2.44	2.42	
2.20	2.15	2.09	2.05	2.00	1.96	1.93	1.89	1.87	1.84	1.82	1.81	21
3.07	2.99	2.88	2.80	2.72	2.63	2.58	2.51	2.47	2.42	2.38	2.36	
2.18	2.13	2.07	2.03	1.98	1.93	1.91	1.87	1.84	1.81	1.80	1.78	22
3.02	2.94	2.83	2.75	2.67	2.58	2.53	2.46	2.42	2.37	2.33	2.31	
2.14	2.10	2.04	2.00	1.96	1.91	1.88	1.84	1.82	1.79	1.77	1.76	23
2.97	2.89	2.78	2.70	2.62	2.53	2.48	2.41	2.37	2.32	2.28	2.26	
2.13	2.09	2.02	1.98	1.94	1.89	1.86	1.82	1.80	1.76	1.74	1.73	24
2.93	2.85	2.74	2.66	2.58	2.49	2.44	2.36	2.33	2.27	2.23	2.21	
2.11	2.06	2.00	1.96	1.92	1.87	1.84	1.80	1.77	1.74	1.72	1.71	25
2.89	2.81	2.70	2.62	2.54	2.45	2.40	2.32	2.29	2.23	2.19	2.17	
2.10	2.05	1.99	1.95	1.90	1.85	1.82	1.78	1.76	1.72	1.70	1.69	26
2.86	2.77	2.66	2.58	2.50	2.41	2.36	2.28	2.25	2.19	2.15	2.13	
2.08	2.03	1.97	1.93	1.88	1.84	1.80	1.76	1.74	1.71	1.68	1.67	27
2.83	2.74	2.63	2.55	2.47	2.38	2.33	2.25	2.21	2.16	2.12	2.10	
2.06	2.02	1.96	1.91	1.87	1.81	1.78	1.75	1.72	1.69	1.67	1.65	28
2.80	2.71	2.60	2.52	2.44	2.35	2.30	2.22	2.18	2.13	2.09	2.06	
2.05	2.00	1.94	1.90	1.85	1.80	1.77	1.73	1.71	1.68	1.65	1.64	29
2.77	2.68	2.57	2.49	2.41	2.32	2.27	2.19	2.15	2.10	2.06	2.03	
2.04	1.99	1.93	1.89	1.84	1.79	1.76	1.72	1.69	1.66	1.64	1.62	30
2.74	2.66	2.55	2.47	2.38	2.29	2.24	2.16	2.13	2.07	2.03	2.01	
2.02	1.97	1.91	1.86	1.82	1.76	1.74	1.69	1.67	1.64	1.61	1.59	32
2.70	2.62	2.51	2.42	2.34	2.25	2.20	2.12	2.08	2.02	1.98	1.96	
2.00	1.95	1.89	1.84	1.80	1.74	1.71	1.67	1.64	1.61	1.59	1.57	34
2.66	2.58	2.47	2.38	2.30	2.21	2.15	2.08	2.04	1.98	1.94	1.91	
1.98	1.93	1.87	1.82	1.78	1.72	1.69	1.65	1.62	1.59	1.56	1.55	36
2.62	2.54	2.43	2.35	2.26	2.17	2.12	2.04	2.00	1.94	1.90	1.87	
1.96	1.92	1.85	1.80	1.76	1.71	1.67	1.63	1.60	1.57	1.54	1.53	38
2.59	2.51	2.40	2.32	2.22	2.14	2.08	2.00	1.97	1.90	1.86	1.84	
1.95	1.90	1.84	1.79	1.74	1.69	1.66	1.61	1.59	1.55	1.53	1.51	40
2.56	2.49	2.37	2.29	2.20	2.11	2.05	1.97	1.94	1.88	1.84	1.81	
1.94	1.89	1.82	1.78	1.73	1.68	1.64	1.60	1.57	1.54	1.51	1.49	42
2.54	2.46	2.35	2.26	2.17	2.08	2.02	1.94	1.91	1.85	1.80	1.78	
1.92	1.88	1.81	1.76	1.72	1.66	1.63	1.58	1.56	1.52	1.50	1.48	44
2.52	2.44	2.32	2.24	2.15	2.06	2.00	1.92	1.88	1.82	1.78	1.75	

TABLE V

f_2	1	2	3	4	5	6	7	8	9	10	11	12
							f_1 Degrees of Freedom (for					
46	4.05	3.20	2.81	2.57	2.42	2.30	2.22	2.14	2.09	2.04	2.00	1.97
	7.21	**5.10**	**4.24**	**3.76**	**3.44**	**3.22**	**3.05**	**2.92**	**2.82**	**2.73**	**2.66**	**2.60**
48	4.04	3.19	2.80	2.56	2.41	2.30	2.21	2.14	2.08	2.03	1.99	1.96
	7.19	**5.08**	**4.22**	**3.74**	**3.42**	**3.20**	**3.04**	**2.90**	**2.80**	**2.71**	**2.64**	**2.58**
50	4.03	3.18	2.79	2.56	2.40	2.29	2.20	2.13	2.07	2.02	1.98	1.95
	7.17	**5.06**	**4.20**	**3.72**	**3.41**	**3.18**	**3.02**	**2.88**	**2.78**	**2.70**	**2.62**	**2.56**
55	4.02	3.17	2.78	2.54	2.38	2.27	2.18	2.11	2.05	2.00	1.97	1.93
	7.12	**5.01**	**4.16**	**3.68**	**3.37**	**3.15**	**2.98**	**2.85**	**2.75**	**2.66**	**2.59**	**2.53**
60	4.00	3.15	2.76	2.52	2.37	2.25	2.17	2.10	2.04	1.99	1.95	1.92
	7.08	**4.98**	**4.13**	**3.65**	**3.34**	**3.12**	**2.95**	**2.82**	**2.72**	**2.63**	**2.56**	**2.50**
65	3.99	3.14	2.75	2.51	2.36	2.24	2.15	2.08	2.02	1.98	1.94	1.90
	7.04	**4.95**	**4.10**	**3.62**	**3.31**	**3.09**	**2.93**	**2.79**	**2.70**	**2.61**	**2.54**	**2.47**
70	3.98	3.13	2.74	2.50	2.35	2.23	2.14	2.07	2.01	1.97	1.93	1.89
	7.01	**4.92**	**4.08**	**3.60**	**3.29**	**3.07**	**2.91**	**2.77**	**2.67**	**2.59**	**2.51**	**2.45**
80	3.96	3.11	2.72	2.48	2.33	2.21	2.12	2.05	1.99	1.95	1.91	1.88
	6.96	**4.88**	**4.04**	**3.56**	**3.25**	**3.04**	**2.87**	**2.74**	**2.64**	**2.55**	**2.48**	**2.41**
100	3.94	3.09	2.70	2.46	2.30	2.19	2.10	2.03	1.97	1.92	1.88	1.85
	6.90	**4.82**	**3.98**	**3.51**	**3.20**	**2.99**	**2.82**	**2.69**	**2.59**	**2.51**	**2.43**	**2.36**
125	3.92	3.07	2.68	2.44	2.29	2.17	2.08	2.01	1.95	1.90	1.86	1.83
	6.84	**4.78**	**3.94**	**3.47**	**3.17**	**2.95**	**2.79**	**2.65**	**2.56**	**2.47**	**2.40**	**2.33**
150	3.91	3.06	2.67	2.43	2.27	2.16	2.07	2.00	1.94	1.89	1.85	1.82
	6.81	**4.75**	**3.91**	**3.44**	**3.14**	**2.92**	**2.76**	**2.62**	**2.53**	**2.44**	**2.37**	**2.30**
200	3.89	3.04	2.65	2.41	2.26	2.14	2.05	1.98	1.92	1.87	1.83	1.80
	6.76	**4.71**	**3.88**	**3.41**	**3.11**	**2.90**	**2.73**	**2.60**	**2.50**	**2.41**	**2.34**	**2.28**
400	3.86	3.02	2.62	2.39	2.23	2.12	2.03	1.96	1.90	1.85	1.81	1.78
	6.70	**4.66**	**3.83**	**3.36**	**3.06**	**2.85**	**2.69**	**2.55**	**2.46**	**2.37**	**2.29**	**2.23**
1000	3.85	3.00	2.61	2.38	2.22	2.10	2.02	1.95	1.89	1.84	1.80	1.76
	6.66	**4.62**	**3.80**	**3.34**	**3.04**	**2.82**	**2.66**	**2.53**	**2.43**	**2.34**	**2.26**	**2.20**
∞	3.84	2.99	2.60	2.37	2.21	2.09	2.01	1.94	1.88	1.83	1.79	1.75
	6.64	**4.60**	**3.78**	**3.32**	**3.02**	**2.80**	**2.64**	**2.51**	**2.41**	**2.32**	**2.24**	**2.18**

Greater Mean Square)

14	16	20	24	30	40	50	75	100	200	500	∞	f_2
1.91	1.87	1.80	1.75	1.71	1.65	1.62	1.57	1.54	1.51	1.48	1.46	46
2.50	**2.42**	**2.30**	**2.22**	**2.13**	**2.04**	**1.98**	**1.90**	**1.86**	**1.80**	**1.76**	**1.72**	
1.90	1.86	1.79	1.74	1.70	1.64	1.61	1.56	1.53	1.50	1.47	1.45	48
2.48	**2.40**	**2.28**	**2.20**	**2.11**	**2.02**	**1.96**	**1.88**	**1.84**	**1.78**	**1.73**	**1.70**	
1.90	1.85	1.78	1.74	1.69	1.63	1.60	1.55	1.52	1.48	1.46	1.44	50
2.46	**2.39**	**2.26**	**2.18**	**2.10**	**2.00**	**1.94**	**1.86**	**1.82**	**1.76**	**1.71**	**1.68**	
1.88	1.83	1.76	1.72	1.67	1.61	1.58	1.52	1.50	1.46	1.43	1.41	55
2.43	**2.35**	**2.23**	**2.15**	**2.06**	**1.96**	**1.90**	**1.82**	**1.78**	**1.71**	**1.66**	**1.64**	
1.86	1.81	1.75	1.70	1.65	1.59	1.56	1.50	1.48	1.44	1.41	1.39	60
2.40	**2.32**	**2.20**	**2.12**	**2.03**	**1.93**	**1.87**	**1.79**	**1.74**	**1.68**	**1.63**	**1.60**	
1.85	1.80	1.73	1.68	1.63	1.57	1.54	1.49	1.46	1.42	1.39	1.37	65
2.37	**2.30**	**2.18**	**2.09**	**2.00**	**1.90**	**1.84**	**1.76**	**1.71**	**1.64**	**1.60**	**1.56**	
1.84	1.79	1.72	1.67	1.62	1.56	1.53	1.47	1.45	1.40	1.37	1.35	70
2.35	**2.28**	**2.15**	**2.07**	**1.98**	**1.88**	**1.82**	**1.74**	**1.69**	**1.62**	**1.56**	**1.53**	
1.82	1.77	1.70	1.65	1.60	1.54	1.51	1.45	1.42	1.38	1.35	1.32	80
2.32	**2.24**	**2.11**	**2.03**	**1.94**	**1.84**	**1.78**	**1.70**	**1.65**	**1.57**	**1.52**	**1.49**	
1.79	1.75	1.68	1.63	1.57	1.51	1.48	1.42	1.39	1.34	1.30	1.28	100
2.26	**2.19**	**2.06**	**1.98**	**1.89**	**1.79**	**1.73**	**1.64**	**1.59**	**1.51**	**1.46**	**1.43**	
1.77	1.72	1.65	1.60	1.55	1.49	1.45	1.39	1.36	1.31	1.27	1.25	125
2.23	**2.15**	**2.03**	**1.94**	**1.85**	**1.75**	**1.68**	**1.59**	**1.54**	**1.46**	**1.40**	**1.37**	
1.76	1.71	1.64	1.59	1.54	1.47	1.44	1.37	1.34	1.29	1.25	1.22	150
2.20	**2.12**	**2.00**	**1.91**	**1.83**	**1.72**	**1.66**	**1.56**	**1.51**	**1.43**	**1.37**	**1.33**	
1.74	1.69	1.62	1.57	1.52	1.45	1.42	1.35	1.32	1.26	1.22	1.19	200
2.17	**2.09**	**1.97**	**1.88**	**1.79**	**1.69**	**1.62**	**1.53**	**1.48**	**1.39**	**1.33**	**1.28**	
1.72	1.67	1.60	1.54	1.49	1.42	1.38	1.32	1.28	1.22	1.16	1.13	400
2.12	**2.04**	**1.92**	**1.84**	**1.74**	**1.64**	**1.57**	**1.47**	**1.42**	**1.32**	**1.24**	**1.19**	
1.70	1.65	1.58	1.53	1.47	1.41	1.36	1.30	1.26	1.19	1.13	1.08	1000
2.09	**2.01**	**1.89**	**1.81**	**1.71**	**1.61**	**1.54**	**1.44**	**1.38**	**1.28**	**1.19**	**1.11**	
1.69	1.64	1.57	1.52	1.46	1.40	1.35	1.28	1.24	1.17	1.11	1.00	∞
2.07	**1.99**	**1.87**	**1.79**	**1.69**	**1.59**	**1.52**	**1.41**	**1.36**	**1.25**	**1.15**	**1.00**	

TABLE VI. Values of *r* for Different Levels of Significance

df	.1	.05	.02	.01	.001
1	.98769	.99692	.999507	.999877	.9999988
2	.90000	.95000	.98000	.990000	.99900
3	.8054	.8783	.93433	.95873	.99116
4	.7293	.8114	.8822	.91720	.97406
5	.6694	.7545	.8329	.8745	.95074
6	.6215	.7067	.7887	.8343	.92493
7	.5822	.6664	.7498	.7977	.8982
8	.5494	.6319	.7155	.7646	.8721
9	.5214	.6021	.6851	.7348	.8471
10	.4973	.5760	.6581	.7079	.8233
11	.4762	.5529	.6339	.6835	.8010
12	.4575	.5324	.6120	.6614	.7800
13	.4409	.5139	.5923	.6411	.7603
14	.4259	.4973	.5742	.6226	.7420
15	.4124	.4821	.5577	.6055	.7246
16	.4000	.4683	.5425	.5897	.7084
17	.3887	.4555	.5285	.5751	.6932
18	.3783	.4438	.5155	.5614	.6787
19	.3687	.4329	.5034	.5487	.6652
20	.3598	.4227	.4921	.5368	.6524
25	.3233	.3809	.4451	.4869	.5974
30	.2960	.3494	.4093	.4487	.5541
35	.2746	.3246	.3810	.4182	.5189
40	.2573	.3044	.3578	.3932	.4896
45	.2428	.2875	.3384	.3721	.4648
50	.2306	.2732	.3218	.3541	.4433
60	.2108	.2500	.2948	.3248	.4078
70	.1954	.2319	.2737	.3017	.3799
80	.1829	.2172	.2565	.2830	.3568
90	.1726	.2050	.2422	.2673	.3375
100	.1638	.1946	.2301	.2540	.3211

SOURCE: Table VI is reprinted from Table VI of R. A. Fisher and F. Yates: *Statistical Tables for Biological, Agricultural, and Medical Research*, published by Oliver and Boyd Ltd., Edinburgh, by permission of the authors and publishers.

TABLE VII. Table of z Values for r[a]

r	z	r	z	r	z	r	z	r	z
.000	.000	.200	.203	.400	.424	.600	.693	.800	1.099
.005	.005	.205	.208	.405	.430	.605	.701	.805	1.113
.010	.010	.210	.213	.410	.436	.610	.709	.810	1.127
.015	.015	.215	.218	.415	.442	.615	.717	.815	1.142
.020	.020	.220	.224	.420	.448	.620	.725	.820	1.157
.025	.025	.225	.229	.425	.454	.625	.733	.825	1.172
.030	.030	.230	.234	.430	.460	.630	.741	.830	1.188
.035	.035	.235	.239	.435	.466	.635	.750	.835	1.204
.040	.040	.240	.245	.440	.472	.640	.758	.840	1.221
.045	.045	.245	.250	.445	.478	.645	.767	.845	1.238
.050	.050	.250	.255	.450	.485	.650	.775	.850	1.256
.055	.055	.255	.261	.455	.491	.655	.784	.855	1.274
.060	.060	.260	.266	.460	.497	.660	.793	.860	1.293
.065	.065	.265	.271	.465	.504	.665	.802	.865	1.313
.070	.070	.270	.277	.470	.510	.670	.811	.870	1.333
.075	.075	.275	.282	.475	.517	.675	.820	.875	1.354
.080	.080	.280	.288	.480	.523	.680	.829	.880	1.376
.085	.085	.285	.293	.485	.530	.685	.838	.885	1.398
.090	.090	.290	.299	.490	.536	.690	.848	.890	1.422
.095	.095	.295	.304	.495	.543	.695	.858	.895	1.447
.100	.100	.300	.310	.500	.549	.700	.867	.900	1.472
.105	.105	.305	.315	.505	.556	.705	.877	.905	1.499
.110	.110	.310	.321	.510	.563	.710	.887	.910	1.528
.115	.116	.315	.326	.515	.570	.715	.897	.915	1.557
.120	.121	.320	.332	.520	.576	.720	.908	.920	1.589
.125	.126	.325	.337	.525	.583	.725	.918	.925	1.623
.130	.131	.330	.343	.530	.590	.730	.929	.930	1.658
.135	.136	.335	.348	.535	.597	.735	.940	.935	1.697
.140	.141	.340	.354	.540	.604	.740	.950	.940	1.738
.145	.146	.345	.360	.545	.611	.745	.962	.945	1.783
.150	.151	.350	.365	.550	.618	.750	.973	.950	1.832
.155	.156	.355	.371	.555	.626	.755	.984	.955	1.886
.160	.161	.360	.377	.560	.633	.760	.996	.960	1.946
.165	.167	.365	.383	.565	.640	.765	1.008	.965	2.014
.170	.172	.370	.388	.570	.648	.770	1.020	.970	2.092
.175	.177	.375	.394	.575	.655	.775	1.033	.975	2.185
.180	.182	.380	.400	.580	.662	.780	1.045	.980	2.298
.185	.187	.385	.406	.585	.670	.785	1.058	.985	2.443
.190	.192	.390	.412	.590	.678	.790	1.071	.990	2.647
.195	.198	.395	.418	.595	.685	.795	1.085	.995	2.994

[a] Table VII was constructed by F. P. Kilpatrick and D. A. Buchanan from the formula

$$z = \tfrac{1}{2}[\log_e (1 + r) - \log_e (1 - r)]$$

SOURCE: A. L. Edwards. *Statistical Methods for the Behavioral Sciences.* New York: Rinehart, 1954. Reprinted by permission of the publisher.

TABLE VIII. Estimates of r_{tet} for Various Values of ad/bc

r_{tet}	ad/bc	r_{tet}	ad/bc	r_{tet}	ad/bc
.00	0–1.00	.35	2.49–2.55	.70	8.50–8.90
.01	1.01–1.03	.36	2.56–2.63	.71	8.91–9.35
.02	1.04–1.06	.37	2.64–2.71	.72	9.36–9.82
.03	1.07–1.08	.38	2.72–2.79	.73	9.83–10.33
.04	1.09–1.11	.39	2.80–2.87	.74	10.34–10.90
.05	1.12–1.14	.40	2.88–2.96	.75	10.91–11.51
.06	1.15–1.17	.41	2.97–3.05	.76	11.52–12.16
.07	1.18–1.20	.42	3.06–3.14	.77	12.17–12.89
.08	1.21–1.23	.43	3.15–3.24	.78	12.90–13.70
.09	1.24–1.27	.44	3.25–3.34	.79	13.71–14.58
.10	1.28–1.30	.45	3.35–3.45	.80	14.59–15.57
.11	1.31–1.33	.46	3.46–3.56	.81	15.58–16.65
.12	1.34–1.37	.47	3.57–3.68	.82	16.66–17.88
.13	1.38–1.40	.48	3.69–3.80	.83	17.89–19.28
.14	1.41–1.44	.49	3.81–3.92	.84	19.29–20.85
.15	1.45–1.48	.50	3.93–4.06	.85	20.86–22.68
.16	1.49–1.52	.51	4.07–4.20	.86	22.69–24.76
.17	1.53–1.56	.52	4.21–4.34	.87	24.77–27.22
.18	1.57–1.60	.53	4.35–4.49	.88	27.23–30.09
.19	1.61–1.64	.54	4.50–4.66	.89	30.10–33.60
.20	1.65–1.69	.55	4.67–4.82	.90	33.61–37.79
.21	1.70–1.73	.56	4.83–4.99	.91	37.80–43.06
.22	1.74–1.78	.57	5.00–5.18	.92	43.07–49.83
.23	1.79–1.83	.58	5.19–5.38	.93	49.84–58.79
.24	1.84–1.88	.59	5.39–5.59	.94	58.80–70.95
.25	1.89–1.93	.60	5.60–5.80	.95	70.96–89.01
.26	1.94–1.98	.61	5.81–6.03	.96	89.02–117.54
.27	1.99–2.04	.62	6.04–6.28	.97	117.55–169.67
.28	2.05–2.10	.63	6.29–6.54	.98	169.68–293.12
.29	2.11–2.15	.64	6.55–6.81	.99	293.13–923.97
.30	2.16–2.22	.65	6.82–7.10	1.00	923.98 . . .
.31	2.23–2.28	.66	7.11–7.42		
.32	2.29–2.34	.67	7.43–7.75		
.33	2.35–2.41	.68	7.76–8.11		
.34	2.42–2.48	.69	8.12–8.49		

SOURCE: M. D. Davidoff and H. W. Goheen. A table for the rapid determination of the tetrachoric correlation coefficient. *Psychometrika*, 1953, **18**, 115–121. Reprinted with the permission of the authors and publisher.

TABLE IX. Table of Critical Values of *T* in the Wilcoxon Matched-Pairs Signed-Ranks Test

	Level of Significance for One-Tailed Test		
	.025	.01	.005
N	Level of Significance for Two-Tailed Test		
	.05	.02	.01
6	0	—	—
7	2	0	—
8	4	2	0
9	6	3	2
10	8	5	3
11	11	7	5
12	14	10	7
13	17	13	10
14	21	16	13
15	25	20	16
16	30	24	20
17	35	28	23
18	40	33	28
19	46	38	32
20	52	43	38
21	59	49	43
22	66	56	49
23	73	62	55
24	81	69	61
25	89	77	68

SOURCE: Adapted from Table I of F. Wilcoxon. *Some Rapid Approximate Statistical Procedures.* New York: American Cyanamid Company, 1949, p. 13. Reproduced from S. Siegel. *Nonparametric Statistics for the Behavioral Sciences.* New York: McGraw-Hill, 1956. Reprinted by permission of the author, American Cyanamid Company, and McGraw-Hill Book Company.

TABLE X. Table of Critical Values of U in the Mann-Whitney Test

(a) Critical Values of U for a One-Tailed Test at .001 or for a
Two-Tailed Test at .002

n_1 \ n_2	9	10	11	12	13	14	15	16	17	18	19	20
1												
2												
3								–	0	0	0	0
4		0	0	0	1	1	1	2	2	3	3	3
5	1	1	2	2	3	3	4	5	5	6	7	7
6	2	3	4	4	5	6	7	8	9	10	11	12
7	3	5	6	7	8	9	10	11	13	14	15	16
8	5	6	8	9	11	12	14	15	17	18	20	21
9	7	8	10	12	14	15	17	19	21	23	25	26
10	8	10	12	14	17	19	21	23	25	27	29	32
11	10	12	15	17	20	22	24	27	29	32	34	37
12	12	14	17	20	23	25	28	31	34	37	40	42
13	14	17	20	23	26	29	32	35	38	42	45	48
14	15	19	22	25	29	32	36	39	43	46	50	54
15	17	21	24	28	32	36	40	43	47	51	55	59
16	19	23	27	31	35	39	43	48	52	56	60	65
17	21	25	29	34	38	43	47	52	57	61	66	70
18	23	27	32	37	42	46	51	56	61	66	71	76
19	25	29	34	40	45	50	55	60	66	71	77	82
20	26	32	37	42	48	54	59	65	70	76	82	88

(b) Critical Values of U for a One-Tailed Test at .01 or for a
Two-Tailed Test at .02

n_1 \ n_2	9	10	11	12	13	14	15	16	17	18	19	20
1												
2					0	0	0	0	0	0	1	1
3	1	1	1	2	2	2	3	3	4	4	4	5
4	3	3	4	5	5	6	7	7	8	9	9	10
5	5	6	7	8	9	10	11	12	13	14	15	16
6	7	8	9	11	12	13	15	16	18	19	20	22
7	9	11	12	14	16	17	19	21	23	24	26	28
8	11	13	15	17	20	22	24	26	28	30	32	34
9	14	16	18	21	23	26	28	31	33	36	38	40
10	16	19	22	24	27	30	33	36	38	41	44	47
11	18	22	25	28	31	34	37	41	44	47	50	53
12	21	24	28	31	35	38	42	46	49	53	56	60
13	23	27	31	35	39	43	47	51	55	59	63	67
14	26	30	34	38	43	47	51	56	60	65	69	73
15	28	33	37	42	47	51	56	61	66	70	75	80
16	31	36	41	46	51	56	61	66	71	76	82	87
17	33	38	44	49	55	60	66	71	77	82	88	93
18	36	41	47	53	59	65	70	76	82	88	94	100
19	38	44	50	56	63	69	75	82	88	94	101	107
20	40	47	53	60	67	73	80	87	93	100	107	114

SOURCE: Adapted and abridged from Tables 1, 3, 5, and 7 of D. Aube. Extended tables for the Mann-Whitney statistic. *Bulletin of the Institute of Educational Research at Indiana University*, 1953, **1**, No. 2. Reproduced from S. Siegel. *Nonparametric Statistics for the Behavioral Sciences.* New York: McGraw-Hill, 1956. Reprinted by permission of the author, Institute of Educational Research, and McGraw-Hill Book Company.

Table X (*Continued*)

(c) Critical Values of U for a One-Tailed Test at .025 or for a Two-Tailed Test at .05

n_1 \ n_2	9	10	11	12	13	14	15	16	17	18	19	20
1												
2	0	0	0	1	1	1	1	1	2	2	2	2
3	2	3	3	4	4	5	5	6	6	7	7	8
4	4	5	6	7	8	9	10	11	11	12	13	13
5	7	8	9	11	12	13	14	15	17	18	19	20
6	10	11	13	14	16	17	19	21	22	24	25	27
7	12	14	16	18	20	22	24	26	28	30	32	34
8	15	17	19	22	24	26	29	31	34	36	38	41
9	17	20	23	26	28	31	34	37	39	42	45	48
10	20	23	26	29	33	36	39	42	45	48	52	55
11	23	26	30	33	37	40	44	47	51	55	58	62
12	26	29	33	37	41	45	49	53	57	61	65	69
13	28	33	37	41	45	50	54	59	63	67	72	76
14	31	36	40	45	50	55	59	64	67	74	78	83
15	34	39	44	49	54	59	64	70	75	80	85	90
16	37	42	47	53	59	64	70	75	81	86	92	98
17	39	45	51	57	63	67	75	81	87	93	99	105
18	42	48	55	61	67	74	80	86	93	99	106	112
19	45	52	58	65	72	78	85	92	99	106	113	119
20	48	55	62	69	76	83	90	98	105	112	119	127

(d) Critical Values of U for a One-Tailed Test at .05 or for a Two-Tailed Test at .10

n_2 \ n_1	9	10	11	12	13	14	15	16	17	18	19	20
1											0	0
2	1	1	1	2	2	2	3	3	3	4	4	4
3	3	4	5	5	6	7	7	8	9	9	10	11
4	6	7	8	9	10	11	12	14	15	16	17	18
5	9	11	12	13	15	16	18	19	20	22	23	25
6	12	14	16	17	19	21	23	25	26	28	30	32
7	15	17	19	21	24	26	28	30	33	35	37	39
8	18	20	23	26	28	31	33	36	39	41	44	47
9	21	24	27	30	33	36	39	42	45	48	51	54
10	24	27	31	34	37	41	44	48	51	55	58	62
11	27	31	34	38	42	46	50	54	57	61	65	69
12	30	34	38	42	47	51	55	60	64	68	72	77
13	33	37	42	47	51	56	61	65	70	75	80	84
14	36	41	46	51	56	61	66	71	77	82	87	92
15	39	44	50	55	61	66	72	77	83	88	94	100
16	42	48	54	60	65	71	77	83	89	95	101	107
17	45	51	57	64	70	77	83	89	96	102	109	115
18	48	55	61	68	75	82	88	95	102	109	116	123
19	51	58	65	72	80	87	94	101	109	116	123	130
20	54	62	69	77	84	92	100	107	115	123	130	138

TABLE XI.   Table of Critical Values of r in the Runs Test

In the bodies of Tables XI(a) and XI(b) are various critical values of r for various values of n_1 and n_2.   For the one-sample runs test, any value of r which is equal to or smaller than that shown in Table XI(a) or equal to or larger than that shown in Table XI(b) is significant at the .05 level.   For the Wald-Wolfowitz two-sample runs test, any value of r which is equal to or smaller than that shown in Table XI(a) is significant at the .05 level.

(a)

n_1 \ n_2	2	3	4	5	6	7	8	9	10	11	12	13	14	15	16	17	18	19	20
2											2	2	2	2	2	2	2	2	2
3			2	2	2	2	2	2	2	2	2	2	2	3	3	3	3	3	3
4		2	2	2	2	2	3	3	3	3	3	3	3	3	4	4	4	4	4
5		2	2	3	3	3	3	3	3	4	4	4	4	4	4	4	5	5	5
6		2	2	3	3	3	4	4	4	4	4	5	5	5	5	5	5	6	6
7		2	2	3	3	3	4	5	5	5	5	5	5	6	6	6	6	6	6
8		2	3	3	4	4	5	5	5	5	6	6	6	6	6	7	7	7	7
9		2	3	3	4	5	5	5	6	6	6	6	7	7	7	7	8	8	8
10		2	3	3	4	5	5	6	6	7	7	7	7	8	8	8	8	8	9
11		2	3	4	4	5	5	6	6	7	7	7	8	8	8	9	9	9	9
12	2	2	3	4	4	5	6	6	7	7	7	8	8	8	9	9	9	10	10
13	2	2	3	4	5	5	6	6	7	7	8	8	9	9	9	10	10	10	10
14	2	2	3	4	5	5	6	7	7	8	8	9	9	9	10	10	10	11	11
15	2	3	3	4	5	6	6	7	7	8	8	9	9	10	10	11	11	11	12
16	2	3	4	4	5	6	6	7	8	8	9	9	10	10	11	11	11	12	12
17	2	3	4	4	5	6	7	7	8	9	9	10	10	11	11	11	12	12	13
18	2	3	4	5	5	6	7	8	8	9	9	10	10	11	11	12	12	13	13
19	2	3	4	5	6	6	7	8	8	9	10	10	11	11	12	12	13	13	13
20	2	3	4	5	6	6	7	8	9	9	10	10	11	12	12	13	13	13	14

(b)

n_1 \ n_2	2	3	4	5	6	7	8	9	10	11	12	13	14	15	16	17	18	19	20
2																			
3																			
4				9	9														
5			9	10	10	11	11												
6			9	10	11	12	12	13	13	13	13								
7				11	12	13	13	14	14	14	14	15	15	15					
8				11	12	13	14	14	15	15	16	16	16	16	17	17	17	17	17
9					13	14	15	16	16	16	17	17	18	18	18	18	18	18	18
10					13	14	15	16	16	17	17	18	18	18	19	19	19	20	20
11					13	14	15	16	17	17	18	19	19	19	20	20	20	21	21
12					13	14	16	16	17	18	19	19	20	20	21	21	21	22	22
13						15	16	17	18	19	19	20	20	21	21	22	22	23	23
14						15	16	17	18	19	20	20	21	22	22	23	23	23	24
15						15	16	18	18	19	20	21	22	22	23	23	24	24	25
16							17	18	19	20	21	21	22	23	23	24	25	25	25
17							17	18	19	20	21	22	23	23	24	25	25	26	26
18							17	18	19	20	21	22	23	24	25	25	26	26	27
19							17	18	20	21	22	23	23	24	25	26	26	27	27
20							17	18	20	21	22	23	24	25	25	26	27	27	28

SOURCE: Adapted from Frieda S. Swed and C. Eisenhart.   Tables for testing randomness of grouping in a sequence of alternatives.   *Annals of Mathematical Statistics*, 1943, **14**, 83–86. Reproduced from S. Siegel.   *Nonparametric Statistics for the Behavioral Sciences*.   New York: McGraw-Hill, 1956.   Reprinted by permission of the authors, Institute of Mathematical Statistics, and McGraw-Hill Book Company.

TABLE XII. Values of H for Three Samples Significant at the 10, 5, and 1 Percent Levels

Sample Sizes			Level		
N_1	N_2	N_3	.10	.05	.01
2	2	2	4.57		
3	2	1	4.29		
3	2	2	4.50	4.71	
3	3	1	4.57	5.14	
3	3	2	4.56	5.36	6.25
3	3	3	4.62	5.60	6.49
4	2	1	4.50		
4	2	2	4.46	5.33	
4	3	1	4.06	5.21	
4	3	2	4.51	5.44	6.30
4	3	3	4.70	5.73	6.75
4	4	1	4.17	4.79	6.67
4	4	2	4.55	5.45	6.87
4	4	3	4.55	5.60	7.14
4	4	4	4.65	5.69	7.54
5	2	1	4.20	5.00	
5	2	2	4.37	5.16	6.53
5	3	1	4.02	4.96	
5	3	2	4.49	5.25	6.82
5	3	3	4.53	5.44	6.98
5	4	1	3.99	4.99	6.84
5	4	2	4.52	5.27	7.12
5	4	3	4.55	5.63	7.40
5	4	4	4.62	5.62	7.74
5	5	1	4.11	5.13	6.84
5	5	2	4.51	5.25	7.27
5	5	3	4.55	5.63	7.54
5	5	4	4.52	5.64	7.79
5	5	5	4.56	5.66	7.98

SOURCE: Abridged from Table 6.1 of W. H. Kruskal and W. A. Wallis. Use of ranks on one-criterion variance analysis. *Journal of the American Statistical Association*, 1952, **47**, 584–621. Reproduced from M. W. Tate and R. C. Clelland. *Nonparametric and Shortcut Statistics*. Danville, Ill.: The Interstate Printers and Publishers, 1957. Reprinted by permission of the authors, Journal of the American Statistical Association, and The Interstate Printers and Publishers.

TABLE XIII. Values of the Coefficient of Concordance W Significant at the 20, 10, 5, and 1 Percent Levels

m	a	3	4	n 5	6	7	8	9	10
	.20	.78	.60	.53	.49	.47	.46	.45	.44
	.10		.73	.62	.58	.55	.53	.52	.51
3	.05	1.00	.82	.71	.65	.62	.60	.58	.56
	.01		.96	.84	.77	.73	.70	.67	.65
	.20	.56	.40	.38	.37	.36	.35	.34	.33
	.10	.75	.52	.47	.44	.42	.41	.40	.39
4	.05	.81	.65	.54	.51	.48	.46	.45	.44
	.01	1.00	.80	.67	.62	.59	.56	.54	.52
	.20	.36	.34	.30	.29	.28	.28	.27	.27
	.10	.52	.42	.38	.36	.34	.33	.32	.31
5	.05	.64	.52	.44	.41	.39	.38	.36	.35
	.01	.84	.66	.56	.52	.49	.46	.44	.43
	.20	.33	.27	.25	.24	.24	.23	.23	.23
	.10	.44	.36	.32	.30	.29	.28	.27	.26
6	.05	.58	.42	.37	.35	.33	.32	.31	.30
	.01	.75	.56	.49	.45	.42	.40	.38	.37
	.20	.27	.23	.22	.21	.20	.20	.20	.19
	.10	.39	.30	.27	.26	.25	.24	.23	.23
7	.05	.51	.36	.32	.30	.29	.27	.26	.26
	.01	.63	.48	.43	.39	.36	.34	.33	.32
	.20	.25	.20	.19	.18	.18	.17	.17	.17
	.10	.33	.26	.24	.23	.22	.21	.20	.20
8	.05	.39	.32	.29	.27	.25	.24	.23	.23
	.01	.56	.43	.38	.35	.32	.31	.29	.28
	.20	.20	.18	.17	.16	.16	.16	.15	.15
	.10	.31	.23	.21	.20	.19	.19	.18	.18
9	.05	.35	.28	.26	.24	.23	.22	.21	.20
	.01	.48	.38	.34	.31	.29	.27	.26	.25
	.20	.19	.16	.15	.15	.14	.14	.14	.13
	.10	.25	.21	.19	.18	.17	.17	.16	.16
10	.05	.31	.25	.23	.21	.20	.20	.19	.18
	.01	.48	.35	.31	.28	.26	.25	.24	.23
	.20	.14	.13	.13	.12	.12	.12	.11	.11
	.10	.19	.17	.16	.15	.15	.14	.14	.13
12	.05	.25	.21	.19	.18	.17	.16	.16	.15
	.01	.36	.30	.26	.24	.22	.21	.20	.19
	.20	.12	.11	.11	.10	.10	.10	.10	.10
	.10	.17	.15	.14	.13	.13	.12	.12	.12
14	.05	.21	.18	.17	.16	.15	.14	.14	.13
	.01	.31	.26	.23	.21	.19	.18	.17	.17

SOURCE: Values at the left of the broken line were derived from Appendix Tables 5A, 5B, 5C, and 5D of M. G. Kendall. *Rank Correlation Methods*. London: Charles Griffin and Co. Ltd., 1948. Other values were obtained by the method described by Kendall, *ibid.*, p. 84. Reproduced from M. W. Tate and R. C. Clelland. *Nonparametric and Shortcut Statistics*. Danville, Ill.: The Interstate Printers and Publishers, 1957. Reprinted by permission of the author, Charles Griffin and Co., Ltd., and The Interstate Printers and Publishers.

TABLE XIII (*Continued*)

m	a	3	4	$\overset{n}{5}$	6	7	8	9	10
	.20	.10	.10	.09	.09	.09	.09	.09	.08
	.10	.15	.13	.12	.12	.11	.11	.10	.10
16	.05	.19	.16	.15	.14	.13	.12	.12	.12
	.01	.28	.23	.20	.18	.17	.16	.15	.15
	.20	.09	.09	.08	.08	.08	.08	.08	.07
	.10	.13	.12	.11	.10	.10	.09	.09	.09
18	.05	.17	.14	.13	.12	.11	.11	.11	.10
	.01	.25	.20	.18	.16	.15	.14	.14	.13
	.20	.08	.08	.07	.07	.07	.07	.07	.07
	.10	.11	.10	.10	.09	.09	.08	.08	.08
20	.05	.15	.13	.12	.11	.10	.10	.10	.09
	.01	.22	.18	.16	.15	.14	.13	.12	.11
	.20	.07	.06	.06	.06	.06	.06	.05	.05
	.10	.09	.08	.08	.07	.07	.07	.07	.06
25	.05	.12	.10	.09	.09	.08	.08	.08	.07
	.01	.18	.15	.13	.12	.11	.10	.10	.09
	.20	.05	.05	.05	.05	.05	.05	.05	.04
	.10	.08	.07	.06	.06	.06	.06	.06	.05
30	.05	.10	.09	.08	.07	.07	.07	.07	.06
	.01	.15	.12	.11	.10	.09	.09	.08	.08

TABLE XIV. Random Numbers

Row	1	2	3	4	5	6	7	8	9	10	11	12	13	14	15	16	17	18	19
1	9	8	9	6	9	9	0	9	6	3	2	3	3	8	6	8	4	4	2
2	3	5	6	1	7	4	1	3	2	6	8	6	0	4	7	5	2	0	3
3	4	0	6	1	6	9	6	1	5	9	5	4	5	4	8	6	7	4	0
4	6	5	6	3	1	6	8	6	7	2	0	7	2	3	2	1	5	0	9
5	2	4	9	7	9	1	0	3	9	6	7	4	1	5	4	9	6	9	8
6	7	6	1	2	7	5	6	9	4	8	4	2	8	5	2	4	1	8	0
7	8	2	1	3	4	7	4	6	3	0	7	5	0	9	2	9	0	6	1
8	6	9	5	6	5	6	0	9	0	7	7	1	4	1	8	3	1	9	3
9	7	2	1	9	9	8	0	1	6	1	6	2	3	6	9	5	5	8	4
10	2	9	0	7	3	0	8	9	6	3	3	8	5	5	6	5	2	0	9
11	9	3	5	4	5	7	4	0	3	0	1	0	4	3	3	9	5	3	2
12	9	7	5	7	9	4	8	6	8	7	6	1	6	8	2	5	5	5	3
13	4	1	7	8	6	8	1	0	5	8	8	6	1	6	8	2	9	0	4
14	5	0	8	3	3	4	5	4	4	2	5	3	0	4	9	6	1	2	3
15	3	5	0	2	9	4	1	0	0	3	9	0	5	8	6	0	9	9	6
16	0	3	8	2	3	5	1	0	1	0	6	8	5	2	4	8	0	3	8
17	1	7	2	9	1	2	7	8	4	7	0	3	3	1	5	8	2	7	3
18	5	0	5	7	9	5	8	7	8	9	3	5	3	4	4	6	1	1	3
19	7	7	3	3	5	3	6	1	3	2	8	5	4	1	4	8	3	9	0
20	1	0	9	1	3	8	2	5	3	0	3	8	0	9	3	3	0	4	5
21	1	3	8	5	1	8	5	9	4	1	9	3	9	3	6	5	9	8	4
22	8	6	4	7	8	7	5	9	4	1	9	3	9	3	6	5	9	8	4
23	0	6	9	6	5	1	0	3	2	6	7	7	4	9	6	0	3	4	0
24	7	6	7	4	7	0	8	3	8	7	3	2	5	1	2	4	2	9	7
25	3	2	3	8	1	3	1	8	7	4	5	9	0	0	2	4	1	2	1
26	9	2	1	6	4	2	3	8	7	6	2	6	2	6	4	8	1	0	7
27	3	7	4	2	2	8	1	7	8	0	6	0	0	0	3	2	2	9	7
28	0	7	8	0	8	5	1	5	2	6	5	8	7	5	3	0	5	9	6
29	7	4	2	3	3	2	6	0	0	6	5	2	2	3	6	3	9	0	4
30	1	8	2	7	5	9	5	3	6	5	2	9	9	1	1	7	3	4	3
31	4	3	1	8	7	0	6	0	8	6	5	0	1	0	4	0	6	1	5
32	8	5	8	0	6	1	4	1	2	0	4	4	1	4	7	6	3	5	1
33	4	5	8	5	0	4	5	8	3	9	2	8	7	8	9	0	8	4	3
34	5	0	2	5	4	9	2	2	1	1	0	0	5	4	8	7	6	4	0
35	0	8	1	7	0	6	3	3	4	7	6	2	6	8	9	3	4	1	4
36	2	5	9	3	4	6	0	7	5	2	0	0	9	6	0	8	2	2	5
37	2	1	3	1	3	7	8	9	8	4	9	3	8	0	2	2	1	8	1
38	3	8	8	6	8	5	1	3	3	4	6	7	2	6	3	4	8	6	7
39	0	9	9	8	5	9	8	4	4	2	2	1	1	0	1	7	6	1	3
40	2	2	3	5	3	9	7	4	4	2	1	4	0	5	8	2	3	0	8

TABLE XIV (*Continued*)

								Column Number													
20	21	22	23	24	25	26	27	28	29	30	31	32	33	34	35	36	37	38	39	40	Row
0	9	7	1	1	9	1	2	7	3	5	1	8	4	0	4	1	0	6	0	3	1
8	3	7	7	9	1	4	9	9	5	9	2	0	1	6	1	2	6	6	7	0	2
2	5	6	3	7	8	3	3	8	4	3	9	3	9	0	0	9	8	3	5	2	3
4	7	0	8	6	6	5	9	6	2	7	3	5	9	0	1	8	0	9	6	9	4
0	9	8	7	3	5	6	8	8	1	2	0	2	3	2	6	4	3	1	9	7	5
5	1	8	8	4	7	0	1	7	6	8	2	1	6	3	2	1	8	1	8	3	6
1	3	7	8	6	9	5	4	1	7	3	8	7	1	5	6	5	6	4	3	6	7
5	9	0	1	5	2	8	6	5	5	7	8	1	8	7	1	2	4	0	4	1	8
2	2	5	5	2	1	8	6	9	8	9	8	0	5	8	9	9	4	1	3	4	9
1	3	4	2	8	5	0	7	9	8	4	3	5	8	0	9	4	6	6	0	5	10
2	6	8	6	6	4	7	1	5	1	6	4	6	7	6	0	8	7	3	5	2	11
8	6	0	1	4	2	9	8	6	8	0	7	6	5	1	9	1	3	7	0	3	12
9	5	7	0	9	8	7	6	9	0	6	5	4	0	3	6	5	6	3	5	0	13
2	2	3	4	7	8	0	2	0	8	0	3	4	9	2	5	7	7	8	6	4	14
2	4	6	1	0	5	0	6	1	4	9	4	7	3	9	1	7	6	4	5	8	15
6	3	4	8	1	6	9	5	6	2	0	4	6	1	6	8	1	9	9	1	1	16
9	0	5	1	3	6	1	9	5	4	1	2	5	4	2	9	5	6	2	4	0	17
3	6	7	0	3	5	3	7	4	1	7	5	4	8	3	7	4	8	5	7	2	18
4	3	6	6	3	6	3	0	0	9	4	2	2	5	1	8	9	5	1	9	7	19
1	0	6	9	0	2	7	3	9	8	4	0	6	9	8	2	3	2	8	0	4	20
9	1	3	5	7	9	6	2	4	3	4	6	4	9	1	3	1	7	5	2	2	21
6	4	2	2	2	1	4	5	2	2	8	3	2	1	2	6	6	0	1	8	9	22
7	2	6	9	0	7	5	3	2	5	6	2	7	6	3	8	1	4	1	5	1	23
8	2	8	2	4	4	4	2	9	1	9	8	3	4	4	1	0	4	6	9	6	24
7	3	1	4	3	0	4	7	1	3	7	4	8	6	7	3	2	6	6	2	0	25
0	6	4	5	8	3	1	4	8	1	8	3	1	6	4	3	0	2	8	7	3	26
4	2	2	8	3	2	1	9	3	0	1	7	5	9	0	9	1	2	5	8	2	27
2	9	8	7	2	0	6	4	0	2	7	1	3	1	6	8	7	0	9	2	5	28
0	8	0	5	6	8	2	4	3	6	1	3	5	2	3	5	9	8	6	2	1	29
0	1	7	6	1	5	7	9	0	3	5	3	4	2	4	8	5	6	4	0	6	30
5	1	9	8	5	2	4	5	1	7	5	3	2	4	6	7	9	9	6	7	2	31
0	3	6	6	3	7	8	6	9	7	2	8	9	0	7	2	9	4	0	8	6	32
5	0	0	0	2	0	8	9	0	1	0	6	2	0	4	6	9	6	5	4	9	33
1	9	4	4	2	6	4	2	4	1	0	2	7	9	6	8	7	5	6	9	3	34
0	0	5	3	8	3	2	7	5	0	4	7	6	4	6	3	0	4	7	5	3	35
6	2	6	2	0	6	0	1	4	8	9	6	5	9	7	3	6	7	6	3	4	36
6	3	9	0	3	5	0	9	1	2	0	5	9	7	3	2	5	9	3	0	2	37
9	7	3	3	5	4	0	6	4	9	4	7	9	1	4	3	9	7	7	1	8	38
1	9	6	2	9	4	2	9	7	0	3	8	9	5	7	0	6	9	7	2	5	39
5	9	4	5	8	6	2	3	0	6	2	9	8	6	3	0	4	1	0	7	6	40

INDEX